CHEMISTRY:
THEORY AND PROBLEMS
BOOK TWO

James A. Hebden, Ph.D.
Head, Department of Science
Kamloops Senior Secondary School
Kamloops, B.C.

McGraw-Hill Ryerson Limited
Toronto, Montreal, New York, St. Louis, San Francisco, Auckland,
Bogotá, Guatemala, Hamburg, Lisbon, London, Madrid, Mexico,
New Delhi, Panama, Paris, San Juan, São Paulo, Singapore,
Sydney, Tokyo

CHEMISTRY: THEORY AND PROBLEMS

Book Two

Copyright © McGraw-Hill Ryerson Limited, 1980

ISBN 0-07-077861-2

78910111213141516 D 9876543210

Printed and bound in Canada

Canadian Cataloguing in Publication Data

Hebden, James A., date.
  Chemistry, theory and problems: book two

ISBN 0-07-077861-2

1. Chemistry. I. Title.

QD31.2.H422   540   C80-094216-7

Preface

This book covers 21 different problem topics in chemistry. Answers for all the problems are given at the back of the book.

Many fully worked out example problems are given. In addition, before the actual solution of some of the problems, a brief indication has been given of the way the problem will be solved and *why* we will do the steps that follow.

Most of the problems have a letter A, B or C in front of the problem number. A-type problems are relatively simple and are used to give practice in handling the "basics". B-type problems are somewhat more involved and difficult. B-type problems are the most difficult ones that the average student is expected to be able to solve. C-type problems generally involve an unexpected usage of the background theory. C-type problems will distinguish between students who have simply memorized the procedure to solve a given type of problem and students who have truly mastered the theory behind the method.

How To Use This Problem Book

1. Read and then re-read the theory and examples at the beginning of each topic.
2. Do not attempt any problems until you are convinced that you *understand* the background theory and the examples. How can you do an *original* problem if you don't understand an *example* problem?
3. As you do each of the first few problems, check that you have obtained the correct answer. If you get ANY of the A-type problems wrong, stop immediately and re-read the example problems to try to find out how to arrive at the answer.
4. Avoid writing problem solutions into the book; you will find the problems useful for review purposes if not surrounded by "clues".

Table Of Contents

Section 1

A Simple Way of Using Logarithms

We are familiar with the following way to multiply powers:

$$100 \times 1000 = 10^2 \times 10^3 = 10^5$$

Life would presumably be a little easier if we could multiply numbers other than 10, 100, 1000, etc. by also adding powers. Fortunately, a quick way to multiply ordinary numbers exists. Consider the following problem.

$$2 \times 3 = ? \quad \text{(we will start with a tough one!)}$$

A mathematical table exists which tells us that:

$$2 = 10^{0.3010} \quad \text{and} \quad 3 = 10^{0.4771}$$

Given this information, we can calculate:

$$2 \times 3 = 10^{0.3010} \times 10^{0.4771} = 10^{0.7781}$$

and the same table tells us that:

$$10^{0.7781} = 6$$

Look at the copy of the Table of Logarithms (Appendix Five of this book). Going down the left-hand column we find the number which we want to express as a power of 10 (for example, "2") and we see from the body of the table that the power we need is 0.3010. On the other hand, if we know the power (for example, "0.7781" in the answer to our above problem) then we first find the power in the body of the table and then look across to the left-hand column to see that $10^{0.7781}$ must be equal to 6. This table is just a means of listing numbers as a power of 10.

Example 1: $125 \times 20 = ?$

We first re-write the numbers in scientific notation:

$$125 \times 20 = (1.25 \times 10^2) \times (2.0 \times 10^1)$$

1

We have to re-write the numbers because the table only lists *numbers* between 1 and 10, and *powers* between 0 and 1 (because $1 = 10^0$ and $10 = 10^1$). Now: (check the results in your table)

$$1.25 \times 10^2 \times 2.0 \times 10^1 = 10^{0.0969} \times 10^2 \times 10^{0.3010} \times 10^1$$

$$= 10^{0.3979} \times 10^3 \quad \text{(collecting powers)}$$

$$= \underline{\underline{2.50 \times 10^3}}$$

Note that we handle the whole-number powers separately from the fractional powers. As an added bonus, we automatically get an answer in *scientific notation*!

Example 2:

$$0.005 \times 0.06 = 5 \times 10^{-3} \times 6 \times 10^{-2}$$

$$= 10^{0.6990} \times 10^{0.7782} \times 10^{-5}$$

$$= 10^{1.4772} \times 10^{-5}$$

But: $\underbrace{10^{1.4772} \times 10^{-5} = 10^1 \times 10^{0.4772} \times 10^{-5}}_{\substack{\text{we can only look up powers of} \\ \text{10 which are between 0 and 1}}} = 10^{0.4772} \times 10^{-4}$

$$= \underline{\underline{3.00 \times 10^{-4}}}$$

Example 3: (Recall that $10^p/10^q = 10^{p-q}$)

$$\frac{500}{0.002} = \frac{5 \times 10^2}{2 \times 10^{-3}} = \frac{10^{0.6990}}{10^{0.3010}} \times 10^5 = 10^{0.3980} \times 10^5 = \underline{\underline{2.5 \times 10^5}}$$

Example 4:

$$\frac{0.002}{500} = \frac{2 \times 10^{-3}}{5 \times 10^2} = \frac{10^{0.3010}}{10^{0.6990}} \times 10^{-5} = 10^{-0.3980} \times 10^{-5}$$

Now, the exponential $10^{-0.3980}$ poses a bit of a problem since the table does not list NEGATIVE POWERS. But:

$$-0.3980 = 0.6020 - 1$$

that is, we *add 1* to -0.3980 (to get 0.6020) and then we *subtract 1* [*i.e.*, $(-0.3980 + 1) - 1 = (0.6020) - 1$]
Hence:

$$10^{-0.3980} \times 10^{-5} = 10^{0.6020} \times 10^{-1} \times 10^{-5}$$

$$= 10^{0.6020} \times 10^{-6}$$

$$= \underline{\underline{4.0 \times 10^{-6}}}$$

2

Up to now, we have not used the terms "log" and "antilog", but sometimes these terms cannot be avoided.

> The *logarithm* (or "log") of a number is defined to be the power of 10 used to express the number.

$$e.g., \qquad 2 = 10^{\widehat{0.3010}} \longleftarrow \text{this is the log of 2}$$
$$i.e., \qquad \log 2 = 0.3010 \qquad (\text{"the power of 10 used to express 2"} = 0.3010)$$

The process of "taking the log" of a number is just the process of *writing down* the logarithm:

$$\log(2) = \log(10^{0.3010}) = 0.3010$$

or $\qquad \boxed{\log(10^a) = a} \qquad$: "Taking the log"

Example 5:
$$\log(10^{-3}) = -3$$
$$\log(2 \times 10^4) = \log(10^{0.3010} \times 10^4) = 0.3010 + 4 = 4.3010$$
$$\log(2 \times 10^{-5}) = \log(10^{0.3010} \times 10^{-5}) = 0.3010 - 5$$
$$= -4.6990$$

Hence, to repeat our above statement, when "taking the log" we just write down the powers of 10.

> Similarly, to "take the *antilog*" of a number we just raise 10 to the power of that number:
>
> $$\text{antilog}(b) = 10^b$$

Example 6:
$$\text{antilog}(-6) = 10^{-6}$$
$$\text{antilog}(0.4771) = 10^{0.4771} = 3.00$$
$$\text{antilog}(-4.6990) = \text{antilog}(0.3010 - 5)$$
$$= 10^{0.3010} \times 10^{-5} = 2 \times 10^{-5}$$
$$\text{antilog}(-7.3520) = \text{antilog}(0.6480 - 8)$$
$$= 10^{0.6480} \times 10^{-8} = 4.45 \times 10^{-8}$$

3

Notes

1. When we take the log we get a "cancelling effect" between the functions "log" and "10 to the power of" (*i.e.*, antilog):

$$\log(10^a) = a$$

these two functions cancel the effect of each other, so that we just get "*a*" back again.

2. When we take the log of a number, and then take 10 to the power of the log, we end up with our original number:

$$10^{\log a} = a \text{ (this is just the definition of "log } a\text{")}$$

these two functions cancel the effect of each other

Overall, we have the following relationships:

$$\log(10^a) = a$$
or simply: $\log(\text{antilog}(a)) = a$

and

$$10^{\log a} = a$$
or simply: $\text{antilog}(\log a) = a$

"log" and "antilog" cancel each other

We can deal with square roots, cube roots, etc. by expressing the roots as fractional powers. Recall that: $\sqrt{x} = x^{1/2}$, $\sqrt[3]{x} = x^{1/3}$, etc.

Example 7: Calculate $\sqrt{400}$

$$\sqrt{400} = (400)^{1/2} = (4.00 \times 10^2)^{1/2}$$
$$= (10^{0.6021} \times 10^2)^{1/2} = (10^{2.6021})^{1/2}$$
$$= 10^{1.3010} = 10^{0.3010} \times 10^1 = \underline{\underline{2.00 \times 10^1}}$$

Note that since the whole-number power of 10 is exactly divisible by 2, we could also take the shorter route:

$$(10^{0.6021} \times 10^2)^{1/2} = 10^{0.3010} \times 10^1 = \underline{\underline{2.00 \times 10^1}}$$

4

Example 8: Calculate $\sqrt[3]{160}$

$$\sqrt[3]{160} = (1.60 \times 10^2)^{1/3} = (10^{0.2041} \times 10^2)^{1/3} = (10^{2.2041})^{1/3}$$
$$= 10^{0.7347} = \underline{\underline{5.43}}$$

(In this case we combine the two powers of 10 before dividing by 3. If the whole-number power *had* been divisible by 3 we could have simply divided the fractional and whole-number powers by 3 directly, without combining them beforehand.)

Example 9: Calculate $(1.60 \times 10^{-18})^{1/3}$

$$(1.60 \times 10^{-18})^{1/3} = (10^{0.2041} \times 10^{-18})^{1/3} = 10^{0.0680} \times 10^{-6}$$
$$= \underline{\underline{1.17 \times 10^{-6}}}$$

Example 10: Solve for s.

$$s^4 = 3.60 \times 10^{-15}$$

When dealing with numbers involving a negative power of 10, the following procedure is convenient. We re-write the number so as to *increase* the decimal part and simultaneously *decrease* the exponential part until it is exactly divisible by 4 (since we want the 4th root).

$s^4 = 36.0 \times 10^{-16}$ (note that we have adjusted the exponential part so as to be divisible by 4)

$s = (36.0 \times 10^{-16})^{1/4} = (10^{1.5563} \times 10^{-16})^{1/4}$

(Note that: $36.0 = 3.60 \times 10^1 = 10^{0.5563} \times 10^1 = 10^{1.5563}$.) Now:

$$s = 10^{1.5563/4} \times 10^{-16/4} = 10^{0.3891} \times 10^{-4}$$
$$= \underline{\underline{2.45 \times 10^{-4}}}$$

Example 11: Solve for s.

$$s^3 = 5.94 \times 10^{-28}$$

Re-writing so that the power of 10 is divisible by 3:

$s^3 = 594.0 \times 10^{-30}$ (recall that we always *increase* the decimal part)

$s = (10^{2.7738} \times 10^{-30})^{1/3} = 10^{0.9246} \times 10^{-10}$

$= \underline{\underline{8.41 \times 10^{-10}}}$.

EXERCISES

1. Write in exponential form, using fractional powers of 10 (separate the fractional and whole-number parts).
   - a) 5
   - b) 6.1
   - c) 7.3
   - d) 48.1
   - e) 478.0
   - f) 0.0047
   - g) 6.45×10^3
   - h) 0.0461×10^{-4}
   - i) 517×10^2
   - j) 1030×10^{-6}

2. Perform the indicated operations using the exponential method
   - a) 1.7×4.9
   - b) 23.4×12.2
   - c) 351×216
   - d) 0.0035×0.0216
   - e) $5.62 \times 10^2 / 4.36 \times 10^{-3}$
   - f) $1.41 \times 10^{-6} / 9.62 \times 10^{-8}$
   - g) $6.40 \times 10^2 \times 5.94 \times 10^{-6}$
   - h) $4.25 \times 10^{-7} / 7.43 \times 10^4$
   - i) $6.02 \times 9.47 \times 10^{-3}$
   - j) $947 / 9.92 \times 10^{-3}$

3. Write the value of the following functions.
   - a) $\log(7.0)$
   - b) $\log(6.0 \times 10^2)$
   - c) $\log(4.5 \times 10^{-3})$
   - d) $\log(0.0475)$
   - e) $\text{antilog}(3)$
   - f) $\text{antilog}(-0.6)$
   - g) $\text{antilog}(-7.623)$
   - h) $\log(6.93 \times 10^{-4})$
   - i) $\text{antilog}(3.715)$
   - j) $\log(53.6 \times 10^4)$
   - k) $\text{antilog}(-4.075)$
   - l) $\log(0.0415 \times 10^{-8})$

4. Perform the indicated operations, using logarithms.
   - a) $\sqrt{35}$
   - b) $(2.9 \times 10^3)^{1/2}$
   - c) $(5.63 \times 10^4)^{1/4}$
   - d) $(6.41 \times 10^{-4})^{1/2}$
   - e) solve: $s^3 = 3.5 \times 10^{-5}$
   - f) solve: $s^4 = 6.55 \times 10^3$
   - g) solve: $s^6 = 4.76 \times 10^{-3}$
   - h) solve: $s^5 = 38.7 \times 10^3$
   - i) solve: $s^3 = 7.15 \times 10^{-13}$

Section 2

Specific Heat, Heat of Fusion and Heat of Vaporization

> The *molar heat of vaporization* is the amount of heat required to change one mole of a pure liquid at its boiling temperature into a gas.

> The *molar heat of fusion* is the amount of heat required to change one mole of a pure solid at its melting temperature into a liquid.

> The *specific heat capacity* of a substance is the amount of heat (in joules) required to raise the temperature of 1 kg of the substance by 1°C.

For calculation purposes, we normally use the *heat of fusion* and *heat of vaporization*, which are expressed in joules per gram, rather than the corresponding *molar heats*.

Example: For water we have

$$H_{vap}(H_2O(l)) = 2.25 \text{ kJ/g}$$
$$H_{fus}(H_2O(s)) = 0.334 \text{ kJ/g}$$

where "H" is the symbol for "heat"

The specific heat capacity (c), or simply "*specific heat*", of a substance will be different for different phases of the substance.

Example: For water in its three phases we have

$$c(H_2O(s)) = 2.09 \text{ kJ/(kg} \cdot °\text{C)}$$

$$c(H_2O(l)) = 4.18 \text{ kJ/(kg} \cdot °\text{C)}$$

$$c(H_2O(g)) = 2.00 \text{ kJ/(kg} \cdot °\text{C)}$$

We will adopt the Greek letter for "D", namely "Δ" (pronounced "delta"), to mean "the change in".

Example:

ΔT means "the change in temperature"

ΔH means "the change in heat"

To find the amount of heat required to change the temperature of a given mass of a substance, we use the equation

$$\boxed{\Delta H = c \cdot m \cdot \Delta T}$$

where ΔH = the amount of heat which was added to or lost from the substance
c = the specific heat of the substance
m = the mass of the substance
ΔT = the temperature change of the substance

Example: Calculate the heat lost when 60 g of steam at 180°C is cooled to 110°C.

Mass = 60 g = 0.060 kg

Temperature change = ΔT = 180 − 110 = 70°C

$c(H_2O(g)) = 2.00 \text{ kJ/(kg} \cdot °\text{C)}$ (From example at top of page)

Heat lost = $\Delta H = c \cdot m \cdot \Delta T$

$$= \frac{2.00 \text{ kJ}}{\text{kg} \cdot °\text{C}} \times 0.060 \text{ kg} \times 70°\text{C} = \underline{\underline{8.4 \text{ kJ}}}$$

Example: What mass of glass can be heated from 20°C to 80°C if 800 J of heat are added to the glass?

$c(\text{glass}) = 0.84 \text{ kJ/(kg} \cdot °\text{C)}$

Temperature change = ΔT = 80 − 20 = 60°C

Heat change = ΔH = 800 J = 0.800 kJ

8

Now: $$\Delta H = c \cdot m \cdot \Delta T$$

so that: $$m = \frac{\Delta H}{c \cdot \Delta T} = \frac{0.800 \text{ kJ}}{0.84 \text{ kJ/(kg} \cdot °\text{C)} \times 60°\text{C}} = \underline{\underline{0.016 \text{ kg}}}$$

When heat is applied to make a substance melt or boil there is NO change in temperature during the melting or boiling process, just a phase change. Hence, we need only to know the mass of the substance and its heat of fusion or vaporization.

To find the amount of heat required to melt or boil a given mass of a substance, we use the equations

$$\Delta H = H_{\text{vap}} \cdot m$$

or

$$\Delta H = H_{\text{fus}} \cdot m$$

Example: Calculate the amount of heat required to change 90.0 g of water at 100°C into steam at 100°C.

$$\text{Heat required} = \Delta H = H_{\text{vap}} \cdot m$$

$$= 2.25 \frac{\text{kJ}}{\text{g}} \times 90.0 \text{ g} = \underline{\underline{203 \text{ kJ}}}$$

Note: Since the change from solid to liquid is reversible, then we have, for example:

$$H_2O(s) + 0.334 \frac{\text{kJ}}{\text{g}} \rightleftharpoons H_2O(l)$$

Hence, $H_2O(s)$ requires the *addition* of 0.334 kJ/g in order to form $H_2O(l)$. Similarly, $H_2O(l)$ *gives off* 0.334 kJ/g when forming $H_2O(s)$. In a similar manner we have:

$$H_2O(l) + 2.25 \frac{\text{kJ}}{\text{g}} \rightleftharpoons H_2O(g)$$

so that heat is added to water in order to form steam, and heat is given off when steam condenses to form water.

The diagram on the next page shows the effect of adding heat to ice. (Note: s = solid phase, l = liquid phase, g = gas phase.)

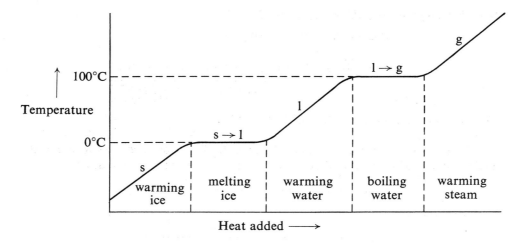

This diagram is actually very general and can be applied to the warming (or cooling, if the curve is reversed) of almost any substance. Using such a diagram, we can deal with problems such as the following.

Example: Calculate the heat required to change 90.0 g of ice at $-30.0°C$ into steam at $150.0°C$.

a) Heating the solid ($\Delta H = c_{ice} \cdot m \cdot \Delta T$)

$$m = 90.0 \text{ g} = 0.090 \text{ kg}$$

$$\Delta T = 0 - (-30.0) = 30.0°C$$

$$\Delta H = \frac{2.09 \text{ kJ}}{\text{kg} \cdot °C} \times 0.090 \text{ kg} \times 30.0°C = 5.64 \text{ kJ}$$

b) Melting the solid ($\Delta H = H_{fus} \cdot m$)

$$\Delta H = \frac{0.334 \text{ kJ}}{\text{g}} \times 90.0 \text{ g} \qquad = 30.1 \text{ kJ}$$

c) Heating the liquid ($\Delta H = c_{water} \cdot m \cdot \Delta T$)

$$\Delta T = 100 - 0 = 100°C$$

$$\Delta H = \frac{4.18 \text{ kJ}}{\text{kg} \cdot °C} \times 0.090 \text{ kg} \times 100°C = 37.6 \text{ kJ}$$

d) Boiling the liquid ($\Delta H = H_{vap} \cdot m$)

$$\Delta H = \frac{2.25 \text{ kJ}}{\text{g}} \times 90.0 \text{ g} \qquad = 203.0 \text{ kJ}$$

e) Heating the gas ($\Delta H = c_{\text{steam}} \cdot m \cdot \Delta T$)

$$\Delta T = 150.0 - 100.0 = 50.0°C$$

$$\Delta H = \frac{2.00 \text{ kJ}}{\text{kg} \cdot °C} \times 0.090 \text{ kg} \times 50.0°C \quad = \quad 9.00 \text{ kJ}$$

$$\text{total heat required} = 285.0 \text{ kJ}$$

Note that we always assume that ΔT is *POSITIVE*.

When we mix a hot and a cold substance, the hot substance loses heat and the cold substance gains heat until both substances have the same temperature.

$$(\textit{i.e.,} \text{ hot water} + \text{cold water} = \text{warm water})$$

Hence we can say:

$$\boxed{\text{HEAT LOST} = \text{HEAT GAINED}}$$

where:

$$\text{HEAT LOST} = \text{the } \textit{total} \text{ heat lost by the hotter substance}$$

$$\text{HEAT GAINED} = \text{the } \textit{total} \text{ heat gained by the colder substance}$$

Example: If 0.100 kg of H_2O at 10.0°C is added to 0.080 kg of H_2O at 90.0°C, what is the final temperature of the mixture?

Let T = the final temperature
For the hot water: $\Delta T = (90.0 - T)°C$

and: $\quad \text{heat lost} = c_{\text{water}} \cdot m \cdot \Delta T$

$$= \frac{4.18 \text{ kJ}}{\text{kg} \cdot °C} \times 0.080 \text{ kg}$$

$$\times (90.0 - T)°C$$

$$= (30.1 - 0.334T) \text{ kJ}$$

Similarly, for cold water: $\Delta T = (T - 10.0)°C$

and: $\quad \text{Heat gained} = c_{\text{water}} \cdot m \cdot \Delta T$

$$= \frac{4.18 \text{ kJ}}{\text{kg} \cdot °C} \times 0.100 \text{ kg} \times (T - 10.0)°C$$

$$= (0.418T - 4.18) \text{ kJ}$$

11

Since: Heat lost = Heat gained,

then: $30.1 - 0.334T = 0.418T - 4.18$

and: $T = \underline{45.6°C}$

Example: What is the final temperature when 0.090 kg of steam at 120.0°C is added to 0.350 kg of ice at $-50.0°C$?

Referring to the heating diagram:

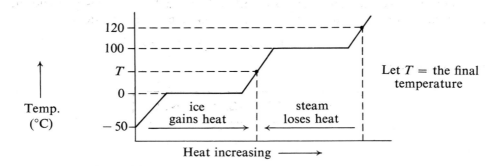

We will ASSUME that the final result will be *water* when steam and ice are mixed. This assumption will always be correct in the problems we will consider.

Total heat lost:

a) Cooling the steam ($\Delta H = c_{steam} \cdot m \cdot \Delta T$)

$$\Delta T = 120.0 - 100.0 = 20.0°C$$

$$\Delta H = \frac{2.00 \text{ kJ}}{\text{kg} \cdot °\text{C}} \times 0.090 \text{ kg} \times 20.0°C = 3.60 \text{ kJ}$$

b) Condensing the steam ($\Delta H = H_{vap} \cdot m$)

$$\Delta H = \frac{2.25 \text{ kJ}}{\text{g}} \times 0.090 \text{ kg} \times \frac{1000 \text{ g}}{\text{kg}} = 203.0 \text{ kJ}$$

c) Cooling the water ($\Delta H = c_{water} \cdot m \cdot \Delta T$)

$$\Delta T = (100.0 - T)°C$$

$$\Delta H = \frac{4.18 \text{ kJ}}{\text{kg} \cdot °\text{C}} \times 0.090 \text{ kg} \times (100.0 - T)°C = (37.6 - 0.376T) \text{ kJ}$$

$$\text{Total heat lost} = (3.60 + 203.0 + 37.6 - 0.376T) \text{ kJ}$$

$$= (244.0 - 0.376T) \text{ kJ}$$

12

Total heat gained:
  d) Warming the ice ($\Delta H = c_{ice} \cdot m \cdot \Delta T$)

$$\Delta T = 0.0 - (-50.0) = 50.0°C$$

$$\Delta H = \frac{2.09 \text{ kJ}}{\text{kg} \cdot °C} \times 0.350 \text{ kg} \times 50.0°C = 36.6 \text{ kJ}$$

  e) Melting the ice ($\Delta H = H_{fus} \cdot m$)

$$\Delta H = \frac{0.334 \text{ kJ}}{g} \times 0.350 \text{ kg} \times \frac{1000 \text{ g}}{\text{kg}} = 117.0 \text{ kJ}$$

  f) Warming the water ($\Delta H = c_{water} \cdot m \cdot \Delta T$)

$$\Delta T = (T - 0.0)°C = T°C$$

$$\Delta H = \frac{4.18 \text{ kJ}}{\text{kg} \cdot °C} \times 0.350 \text{ kg} \times T°C = 1.46T \text{ kJ}$$

$$\text{Total heat gained} = (36.6 + 117.0 + 1.46T) \text{ kJ}$$
$$= (154.0 + 1.46T) \text{ kJ}$$

Now: Heat lost = heat gained

and: $244 - 0.376T = 154 + 1.46T$

$$T = \underline{\underline{49.0°C}}$$

EXERCISES

A-1. a) How many kilojoules are required to heat 0.200 kg of gold from 15.0°C to 85.0°C? $c_{Au} = 0.130 \text{ kJ}/(\text{kg} \cdot °C)$
      b) If the same amount of heat is added to 0.200 kg of water at 15.0°C, what will be the final temperature?

A-2. How much heat is required to change the temperature of each of the following from 15°C to 60°C?
      a) 35 g of water
      b) 4.98 g of pyrex glass ($c_{pyrex} = 0.84 \text{ kJ}/(\text{kg} \cdot °C)$)
      c) 20.7 g of Pt ($c_{Pt} = 0.13 \text{ kJ}/(\text{kg} \cdot °C)$)

A-3. Using the values for the heat of vaporization and fusion of water, calculate the *molar* heat of vaporization and fusion of water.

A-4. If $c_{Cu} = 0.39 \text{ kJ}/(\text{kg} \cdot °C)$ and $c_{Al} = 0.91 \text{ kJ}/(\text{kg} \cdot °C)$:
      a) How many kilojoules are required to heat 0.100 kg of Cu from 10°C to 100°C?

     b) The same quantity of heat is added to 0.100 kg of Al at 10°C. Which metal reaches the higher temperature, the Cu or Al?

A-5. One gram of anthracite coal gives off about 30.6 kJ when burned. What mass of coal is required to heat 3.50 L of water from 10.0°C to 95.0°C?

A-6. Determine the resulting temperature when 1.00 kg of ice at 0.00°C is mixed with 9.00 kg of water at 50.0°C.

B-7. Determine the resulting temperature when 150.0 g of ice at -20.0°C is mixed with 360.0 g of water at 65.0°C.

B-8. How much heat is given up when 20 g of steam at 120°C is cooled to -15°C?

B-9. How much heat is required to convert 45 g of ice at -115°C into steam at 220°C?

B-10. a) How many kilojoules are required to heat 0.450 kg of gold from -25°C to 215°C? $c_{Au} = 0.13$ kJ/(kg·°C)

     b) If the same amount of heat is added to 0.035 kg of ice at -10°C, what will be the final water temperature?

B-11. a) If 150 g of water 0°C is added to 100 g of water at 90°C, what will be the final temperature of the water?

     b) If 250 g of gold at 100°C is added to 500 g of water at 5°C, what will be the final temperature of the gold? $c_{Au} = 0.13$ kJ/(kg·°C)

     c) When 2.1 kJ of heat were added to 40 g of Pb, the temperature of the lead rose from 20°C to 423°C. What is the specific heat of lead?

B-12. If 50.0 g of steam at 165°C is added to 200 g of ice at -45°C, what will be the final temperature of the system?

B-13. If 85.0 g of steam at 130°C is added to 300.0 g of ice at -20°C, what will be the final temperature of the system?

B-14. When 1.00 g of propane, C_3H_8, is burned, about 2.36 kJ of heat is given off. What mass of water at 50°C can be converted into steam at 100°C when 4.00 mol of propane are burned? What mass of water at 50°C can be converted into super-heated steam at 170°C?

B-15. The average body temperature of a healthy human is 37°C. What mass of steam at 140°C must be added to 250 g of ice at -30°C to produce water having the same temperature as a human body?

B-16. What mass of ice at -10°C must be added to 125 g of steam at 220°C to produce water at 100°C?

B-17. If a 2.00 kg block of aluminum at 5.0°C ($c_{Al} = 0.900$ kJ/(kg·°C)) is put in contact with 0.050 kg of steam at 110.0°C, what is the final temperature of the aluminum block?

B-18. What mass of steam at 180.0°C is required to raise the temperature of 0.470 kg of vanadium ($c_V = 0.486$ kJ/(kg·°C)) from -5.0°C to 60.0°C?

Section 3
Reaction Heats

INTRODUCTION

> An ENDOTHERMIC reaction is a reaction which ABSORBS heat.

Example: Experimentally, it is found that HCl and I_2 require the addition of heat to react.

$$HCl(g) + \tfrac{1}{2} I_2(g) + 118 \text{ kJ} \rightarrow HI(g) + \tfrac{1}{2} Cl_2(g)$$

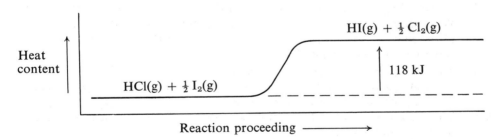

As we can see from the diagram, the products (1 mol of HI and 0.5 mol of Cl_2) contain 118 kJ more heat energy than the reactants (1 mol of HCl and 0.5 mol of I_2), and hence the reaction is *endothermic*.

> An EXOTHERMIC reaction is a reaction which GIVES OFF heat.

15

Example: The reaction in the previous example is reversible. When 1 mol of HI and 0.5 mol of Cl_2 react, 118 kJ of heat is given off as the reaction proceeds.

$$HI(g) + \tfrac{1}{2} Cl_2(g) \rightarrow HCl(g) + \tfrac{1}{2} I_2(g) + 118 \text{ kJ}$$

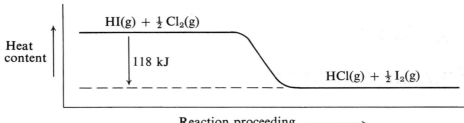

Since the products (HCl and I_2) have less heat energy than the reactants (HI and Cl_2), the reaction is *exothermic*.

We define the ENTHALPY of a substance to be the heat contained in the substance. Enthalpy is given the symbol "H".

If we let: H_{prod} = the *combined* enthalpies of *all* the products

and: H_{react} the *combined* enthalpies of *all* the reactants

then we can define:

             ΔH_{rx} = the change in enthalpy during the reaction,

and

$$\Delta H_{rx} = H_{prod} - H_{react}$$

For an endothermic reaction, the heat contained in the products is greater than the heat contained in the reactants, which means that $H_{prod} > H_{react}$. Hence we have:

$$\Delta H_{rx} > 0 \text{ for an endothermic reaction}$$

Similarly, in an exothermic reaction we have $H_{react} > H_{prod}$, which means that:

$$\Delta H_{rx} < 0 \text{ for an exothermic reaction}$$

We should note that the following expressions are equivalent:

$$HCl(g) + \tfrac{1}{2} I_2(g) + 118 \text{ kJ} \rightarrow HI(g) + \tfrac{1}{2} Cl_2(g)$$

and:

$$HCl(g) + \tfrac{1}{2} I_2(g) \rightarrow HI(g) + \tfrac{1}{2} Cl_2(g); \qquad \Delta H_{rx} = 118 \text{ kJ}$$

Similarly,

$$HI(g) + \tfrac{1}{2} Cl_2(g) \rightarrow HCl(g) + \tfrac{1}{2} I_2(g) + 118 \text{ kJ}$$

and:

$$HI(g) + \tfrac{1}{2} Cl_2(g) \rightarrow HCl(g) + \tfrac{1}{2} I_2(g); \qquad \Delta H_{rx} = -118 \text{ kJ}$$

are equivalent expressions.

Note also that if we "turn the reaction around", we change the sign of ΔH_{rx}.

i.e.,

$$HCl(g) + \tfrac{1}{2} I_2(g) \rightarrow HI(g) + \tfrac{1}{2} Cl_2(g); \qquad \Delta H_{rx} = +118 \text{ kJ}$$

and

$$HI(g) + \tfrac{1}{2} Cl_2(g) \rightarrow HCl(g) + \tfrac{1}{2} I_2(g); \qquad \Delta H_{rx} = -118 \text{ kJ}$$

SOME DEFINITIONS

STANDARD STATE = the phase in which a substance is found at 25°C
and 101.3 kPa pressure.

Example: H_2O is a liquid in its standard state, O_2 is a gas in its standard state.

ΔH_{rx}° = the standard enthalpy of reaction
= the heat change which occurs when a particular reaction occurs according to a given equation, such that all the reactants and products are in their standard states (the "°" in ΔH_{rx}° tells us that ΔH_{rx}° refers to a standard state).

Example:

$$HI(g) + \tfrac{1}{2} Cl_2(g) \rightarrow HCl(g) + \tfrac{1}{2} I_2(g); \qquad \Delta H_{rx}^{\circ} = -118 \text{ kJ}$$

ΔH_f° = the standard enthalpy of formation of a compound
= the heat required to make one mole of the compound from elements in their *standard* state.

Example:

$$H_2(g) + S(s) + 2 O_2(g) \rightarrow H_2SO_4(l); \qquad \Delta H_f^{\circ} = -814.3 \text{ kJ}$$

Note: We define $\Delta H_f^{\circ} = 0$ for an ELEMENT in its standard state.

ΔH_{soln} = the enthalpy of solution
= the change in enthalpy which occurs when one mole of a substance is dissolved in water.

Example:

$$KOH(s) \rightarrow K^+(aq) + OH^-(aq); \qquad \Delta H_{soln} = -57.8 \text{ kJ}$$

ΔH_{comb}° = the standard enthalpy of combustion.
= the change in enthalpy which occurs when one mole of a substance is burned.

Example:

$$CH_4(g) + 2 O_2(g) \rightarrow CO_2(g) + 2 H_2O(l); \qquad \Delta H_{comb}^{\circ} = -891.0 \text{ kJ}$$

ΔH_{diss}° = the standard enthalpy of dissociation (also called the "bond dissociation energy" or simply "bond energy").
= the heat required to dissociate two atoms joined by a covalent bond (will be positive since energy is required to break a bond).

Example:

$$Cl_2(g) \rightarrow 2 Cl(g); \qquad \Delta H_{diss}^{\circ} = \frac{+121 \text{ kJ}}{\text{mol of } Cl_2}$$

ΔH_{fus}° = the standard enthalpy of fusion
= the heat required to change one mole of a solid compound at its melting point into a liquid, at a pressure of 101.3 kPa.

Example:

$$H_2O(s; 0°C, 101.3 \text{ kPa}) \rightarrow H_2O(l; 0°C, 101.3 \text{ kPa}); \qquad \Delta H_{fus}^{\circ} = 6.0 \text{ kJ}$$

ΔH_{vap}° = the standard enthalpy of vaporization
= the heat required to change one mole of a liquid compound at its boiling point into a gas, at a pressure of 101.3 kPa.

Example:

$$H_2O(l; 100°C, 101.3 \text{ kPa}) \rightarrow H_2O(g; 100°C, 101.3 \text{ kPa}); \qquad \Delta H_{vap}^{\circ} = 41 \text{ kJ}$$

ADDITION OF REACTION HEATS

Consider the following sequence of reactions:

$$C_2H_2(g) + H_2(g) \rightarrow C_2H_4(g) + 175 \text{ kJ}$$

$$C_2H_4(g) + H_2(g) \rightarrow C_2H_6(g) + 137 \text{ kJ}$$

We can represent this sequence as follows.

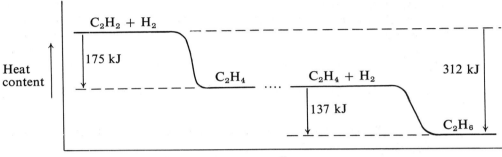

As can be seen from the above diagram, the heat given off in the reaction $C_2H_2(g) + 2 H_2(g) \rightarrow C_2H_6(g)$ is just the sum of the heats given off by $C_2H_2(g) + H_2(g) \rightarrow C_2H_4(g)$ followed by $C_2H_4(g) + H_2(g) \rightarrow C_2H_6(g)$. In other words, we can treat reactions and reaction heats by an algebraic method.

$$C_2H_2(g) + H_2(g) \rightarrow \cancel{C_2H_4(g)}; \qquad \Delta H = -175 \text{ kJ}$$

$$\cancel{C_2H_4(g)} + H_2(g) \rightarrow C_2H_6(g); \qquad \Delta H = -137 \text{ kJ}$$

adding: $\quad C_2H_2(g) + 2 H_2(g) \rightarrow C_2H_6(g); \qquad \Delta H = -312 \text{ kJ}$

Based on the above, we can make the following general statement:

> *Hess' Law of Heat Summation:* When a reaction is expressed as the algebraic sum of other reactions, the heat of the reaction is the algebraic sum of the heats of the other reactions.

Example: Given

$$S(g) + O_2(g) \rightarrow SO_2(g); \qquad \Delta H_f^\circ = -297 \text{ kJ}$$

$$S(g) + 3/2 O_2(g) \rightarrow SO_3(g); \qquad \Delta H_f^\circ = -396 \text{ kJ}$$

Predict ΔH for $SO_2(g) + \frac{1}{2} O_2(g) \rightarrow SO_3(g)$.

Since we require SO_2 as a reactant and SO_3 as a product, we can write:

$$SO_2(g) \rightarrow \cancel{S(g)} + O_2(g); \qquad \Delta H = +297 \text{ kJ}$$

$$\cancel{S(g)} + 3/2\ O_2(g) \rightarrow SO_3(g); \qquad \Delta H = -396 \text{ kJ}$$

$$SO_2(g) + \tfrac{1}{2} O_2(g) \rightarrow SO_3(g); \qquad \Delta H_{rx}^{\circ} = \underline{\underline{-99 \text{ kJ}}}$$

Notes

1. When we inverted the equation $S + O_2 \rightarrow SO_2$ we had to change the sign of ΔH.

2. Once we arranged the first two equations to ensure that the sum of the equations had SO_2 as a reactant and SO_3 as a product, the O_2 term automatically appears as a reactant and the final equation is automatically balanced.

Example: Given $\Delta H_f^{\circ} = -394$ kJ for $CO_2(g)$, $\Delta H_f^{\circ} = -286$ kJ for $H_2O(l)$ and $\Delta H_{comb}^{\circ} = -891$ kJ for $CH_4(g)$, determine ΔH_f° for $CH_4(g)$.

We want to find ΔH_f° for the reaction:

a) $C(s) + 2\ H_2(g) \rightarrow CH_4(g)$.

The given data is:

b) $C(s) + O_2(g) \rightarrow CO_2(g); \qquad \Delta H_f^{\circ} = -394$ kJ

c) $H_2(g) + \tfrac{1}{2} O_2(g) \rightarrow H_2O(l); \qquad \Delta H_f^{\circ} = -286$ kJ

d) $CH_4(g) + 2\ O_2(g) \rightarrow CO_2(g) + 2\ H_2O(l); \qquad \Delta H_{comb}^{\circ} = -891$ kJ

We first rearrange (d) such that $CH_4(g)$ is a product, as required by (a):

e) $CO_2(g) + 2\ H_2O(l) \rightarrow CH_4(g) + 2\ O_2(g); \qquad \Delta H = +891$ kJ

Next, we add in (b) and (c) in such a way as to cancel the "CO_2" and "$2\ H_2O$" in (e) [these compounds are not required in (a)]. Overall we then have:

$$\cancel{CO_2(g)} + \cancel{2\ H_2O(l)} \rightarrow CH_4(g) + \cancel{2\ O_2(g)}; \qquad \Delta H = +891 \text{ kJ}$$

$$C(s) + \cancel{O_2(g)} \rightarrow \cancel{CO_2(g)}; \qquad \Delta H = -394 \text{ kJ}$$

$$2\ H_2(g) + \cancel{O_2(g)} \rightarrow \cancel{2\ H_2O(l)}; \qquad \Delta H = 2 \times (-286 \text{ kJ})$$

$$= -572 \text{ kJ}$$

Add: $\qquad C(s) + 2\ H_2(g) \rightarrow CH_4(g); \qquad \Delta H_f^{\circ} = \underline{\underline{-75 \text{ kJ}}}$

Notes

1. We had to double the equation $H_2 + \tfrac{1}{2} O_2 \rightarrow H_2O$ to cancel the "$2\ H_2O$" in (e), and hence we had to double the amount of heat involved.

2. Not all compounds can be formed directly from the elements which make them up, and hence sometimes the enthalpy of formation of a compound must be found by indirect means, as was the case with the above example.

Example: Given the following bond energies:

$$\Delta H^{\circ}_{\text{diss}} = 416 \text{ kJ for C—H, and}$$

$$\Delta H^{\circ}_{\text{diss}} = 348 \text{ kJ for C—C}$$

calculate the total bond energy of ethane

$$\left(\begin{array}{c} \text{H} \quad \text{H} \\ | \quad | \\ \text{H—C—C—H} \\ | \quad | \\ \text{H} \quad \text{H} \end{array} \right)$$

Since ethane has 6 C—H bonds and 1 C—C bond, then:

$$\text{total bond energy} = 6 \times \Delta H^{\circ}_{\text{diss}}(\text{C—H}) + \Delta H^{\circ}_{\text{diss}}(\text{C—C})$$

$$= 6 \times 416 + 348 = \underline{\underline{2844 \text{ kJ}}}$$

Example: Given

$$\Delta H^{\circ}_{\text{diss}} = 436 \text{ kJ for H}_2(g)$$

$$\Delta H^{\circ}_{\text{diss}} = 416 \text{ kJ for C—H}$$

$$\Delta H^{\circ}_{\text{diss}} = 348 \text{ kJ for C—C}$$

and

$$\Delta H = 716 \text{ kJ for C(s)} \rightarrow \text{C(g)}$$

calculate

$$\Delta H^{\circ}_{f} \text{ for C}_2\text{H}_6(g)$$

Since we require ΔH°_{f} for the reaction

$$2 \text{ C(s)} + 3 \text{ H}_2(g) \rightarrow \text{C}_2\text{H}_6(g)$$

we must (i) change C(s) to C(g), (ii) break H_2 bonds, and (iii) form C—H and C—C bonds from C(g) and H(g). Performing the actual calculations we have:

a) forming gaseous elements

$$2 \text{ C(s)} \rightarrow 2 \text{ C(g)}; \qquad \Delta H = 2 \times 716 = 1432 \text{ kJ}$$

$$3 \text{ H}_2(g) \rightarrow 6 \text{ H(g)}; \qquad \Delta H = 3 \times 436 = 1308 \text{ kJ}$$

b) forming C_2H_6 from gaseous elements (see previous example)

$$2 \text{ C(g)} + 6 \text{ H(g)} \rightarrow \text{C}_2\text{H}_6(g); \qquad \Delta H = 6 \times [-\Delta H^{\circ}_{\text{diss}}(\text{C—H})] + -\Delta H^{\circ}_{\text{diss}}(\text{C—C})$$

$$= -2844 \text{ kJ}$$

Adding the results of (a) and (b):

$$\Delta H_f^\circ = \text{(energy required to change elements into gaseous atoms)}$$
$$+ \text{(energy gained by forming bonds between gaseous atoms)}$$
$$= (1432 + 1308) + (-2844) = \underline{\underline{-104 \text{ kJ}}}$$

Note: The accepted value of ΔH_f° for $C_2H_6(g)$ is -85 kJ.

The agreement with the value calculated in this example is quite good, since we have assumed that *ALL* C—H bonds and C—C bonds have the same ΔH_{diss}° values, regardless of the compound containing the bond. (The ΔH_{diss}° values used here represent the energy required to dissociate a "typical" bond.)

The determination of ΔH_{comb} for a substance is accomplished by means of the CALORIMETRY method. In this method, a known mass of the substance is burned in a sealed combustion chamber, called a CALORIMETER, which also contains a large amount of pure oxygen. The calorimeter is immersed in an insulated container full of water. When the substance is ignited by an electrical spark, the heat produced warms up the calorimeter and the surrounding water. The calculation of ΔH_{comb} is then performed as follows.

Example: A 2.56 g sample of anthracene, $C_{14}H_{10}$, was burned in an iron calorimeter ($c_{Fe} = 0.452$ kJ/(kg·°C) having a mass of 0.948 kg. The calorimeter was immersed in 1.450 kg of water. The initial temperature of the system was 21.8°C and the final temperature was 37.6°C. Calculate the heat of combustion of anthracene, under the conditions present inside the calorimeter.

First, we find the heat absorbed by the calorimeter and water:

$$\Delta H_{calorimeter} = c_{Fe} \cdot m \cdot \Delta T$$

$$= \frac{0.452 \text{ kJ}}{\text{kg} \cdot \text{°C}} \times 0.948 \text{ kg} \times (37.6 - 21.8)\text{°C} = 6.77 \text{ kJ}$$

$$\Delta H_{water} = c_{water} \cdot m \cdot \Delta T$$

$$= \frac{4.18 \text{ kJ}}{\text{kg} \cdot \text{°C}} \times 1.450 \text{ kg} \times (37.6 - 21.8)\text{°C} = 95.8 \text{ kJ}$$

Assuming no heat was lost to the surroundings:

Total heat given off by combustion = heat absorbed by water
+ heat absorbed by calorimeter
$$= 6.77 + 95.8 = 103.0 \text{ kJ}$$

Since molar mass of $C_{14}H_{10} = 178$ g, then:

$$\text{moles } C_{14}H_{10} = 2.56 \text{ g} \times \frac{1 \text{ mol}}{178 \text{ g}} = 0.0144 \text{ mol}$$

$$\Delta H_{comb} = \frac{103.0 \text{ kJ}}{0.0144 \text{ mol}} = \underline{\underline{7.15 \times 10^3 \text{ kJ}}}$$

EXERCISES

A-1. Given: $N_2(g) + 3 H_2(g) \rightarrow 2 NH_3(g) + 92.5$ kJ, what is ΔH_f° for $NH_3(g)$?

A-2. Determine ΔH_{rx}° for $KClO_3(s) \rightarrow KCl(s) + 3/2 O_2(g)$, given:

$$\Delta H_f^\circ = -391 \text{ kJ for } KClO_3(s); \qquad \Delta H_f^\circ = -436 \text{ kJ for } KCl(s)$$

A-3. Given $\Delta H_f^\circ = -602$ kJ for MgO(s) and $\Delta H_f^\circ = -394$ kJ for $CO_2(g)$, predict ΔH_{rx}° for the reaction:

$$2 MgO(s) + C(s) \rightarrow 2 Mg(s) + CO_2(g)$$

A-4. Given: $CaCO_3(s) \rightarrow CaO(s) + CO_2(g)$; $\qquad \Delta H_{rx}^\circ = 175$ kJ
$\qquad \quad Ca(OH)_2(s) \rightarrow H_2O(l) + CaO(s)$; $\qquad \Delta H_{rx}^\circ = 67$ kJ
$\qquad \quad Ca(OH)_2(s) + 2 HCl(g) \rightarrow CaCl_2(s) + 2 H_2O(l)$; $\qquad \Delta H_{rx}^\circ = -198$ kJ
Predict ΔH_{rx}° for

$$CaCO_3(s) + 2 HCl(g) \rightarrow CaCl_2(s) + H_2O(l) + CO_2(g)$$

A-5. Given $\Delta H_f^\circ = -85$ kJ for $C_2H_6(g)$, $\Delta H_f^\circ = -394$ kJ for $CO_2(g)$ and $\Delta H_f^\circ = -286$ kJ for $H_2O(l)$, calculate ΔH_{comb}° for $C_2H_6(g)$.

A-6. Calculate the heat of decomposition of $CaCO_3(s)$ into CaO(s) and $CO_2(g)$. $\Delta H_f^\circ = -1208$ kJ for $CaCO_3(s)$, $\Delta H_f^\circ = -636$ kJ for CaO(s), $\Delta H_f^\circ = -394$ kJ for $CO_2(g)$.

B-7. The heat of combustion of naphthalene, $C_{10}H_8(s)$, is -5162 kJ. What is the heat of formation of naphthalene? $\Delta H_f^\circ = -286$ kJ for $H_2O(l)$; $\Delta H_f^\circ = -394$ kJ for $CO_2(g)$.

B-8. Given: $\Delta H_f^\circ = -396$ kJ for $SO_3(g)$, $\Delta H_f^\circ = -286$ kJ for $H_2O(l)$ and $H_2O(l) + SO_3(g) \rightarrow H_2SO_4(l)$; $\Delta H_{rx}^\circ = -130$ kJ, predict ΔH_f° for $H_2SO_4(l)$.

B-9. Sugar ferments to form alcohol according to the reaction

$$C_{12}H_{22}O_{11}(s) + 7 H_2O(l) \rightarrow 6 C_2H_5OH(l) + 6 O_2(g)$$

Predict ΔH_{rx}° for the fermentation of sugar, given:

$$\Delta H_{comb}^\circ = -5645 \text{ kJ for } C_{12}H_{22}O_{11}(s)$$

$$\Delta H_{comb}^\circ = -1368 \text{ kJ for } C_2H_5OH(l)$$

$$\Delta H_f^\circ = -286 \text{ kJ for } H_2O(l), \qquad \Delta H_f^\circ = -394 \text{ kJ for } CO_2(g)$$

B-10. Exactly 3.0 g of C(s) was burned to $CO_2(g)$ in a copper calorimeter. The mass of the calorimeter was 1.500 kg and the mass of the water in which the calorimeter was immersed was 2.000 kg. The initial temperature of the system was 20.0°C and the final temperature was 31.0°C. Calculate the heat of formation of $CO_2(g)$, under the conditions present in the calorimeter. $c_{Cu} = 0.39$ kJ/(kg·°C).

B-11. Consider the following standard enthalpies of formation (in kilojoules per mole):

$$NO(g) = 90.4, \qquad NO_2(g) = 33.9, \qquad N_2O(g) = 81.6, \qquad N_2O_4(g) = 9.6$$

Balance the following reactions, predict the heat of reaction and indicate in each case whether the reaction is exothermic or endothermic.
a) $NO_2(g) \rightarrow N_2O_4(g)$
b) $N_2O_4(g) \rightarrow NO(g) + NO_2(g) + O_2(g)$
c) $N_2O(g) + NO_2(g) \rightarrow NO(g)$
d) $N_2O(g) + O_2(g) \rightarrow N_2O_4(g)$

B-12. Given: $\Delta H_f^\circ = 50.0$ kJ for $C_7H_8(l)$, $\Delta H_f^\circ = -286$ kJ for $H_2O(l)$ and $\Delta H_f^\circ = -394$ kJ for $CO_2(g)$, calculate the amount of heat given off when 100.0 g of $C_7H_8(l)$ is burned.

B-13. Given: $\Delta H_{diss}^\circ = 436$ kJ for H_2, $\Delta H_{diss}^\circ = 416$ kJ for C—H, $\Delta H_{diss}^\circ = 348$ kJ for C—C, and $\Delta H = 716$ kJ for $C(s) \rightarrow C(g)$, predict ΔH_f° for $C_3H_8(g)$, *i.e.*, for:

$$\left(\begin{matrix} & H & H & H & \\ & | & | & | & \\ H- & C- & C- & C- & H \\ & | & | & | & \\ & H & H & H & \end{matrix}\right)$$

B-14. The standard enthalpy of combustion of $C_2H_2(g)$ is -1301 kJ. The standard enthalpies of formation of $CO_2(g)$ and $H_2O(l)$ are -394 kJ and -286 kJ, respectively. What is ΔH_f° for $C_2H_2(g)$?

B-15. How much heat will be required to make 1.00 kg of $CaC_2(s)$ according to the reaction given below. The ΔH_f° values are in kilojoules per mole.

$$CaO(s) + 3\ C(s) \rightarrow CaC_2(s) + CO(g)$$
$$\Delta H_f^\circ: \quad -636 \qquad\qquad\qquad -63 \qquad -111$$

B-16. Given: $\Delta H_f^\circ = -46$ kJ for $NH_3(g)$, $\Delta H_{diss}^\circ = 436$ kJ for H_2 and $\Delta H_{diss}^\circ = 391$ kJ for N—H, predict ΔH_{diss}° for N_2.

B-17. Aviation gasoline is almost pure octane, C_8H_{18}. Octane burns according to the equation:

$$C_8H_{18}(l) + O_2(g) \rightarrow CO_2(g) + H_2O(l)$$
$$\text{(a)} \qquad \text{(b)} \qquad \text{(c)} \qquad \text{(d)}$$

($\Delta H_f^\circ = -209$ kJ for C_8H_{18}, $\Delta H_f^\circ = -286$ kJ for $H_2O(l)$ and $\Delta H_f^\circ = -394$ kJ for $CO_2(g)$.)

  i) Balance the equation.

  ii) What is the heat of formation of reactant (b)?

  iii) Calculate ΔH_{comb}° for C_8H_{18}.

  iv) Calculate the heat produced when 1.00 L of $C_8H_{18}(l)$ is burned. The density of $C_8H_{18}(l)$ is 703 g/L.

  v) An aluminum engine block has a mass of 110.0 kg. If only 20% of the heat produced in the engine is available to heat the block, what mass of octane is required to raise the temperature of the block from 15°C to 85°C? $c_{Al} = 0.900$ kJ/(kg·°C).

B-18. If CH_4 $\left(\begin{array}{c} H \\ | \\ H—C—H \\ | \\ H \end{array} \right)$ has a total bond energy of 1663 kJ, and C_2H_2

(H—C≡C—H) has a total bond energy of 1665 kJ, predict the bond strength of a carbon-carbon triple bond (C≡C).

B-19. The specific heat capacity of Ni(s) is 0.444 kJ/(kg·°C). A 3.85 g sample of benzoic acid, $C_6H_5CO_2H(s)$, was burned in a nickel calorimeter having a mass of 0.850 kg and immersed in 1.200 kg of water. The initial temperature of the system was 23.0°C and the final temperature was 41.9°C. Calculate the heat of combustion of benzoic acid, under the conditions present inside the calorimeter.

B-20. How much heat will be evolved in making 15.2 g of $H_2(Sg)$ at STP from FeS(s) and dilute HCl(aq)?

$$FeS(s) + 2\ HCl(aq) \rightarrow FeCl_2(aq) + H_2S(g)$$

ΔH_f° values in kilojoules per mole: HCl(g) $= -93$, $FeCl_2$(s) $= -341$

$$FeS(s) = -95,\ H_2S(g) = -20$$

ΔH_{soln} values in kilojoules per mole: HCl(g) $= -74$, $FeCl_2$(s) $= -79$

B-21. A 2.50 g sample of sucrose, $C_{12}H_{22}O_{11}(s)$ was burned in a 2.100 kg iron calorimeter immersed in 1.450 kg of water. The initial temperature of the system was 24.32°C and the final temperature was 30.20°C. Determine the heat of combustion of sucrose, under the conditions present inside the calorimeter. $c_{Fe} = 0.452$ kJ/(kg·°C).

B-22. One step in the manufacture of $CCl_4(l)$ includes the reaction

$$3 Cl_2(g) + CS_2(l) \rightarrow CCl_4(l) + S_2Cl_2(l).$$

($\Delta H_f^\circ = 88$ kJ for $CS_2(l)$; $\Delta H_f^\circ = -139$ kJ for $CCl_4(l)$; $\Delta H_f^\circ = -60$ kJ for $S_2Cl_2(l)$.)

If the reaction takes place inside a reactor which is cooled by water at 25°C, how many kilograms of water at 12°C must pass through the cooling coils of the reactor for each kilogram of $Cl_2(g)$ reacting in order to keep the temperature at 25°C?

B-23. Given: $Na(s) \rightarrow Na(g)$; $\Delta H = 109$ kJ

$\Delta H_{diss}^\circ = 251$ kJ for O_2; $\qquad\qquad \Delta H_{diss}^\circ = 435$ kJ for H_2;

$\Delta H_{diss}^\circ = 465$ kJ for $O{-}H$; $\qquad\qquad \Delta H_{diss}^\circ = 255$ kJ for $Na{-}O$;

$\Delta H_{soln} = -46$ kJ for $NaOH(s)$; $\qquad \Delta H_f^\circ = -427$ kJ for $NaOH(s)$

Predict ΔH for $NaOH(s) \rightarrow NaOH(g)$.

C-24. Given: $3 NO_2(g) + H_2O(l) \rightarrow 2 HNO_3(l) + NO(g)$; $\Delta H_{rx}^\circ = -72$ kJ

$2 NO(g) + O_2(g) \rightarrow 2 NO_2(g)$; $\qquad \Delta H_{rx}^\circ = -118$ kJ;

$\Delta H_f^\circ = 90$ kJ for $NO(g)$; $\qquad \Delta H_f^\circ = -286$ kJ for $H_2O(l)$

Calculate ΔH_f° for $HNO_3(l)$.

Section 4

Equilibrium Expressions and Le Chatelier's Principle

I. EQUILIBRIUM EXPRESSIONS

The equilibrium expression for the reaction

$$2\,A + B + 3\,C + \cdots \rightleftharpoons 4\,X + 2\,Y + Z + \cdots$$

is:
$$K_{eq} = \frac{[X]^4[Y]^2[Z]\cdots}{[A]^2[B][C]^3\cdots}$$

Note how the *coefficients* (2, 1, 3, etc.) in the reaction equation become *powers* in the equilibrium expression.

If all the reactants are gases, for example:

$$2\,A(g) + B(g) + 3\,C(g) + \cdots \rightleftharpoons 4\,X(g) + 2\,Y(g) + Z(g) + \cdots$$

we can write the equilibrium expression in terms of the partial pressures of each gas:

$$K_{eq} = \frac{P_X{}^4 \cdot P_Y{}^2 \cdot P_Z \cdots}{P_A{}^2 \cdot P_B \cdot P_C{}^3 \cdots}$$

(Partial pressure represents the amount of a particular gas contained in a given volume; that is, partial pressure is just another way to express concentration.)

By convention, the equilibrium expression *only* includes substances which can vary in concentration. Hence:

1. All gases must be included, since we can increase the pressure on a gas and therefore increase its concentration.

2. Aqueous ions (or gases in solution) must be included, since it is possible to change the concentration of solutions (for example, by dilution).

3. Pure solids are NEVER included, since the *density* of a solid (density is a form

27

of expressing concentration) is constant (*e.g.*, we cannot take a 1 cm cube of a solid and compress it appreciably).

4. *Pure* liquids are NEVER included, since the density of a pure liquid is constant (liquids cannot be compressed appreciably).

5. *Mixtures* of liquids must be included, since a change in the relative amounts of two mixed liquids will cause one liquid to dilute the other, and hence change concentrations.

Example: Write the equilibrium expressions for:

a) $2 C(s) + 3 H_2(g) \rightleftharpoons C_2H_6(g)$

$$K_{eq} = \frac{[C_2H_6(g)]}{[H_2(g)]^3} \qquad \text{(do not include solids)}$$

b) $Pb^{2+}(aq) + 2 Br^-(aq) \rightleftharpoons PbBr_2(s)$

$$K_{eq} = \frac{1}{[Pb^{2+}(aq)][Br^-(aq)]^2} \qquad \text{(do not include solids)}$$

c) $2 CH_3OH(l) \rightleftharpoons CH_3OCH_3(l) + H_2O(l)$

$$K_{eq} = \frac{[H_2O(l)][CH_3OCH_3(l)]}{[CH_3OH(l)]^2} \qquad$$ all *three* liquids exist at the same time in the solution and hence dilute each other.

EXERCISES

Write the equilibrium expressions for the following reactions.
1. $2 ICl(g) \rightleftharpoons I_2(g) + Cl_2(g)$
2. $N_2(g) + O_2(g) \rightleftharpoons 2 NO(g)$
3. $3 O_2(g) \rightleftharpoons 2 O_3(g)$
4. $2 Bi^{3+}(aq) + 3 H_2S(g) \rightleftharpoons Bi_2S_3(s) + 6 H^+(aq)$
5. $CaCO_3(s) \rightleftharpoons CaO(s) + CO_2(g)$
6. $CaC_2(s) + 2 H_2O(l) \rightleftharpoons C_2H_2(g) + Ca(OH)_2(s)$
7. $C_6H_6(l) + Br(l) \rightleftharpoons C_6H_5Br(l) + HBr(g)$
8. $Cu(s) + 2 Ag^+(aq) \rightleftharpoons Cu^{2+}(aq) + 2 Ag(s)$
9. $4 NH_3(g) + 5 O_2(g) \rightleftharpoons 6 H_2O(g) + 4 NO(g)$
10. $H_2(g) + \frac{1}{2} O_2(g) \rightleftharpoons H_2O(l)$

II. LE CHATELIER'S PRINCIPLE

Le Chatelier's Principle states that if a closed system at equilibrium is subjected to a change, processes will occur that *tend* to counteract that change.

That is, the equilibrium "shifts" to one side or another in an effort to oppose the change.

A. TEMPERATURE CHANGES

Consider the equilibrium

$$N_2O_4(g) + 59.0 \text{ kJ} \rightleftharpoons 2 NO_2(g)$$

If we increase the temperature, then more heat is available to the reaction, allowing more N_2O_4 to react. Hence the reaction shifts:

$$N_2O_4(g) + 59.0 \text{ kJ} \rightarrow 2 NO_2(g)$$

Note: If we *raise and maintain* the temperature then we continually make more heat available and cause K_{eq} to increase at the higher temperature (more products and less reactants). Note further that K_{eq} for an exothermic reaction will DECREASE when we raise the temperature (heat is used up driving the reverse reaction, producing more reactants and less products).

Graphically, we can show the effect of a temperature increase in the above system as:

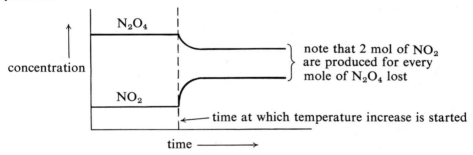

B. CONCENTRATION CHANGES

If we increase the amount of NO_2 by a *single injection* of NO_2 into the system, then the equilibrium will be temporarily upset until some of the extra NO_2 is used up. Hence the reaction shifts:

$$N_2O_4(g) + 59.0 \text{ kJ} \leftarrow 2 NO_2(g)$$

After *some* of the excess NO_2 is used, the equilibrium is re-established. Note, however that K_{eq} REMAINS UNCHANGED IN VALUE.

Graphically, we can show the effect of adding extra NO_2 as:

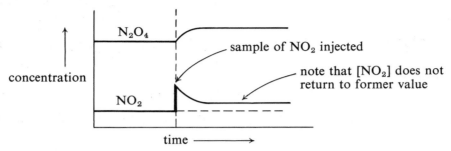

C. VOLUME CHANGES

If we decrease the volume of the container (*i.e.*, compress the mixture, but do not change the amount of gas inside) the concentration (in moles per litre) of all the gases in the container is effectively increased (*i.e.*, have same moles but fewer litres and hence moles per litre increases). To overcome the increased pressure, some of the NO_2 will react to form more N_2O_4. In this way the equilibrium re-establishes itself because 2 mol of NO_2 are consumed for every mole of N_2O_4 created and hence the pressure drops. That is: the increase in pressure is opposed by a tendency to decrease the pressure by shifting the reaction to the side having the fewest molecules:

$$N_2O_4(g) + 59.0 \text{ kJ} \leftarrow 2 NO_2(g)$$

Note that the value of K_{eq} *remains unchanged.*

Graphically, we can show the effect of changing the pressure as:

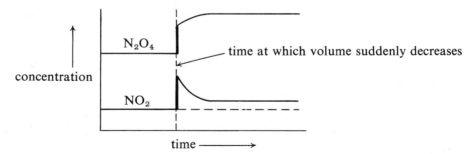

When dealing with pressure changes, we *must* state exactly how the change is accomplished.

i) If the pressure is increased by changing the volume, the reaction shifts to the side having the least number of molecules, as previously stated.

ii) If the pressure is increased by adding an inert gas such as He, *NO* shift occurs because the concentration of the gases involved in the reaction is unchanged.

iii) If the pressure is increased by changing the temperature or number of moles of a reactant or product, we consider the problem to involve *only* a change in temperature or moles (*i.e.*, use previously discussed methods and consider the pressure increase to be an incidental result of the other, more important changes).

D. ADDITION OF A CATALYST

Finally, if we add a catalyst to a system at equilibrium, there will be no change. If the system has not yet attained equilibrium, then equilibrium will be established FASTER, but the value of K_{eq} will be UNALTERED.

EXERCISES

Part I: Use Le Chatelier's Principle to describe the effect of the following changes on the reaction indicated.

A-1. Equilibrium is: $N_2O_3(g) \rightleftharpoons NO(g) + NO_2(g)$
   a) increase [NO]
   b) increase [N_2O_3]
   c) increase the pressure by decreasing the volume
   d) add a catalyst

A-2. Equilibrium is: $2 H_2(g) + 2 NO(g) \rightleftharpoons N_2(g) + 2 H_2O(g)$
   a) decrease [N_2]
   b) decrease [NO]
   c) decrease the pressure by increasing the volume

A-3. Equilibrium is: $CO(g) + \frac{1}{2} O_2(g) \rightleftharpoons CO_2(g) + 283$ kJ
   a) increase temperature
   b) increase [O_2]
   c) introduce a catalyst
   d) increase pressure by adding He(g)

A-4. Equilibrium is: $I_2(g) + Cl_2(g) \rightleftharpoons 2 ICl(g); \Delta H = 35.0$ kJ
   a) decrease temperature
   b) decrease [Cl_2]
   c) increase pressure by decreasing the volume

Part II: Describe the effect on K_{eq} and on the concentration of the underlined substance by the following changes. Write INC for increase, DEC for decrease, NC for no change.

B-5. Equilibrium is: $N_2(g) + 3 \underline{H_2(g)} \rightleftharpoons 2 NH_3(g)$; $\Delta H = -92$ kJ
  a) increase $[N_2]$ b) increase temperature
  c) increase volume   d) add a catalyst
B-6. Equilibrium is: $2 HF(g) \rightleftharpoons \underline{F_2(g)} + H_2(g)$; $\Delta H = 536$ kJ
  a) decrease temperature   b) decrease $[H_2]$
  c) decrease volume
B-7. Equilibrium is: $SnO_2(s) + 2 CO(g) \rightleftharpoons \underline{Sn(s)} + 2 CO_2(g)$; $\Delta H = 13$ kJ
  a) increase temperature   b) add a catalyst
  c) increase $[CO_2]$ d) add Kr(g)

Part III: Show the following situations graphically.
B-8. Equilibrium is: $H_2(g) + I_2(g) \rightleftharpoons 2 HI(g) + 52$ kJ
  a) increase temperature   b) decrease volume
  c) inject some $H_2(g)$ d) add a catalyst
B-9. Equilibrium is: $2 SO_2(g) + O_2(g) \rightleftharpoons 2 SO_3(g)$; $\Delta H = -197$ kJ
  a) inject some $SO_2(g)$ b) decrease temperature
  c) increase volume   d) increase $[SO_3]$
B-10. Equilibrium is: $CO(g) + H_2O(g) \rightleftharpoons CO_2(g) + H_2(g)$; $\Delta H = -41$ kJ
  a) inject some $CO_2(g)$ b) increase temperature
  c) remove some of the $H_2O(g)$ with a very rapidly acting drying agent
  d) decrease pressure by increasing volume

Section 5

Equilibrium Calculations

Consider the equilibrium: $N_2O_4 \rightleftharpoons 2\,NO_2$. In order to determine the value of K_{eq} we must have accurate information on the concentration of N_2O_4 and NO_2 at equilibrium. This information CANNOT be determined without actually doing an experiment.

Example: 1.0 mol of N_2O_4 was introduced into a 1.0 L bulb. After equilibrium was established, only 0.8 mol of N_2O_4 remained. What is the value of K_{eq} for the reaction?
We set up the problem as follows:

$$N_2O_4 \rightleftharpoons 2\,NO_2$$

starting concentration (= "START")	1.0	
+ change in concentration (= "Δ")		
= equilibrium concentration (= "EQUIL")	0.8	

Since no mention was made of any NO_2 initially, we assume that $[NO_2] = 0$, initially. Obviously, $\Delta = -0.2$ for N_2O_4. Now, 1 mol of N_2O_4 yields 2 mol of NO_2. Hence, the *loss* of 0.2 mol of N_2O_4 on the reactant side is accompanied by the *gain* of 0.4 mol of NO_2 on the product side. We now have:

$$N_2O_4 \rightleftharpoons 2\,NO_2$$

START	1.0	0
+ Δ	-0.2	$+0.4$
= EQUIL	0.8	0.4

note that all these numbers are molar concentrations

$$\therefore K_{eq} = \frac{[NO_2]^2}{[N_2O_4]} = \frac{(0.4)^2}{0.8} = 0.2$$

we ALWAYS use the *equilibrium* concentrations in the equilibrium expression

Example: A 10 L bulb is filled with 4.0 mol of SO_2, 2.2 mol of O_2 and 5.6 mol of SO_3. The gases then reach equilibrium according to the equation:

$$2 SO_2(g) + O_2(g) \rightleftharpoons 2 SO_3(g)$$

At equilibrium, the bulb was found to contain 2.6 mol of SO_2. Calculate K_{eq} for the reaction.

Since the gas is contained in a 10 L bulb, then at the start:

$$[SO_2] = \frac{4.0 \text{ mol}}{10 \text{ L}} = 0.40 \text{ kmol/m}^3 \qquad [O_2] = \frac{2.2 \text{ mol}}{10 \text{ L}} = 0.22 \text{ kmol/m}^3$$

$$[SO_3] = \frac{5.6 \text{ mol}}{10 \text{ L}} = 0.56 \text{ kmol/m}^3$$

and at equilibrium: $[SO_2] = \dfrac{2.6 \text{ mol}}{10 \text{ L}} = 0.26 \text{ kmol/m}^3$. Now:

	② SO_2 +	① O_2 $\rightleftharpoons$	2 SO_3
START	0.40	0.22	0.56
+ Δ	−0.14	−0.07	+0.14
= EQUIL	0.26	0.15	0.70

$$\frac{0.14}{2} = \frac{0.07}{1}$$

After all *data* is put in table, the Δ-value for SO_2 is calculated first. All other Δ-values are proportional to this value (in the same ratio as the coefficients in the equilibrium equation).

and:
$$K_{eq} = \frac{[SO_3]^2}{[SO_2]^2[O_2]} = \frac{(0.70)^2}{(0.26)^2(0.15)} = \underline{\underline{48}}$$

Example: Given that $K_{eq} = 48$ for the equilibrium

$$2 SO_2(g) + O_2(g) \rightleftharpoons 2 SO_3(g)$$

predict which way, if any, the reaction will shift when the following *initial* conditions are used: 4 mol SO_2, 3 mol O_2 and 2 mol SO_3 are introduced into a 10 L container.

We first calculate a trial value for K_{eq}:

$$K_{trial} = \frac{[SO_3]^2_{start}}{[SO_2]^2_{start}[O_2]_{start}} = \frac{(0.2)^2}{(0.4)^2(0.3)} = 0.83 < 48 = K_{eq}$$

Hence $K_{trial} < K_{eq}$, so that we must increase the numerator, $[SO_3]^2$, and decrease the denominator, $[SO_2]^2[O_2]$, in order to bring K_{trial} up to the value of K_{eq}. This corresponds to the shift:

$$2\,SO_2(g) + O_2(g) \rightarrow 2\,SO_3(g)$$

Example: At a certain temperature, $K_{eq} = 27$ for the reaction

$$PCl_5(g) \rightleftharpoons PCl_3(g) + Cl_2(g)$$

Some $PCl_5(g)$ was put in a litre vessel and at equilibrium it was found that $[PCl_5] = 3$ kmol/m³. What was the final concentration of PCl_3?

> Since we have no information about the starting amounts, or any changes, a "START, Δ, EQUIL" table will not be the correct way to tackle this problem. On the other hand, we know the value of K_{eq} and one of the equilibrium concentrations, $[PCl_5]$, and are asked to find another final equilibrium concentration, $[PCl_3]$. We will therefore try to solve for $[PCl_3]$ by rearranging the equilibrium expression.

The only source of PCl_3 and Cl_2 is the decomposition of PCl_5. Hence:

$$[PCl_3] = [Cl_2] \quad \text{since} \quad PCl_5 \rightarrow PCl_3 + Cl_2$$

Since we do not know the amount of PCl_3, we let $s = [PCl_3]$. Now:

$$K_{eq} = \frac{[PCl_3][Cl_2]}{[PCl_5]} = \frac{s^2}{3} = 27$$

$$s^2 = 81, \quad \text{and} \quad s = [PCl_3] = \underline{\underline{9 \text{ kmol/m}^3}}$$

Example: The equilibrium mixture

$$SO_2(g) + NO_2(g) \rightleftharpoons NO(g) + SO_3(g)$$

consisted of 0.800 mol of NO, 0.600 mol of SO_3, 0.200 mol of NO_2 and 0.500 mol of SO_2 in a 1.0 L bulb. How many moles of SO_3 would have to be added to the reaction vessel in order to increase the amount of NO_2 to 0.350 mol?

35

We will let the amount of SO_3 added be an unknown.

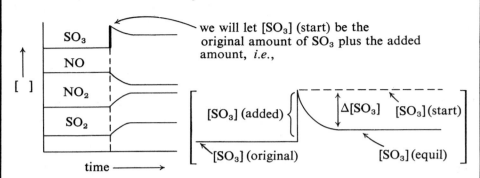

we will let $[SO_3]$ (start) be the original amount of SO_3 plus the added amount, *i.e.*,

The only means of solving for an unknown concentration we have is to use the equilibrium expression. This implies that we will require a value for K_{eq} and all the remaining concentrations in the expression. We can find the other concentrations by means of a "START, Δ, EQUIL" table. We should be able to calculate K_{eq} from the data given. Before the addition of the SO_3, the system was at equilibrium, and after the addition the system will seek to regain equilibrium. Since the addition of more reactants or products has no effect on the K_{eq} value, we can simply use the initial concentrations to calculate K_{eq}.

We first find K_{eq} using the original concentrations.

$$K_{eq} = \frac{[NO][SO_3]}{[SO_2][NO_2]} = \frac{0.80 \times 0.60}{0.50 \times 0.20} = 4.8$$

Let $s =$ the amount of SO_3 added. The starting conditions can now be written as:

	SO_2	$+ \ NO_2$	$\rightleftharpoons \ NO$	$+ \ SO_3$
START	0.50	0.20	0.80	0.60 + s
$+ \Delta$				
= EQUIL				

Since we require $[NO_2] = 0.35$ kmol/m³ at equilibrium, then $\Delta = +0.15$ for NO_2, and hence the full table becomes:

	SO_2	$+ \ NO_2$	$\rightleftharpoons \ NO$	$+ \ SO_3$
START	0.50	0.20	0.80	0.60 + s
$+ \Delta$	+0.15	+0.15	−0.15	−0.15
= EQUIL	0.65	0.35	0.65	0.45 + s

All Δ-values are equal since all the coefficients in the equilibrium equation are equal.

and:

$$K_{eq} = \frac{0.65 \times (s + 0.45)}{0.65 \times 0.35} = 4.8$$

which solves to give $s = 1.23$ mol of SO_3 added.

36

Example: Into a 10 L bulb was introduced 30.4 kPa pressure of SO_2, 40.5 kPa of O_2 and 2.0 kPa of SO_3. After equilibrium was attained according to the reaction $2 SO_2(g) + O_2(g) \rightleftharpoons 2 SO_3(g)$, the partial pressure of SO_3 was found to be 14.2 kPa. What is the value of K_{eq} for the reaction?

We treat partial pressures in the same way as concentrations. The only difference will be that the size of the bulb does not matter (partial pressure in a 1.0 L portion of the bulb is the same as in the full 10 L). Setting up the table we have:

	$2 SO_2 +$	$O_2 \rightleftharpoons$	$2 SO_3$
START	30.4	40.5	2.0
$+ \Delta$	-12.2	-6.1	$+12.2$
$=$ EQUIL	18.2	34.4	14.2

and:
$$K_{eq} = \frac{P_{SO_3}^2}{P_{SO_2}^2 \cdot P_{O_2}} = \frac{(14.2)^2}{(18.2)^2(34.4)} = \underline{\underline{0.018}}$$

EXERCISES

A-1. A 1.0 L reaction vessel contained 0.750 mol of $CO(g)$ and 0.275 mol of $H_2O(g)$. After 1 h, equilibrium was reached according to the equation:

$$CO(g) + H_2O(g) \rightleftharpoons CO_2(g) + H_2(g)$$

Analysis showed that 0.25 mol of CO_2 was present. What is K_{eq} for the reaction?

A-2. A 5.0 L reaction vessel was initially filled with 6.0 mol of SO_2, 2.5 mol of NO_2 and 1.0 mol of SO_3. After equilibrium was established according to the equation

$$SO_2(g) + NO_2(g) \rightleftharpoons SO_3(g) + NO(g)$$

the vessel was found to contain 3.0 mol of SO_3. What is K_{eq} for the reaction?

A-3. Consider the equilibrium:

$$3 I_2(g) + 6 F_2(g) \rightleftharpoons 2 IF_5(g) + I_4F_2(g)$$

a) At a certain temperature 3.0 mol of F_2 and 2.0 mol of I_2 are introduced into a 10.0 L container. At equilibrium the concentration of I_4F_2 is 0.020 kmol/m³. Calculate K_{eq} for the reaction.

b) At a different temperature, 6.0 mol of IF_5 and 8.0 mol of I_4F_2 are introduced into a 5.0 L container. At equilibrium 6.0 mol of I_4F_2 are left. Calculate K_{eq} for the reaction.

A-4. When a 1.0 L reaction vessel was filled with 101.0 kPa of $NH_3(g)$ and allowed to reach equilibrium according to the equation $2 NH_3(g) \rightleftharpoons N_2(g) + 3 H_2(g)$, 91.2 kPa of H_2 was found to be present. Calculate K_{eq} for the reaction.

A-5. At a certain temperature, K_{eq} = 4 for the reaction

$$2\ HF(g) \rightleftharpoons H_2(g) + F_2(g)$$

Predict the direction in which the equilibrium will shift, if any, when the following systems are introduced into a 5.0 L bulb.
a) 3.0 mol of HF, 2.0 mol of H_2 and 4.0 mol of F_2
b) 0.2 mol of HF, 0.5 mol of H_2 and 0.6 mol of F_2
c) 0.3 mol of HF, 1.8 mol of H_2 and 0.2 mol of F_2

A-6. At a certain temperature, K_{eq} = 55 for the reaction

$$2\ O_3(g) \rightleftharpoons 3\ O_2(g)$$

Predict the direction in which the equilibrium will move, if any, when the following systems are introduced into a 10 L bulb.
a) 0.700 mol of O_3 and 3.00 mol of O_2
b) 0.060 mol of O_3 and 0.70 mol of O_2
c) 1.20 mol of O_3 and 2.90 mol of O_2

B-7. K_{eq} = 5.0 at a certain temperature for the reaction

$$2\ SO_2(g) + O_2(g) \rightleftharpoons 2\ SO_3(g)$$

A certain amount of SO_3 was placed in a 2.0 L reaction vessel at the certain temperature. At equilibrium the vessel contained 30.0 kPa of O_2. What pressure of SO_3 was originally present in the vessel?

B-8. K_{eq} = 100 at a certain temperature for the reaction

$$CH_4(g) + 2\ H_2S(g) \rightleftharpoons CS_2(g) + 4\ H_2(g)$$

Some CH_4 and H_2S were introduced into a 1.0 L bulb and at equilibrium 0.10 mol of CH_4 and 0.30 mol of H_2S were found. What was [CS_2] at equilibrium?

B-9. A reaction mixture, $CO(g) + H_2O(g) \rightleftharpoons CO_2(g) + H_2(g)$ when at equilibrium, contains 0.20 mol of H_2, 0.70 mol of CO_2, 0.20 mol of CO and 0.30 mol of H_2O in a 1.0 L bulb. How many moles of CO_2 would have to be added to increase the amount of CO to 0.30 mol?

B-10. A reaction mixture, $CO_2(g) + H_2(g) \rightleftharpoons CO(g) + H_2O(g)$ when at equilibrium, was found to contain 0.8 mol of CO_2, 0.3 mol of H_2, 0.6 mol of CO and 0.5 mol of H_2O in a 1.0 L container. How many moles of CO_2 would have to be removed from the system in order to reduce the amount of CO to 0.5 mol?

B-11. The equilibrium constant for the reaction

$$CO(g) + H_2O(g) \rightleftharpoons CO_2(g) + H_2(g)$$

is 5.0 at a certain temperature. A mixture of 122 kPa of CO and 182 kPa of steam was put into a 3.0 L bulb at this temperature. What pressure of CO_2 was present when the system reached a state of equilibrium?

B-12. K_{eq} = 49.5 for $H_2(g) + I_2(g) \rightleftharpoons 2\,HI(g)$ at a certain temperature. If 0.25 mol of H_2 and 0.25 mol of I_2 are placed into a 10 L vessel and permitted to react, what will be the concentration of each substance at equilibrium?

B-13. K_{eq} = 35.0 for $PCl_5(g) \rightleftharpoons PCl_3(g) + Cl_2(g)$. If there are $1.34 \times 10^{-3}\,kmol/m^3$ of PCl_5 and $2.05 \times 10^{-1}\,kmol/m^3$ of PCl_3 at equilibrium in a certain vessel, what is $[Cl_2]_{eq}$?

B-14. 0.150 mol of H_2, 0.150 mol of I_2 and 0.870 mol of HI are at equilibrium according to the equation $H_2 + I_2 \rightleftharpoons 2\,HI$. The reaction occurs in a 10.0 L vessel. If 0.40 mol of HI are now added to this system and the system allowed to come to equilibrium again, what will be the new concentrations of H_2, I_2 and HI?

B-15. K_{eq} = 125 for $H_2 + I_2 \rightleftharpoons 2\,HI$ at a certain temperature. If 0.15 mol of HI, 0.034 mol of H_2 and 0.096 mol of I_2 are introduced into a 10.0 L vessel, will the reaction proceed to the reactant or product side as the reaction attempts to reach equilibrium?

B-16. 0.50 mol of NOCl was introduced into a 1.00 L flask and allowed to come to equilibrium according to the reaction: $2\,NOCl \rightleftharpoons 2\,NO + Cl_2$. If 0.10 mol of Cl_2 was found at equilibrium, what is K_{eq} for the reaction?

B-17. K_{eq} = 7.5 for $2\,H_2 + S_2 \rightleftharpoons 2\,H_2S$. A certain amount of H_2S was added to a 1.00 L flask and allowed to come to equilibrium. At equilibrium, 0.036 mol of H_2 was found. How much H_2S was originally added to the flask?

B-18. A reaction mixture, $2\,NO + O_2 \rightleftharpoons 2\,NO_2$, was found to contain 0.24 mol of NO, 0.086 mol O_2 and 1.20 mol of NO_2 when at equilibrium in a 2.0 L bulb. How many moles of O_2 would have to be added to the mixture to increase the number of moles of NO_2 to 1.28 when equilibrium was re-established?

B-19. A reaction mixture, $2\,ICl + H_2 \rightleftharpoons I_2 + 2\,HCl$, was found to contain 0.50 mol of ICl, 0.056 mol of H_2, 1.36 mol of I_2 and 0.80 mol of HCl at equilibrium in a 1.0 L bulb. How many moles of ICl would have to be removed to reduce [HCl] to $0.68\,kmol/m^3$ when equilibrium is re-established?

B-20. K_{eq} = 1 for $N_2O_2 + H_2 \rightleftharpoons N_2O + H_2O$. If 150 kPa of N_2O and 250 kPa of H_2O were introduced into a 10.0 L bulb and allowed to come to equilibrium, what pressure of N_2O_2 was present at equilibrium?

B-21. The equilibrium constant for the reaction

$$N_2(g) + 3\,H_2(g) \rightleftharpoons 2\,NH_3(g)$$

is 3.0 at a certain temperature. Enough NH_3 was added to a 1.0 L container such that, after equilibrium was established, the container was found to contain 2.5 mol of N_2. Now many moles of NH_3 were originally introduced into the container?

C-22. An equilibrium mixture, $2\,SO_2(g) + O_2(g) \rightleftharpoons 2\,SO_3(g)$, was found to contain 0.10 mol of SO_2, 0.15 mol of SO_3 and 0.050 mol of O_2 in a 1.0 L bulb. An identical bulb contains 48 g of SO_2 at the same temperature. What mass of O_2

must be added to the second bulb such that half of the SO_2 will be converted to SO_3 at equilibrium?

C-23. An equilibrium mixture, $H_2(g) + I_2(g) \rightleftharpoons 2\ HI(g)$, was found to contain 2.0 mol of H_2, 4.0 mol of I_2 and 3.0 mol of HI in a litre. How many moles of H_2 must be added to the mixture to have 40% of the added H_2 react to form HI? Let s = moles of H_2 added. Just set up the equilibrium expression, but do not attempt to solve.

C-24. A reaction mixture is at equilibrium according to the equation: $LaCl_3(s) + H_2O(g) \rightleftharpoons LaClO(s) + 2\ HCl(g)$. Some more $HCl(g)$ is then added, such that when equilibrium is re-established the amount of $HCl(g)$ in the mixture is found to have doubled. By what factor will the amount of H_2O in the system have been multiplied?

$$\left[\ \begin{array}{l} \textit{Hint:}\ \text{Write an expression for } K_{eq} \text{ in terms of unknown concentrations,} \\ \text{before and after adding HCl. Then: } K_{eq}(\text{before}) = K_{eq}(\text{after}). \end{array}\ \right]$$

40

Section 6

Solubility Product

The SOLUBILITY of a substance in a certain solvent is defined to be the MAXIMUM amount of the substance which will dissolve in a given quantity of the solvent. Hence, a substance is said to be *slightly* soluble if only a small amount of the substance will dissolve.

After the maximum amount of a substance has dissolved, such that no more will go into solution, we say the solution is SATURATED with the substance. When a solution is saturated with a substance, an equilibrium situation will occur. For example:

$$CuCl(s) \rightleftharpoons Cu^+(aq) + Cl^-(aq)$$

Note: For a solution to be saturated an equilibrium must exist and hence *some* undissolved substance must be present (even if only a very small amount).

Once an equilibrium equation has been written, we can also write a *solubility product expression*. For example:

$$K_{sp} = [Cu^+(aq)][Cl^-(aq)]$$

General Note on Solving Solubility Problems

It is good practice to start all solubility problems by writing down first the equilibrium equation and then the corresponding equilibrium expression for the equation. If you are uncertain how to proceed with a problem, it is often only necessary to substitute the information given into the equilibrium expression and solve for any unknown quantities.

Example: $K_{sp} = 3.2 \times 10^{-7}$ for CuCl. What is $[Cu^+]$ in a saturated solution of CuCl?

Since the only source of Cu^+ and Cl^- is CuCl, then:

$$[Cu^+] = [Cl^-]$$

If s mol of CuCl dissolve in 1 L we have:

$$s = [Cu^+] = [Cl^-]$$

and since $\quad\quad [Cu^+][Cl^-] = 3.2 \times 10^{-7}$

then $\quad\quad\quad\quad s^2 = 3.2 \times 10^{-7}$

and $\quad\quad\quad\quad s = \underline{\underline{5.7 \times 10^{-4} \text{ kmol/m}^3 = [Cu^+]}}$

Example: What mass of CuCl will dissolve in 10 L of water? First, we must know $[Cu^+]$ or $[Cl^-]$ in a saturated solution. From the first example we know: $[Cu^+] = 5.7 \times 10^{-4} \text{ kmol/m}^3$.

$\therefore$ In 10 L we can dissolve $5.7 \times 10^{-4} \dfrac{\text{mol}}{\text{L}} \times 10 \text{ L} = 5.7 \times 10^{-3} \text{ mol}$

$\therefore$ Mass of CuCl $= 5.7 \times 10^{-3} \text{ mol} \times \dfrac{99.0 \text{ g}}{\text{mol}} = \underline{\underline{0.56 \text{ g}}}$

Example: A saturated solution of Ag_2CO_3 can be made by dissolving 1.27×10^{-4} mol of solid Ag_2CO_3 in 1.0 L of water. What is K_{sp} for Ag_2CO_3?

We want K_{sp} for the equilibrium: $Ag_2CO_3(s) \rightleftharpoons 2\,Ag^+ + CO_3{}^{2-}$. Now, 1.27×10^{-4} mol of Ag_2CO_3 ionizes as follows:

$$Ag_2CO_3(s) \rightleftharpoons 2\,Ag^+(aq) + CO_3{}^{2-}(aq)$$

$$1.27 \times 10^{-4} \quad (2.54)\times 10^{-4} \quad 1.27 \times 10^{-4}$$

$\therefore K_{sp} = [Ag^+]^2[CO_3{}^{2-}] = (2.54 \times 10^{-4})^2 \times (1.27 \times 10^{-4})$

$$= \underline{\underline{8.19 \times 10^{-12}}}$$

Example: $K_{sp} = 8.3 \times 10^{-9}$ for PbI_2. What is the concentration of Pb^{2+} in a saturated solution of PbI_2?

The solubility product expression for the equilibrium

$$PbI_2(s) \rightleftharpoons Pb^{2+}(aq) + 2\,I^-(aq)$$

is: $\quad\quad\quad\quad K_{sp} = [Pb^{2+}][I^-]^2.$

If s mol of PbI_2 dissolve in 1 L of water, then:

$$s = [Pb^{2+}] \left.\begin{array}{l} \\ \\ \end{array}\right\} PbI_2 \to Pb^{2+} + 2\,I^-$$
$$2s = [I^-] \qquad\qquad s \qquad s \qquad 2\,s$$
$$K_{sp} = s \times (2s)^2 = 8.3 \times 10^{-9}$$
$$4s^3 = 8.3 \times 10^{-9}$$

and:
$$s = 1.28 \times 10^{-3}\ kmol/m^3 = [Pb^{2+}]$$

EXERCISES

A-1. A solution in equilibrium with a precipitate of AgCl was found to contain 3.4×10^{-6} kmol of Ag^+ per cubic metre and 5.0×10^{-5} kmol of Cl^- per cubic metre. Calculate K_{sp} for AgCl.

A-2. What is the equilibrium concentration of Cd^{2+} ions in a saturated aqueous solution of CdS made by shaking CdS(s) with water? $K_{sp} = 6 \times 10^{-27}$ for CdS.

A-3. How many grams of $PbSO_4$ will dissolve in 5.0 L of water? $K_{sp} = 1.3 \times 10^{-8}$ for $PbSO_4$.

A-4. K_{sp} for ferrous oxalate, FeC_2O_4, is 2.1×10^{-7} at 25°C. What is the concentration of ferrous ion in a saturated solution made by dissolving solid ferrous oxalate?

A-5. K_{sp} for barium chromate, $BaCrO_4$, is 1.6×10^{-10} at 18°C. How many grams of $BaCrO_4$ are present in 10 L of a saturated solution of $BaCrO_4$?

A-6. An experiment showed that a maximum of 1.49 g of $AgBrO_3$ can dissolve in 1.0 L of water at 20°C. What is K_{sp} for $AgBrO_3$?

A-7. K_{sp} for $Mg(OH)_2$ is 1.0×10^{-11}. Calculate the solubility of $Mg(OH)_2$ in kilomoles per cubic metre.

A-8. K_{sp} for $PbCO_3$ is 1.0×10^{-13}. Calculate the solubility of $PbCO_3$ in grams per litre.

A-9. K_{sp} for $CaSO_4$ is 2.4×10^{-5}. Calculate the solubility of $CaSO_4$ in kilomoles per cubic metre.

A-10. K_{sp} for $Ni(OH)_2$ is 1.6×10^{-16}. Calculate the solubility of $Ni(OH)_2$ in grams per litre.

B-11. A solution in equilibrium with a precipitate of Ag_2S was found to contain 1.6×10^{-16} kmol of S^{2-} per cubic metre and 2.5×10^{-18} kmol of Ag^+ per cubic metre. Calculate the solubility product of Ag_2S.

B-12. A solution in equilibrium with a precipitate of $Pb_3(PO_4)_2$ was found to contain 2.9×10^{-3} kmol of $PO_4{}^{3-}$ per cubic metre and 1.2×10^{-9} kmol of Pb^{2+} per cubic metre. Calculate the solubility product for $Pb_3(PO_4)_2$.

B-13. A solution in equilibrium with a precipitate of Ag_2CO_3 was found to contain 1.86×10^{-2} g of CO_3^{2-} per litre and 1.51×10^{-2} g of Ag^+ per litre. Calculate K_{sp} for Ag_2CO_3. 2.49×10^{-6}

B-14. A speck of chalk dust with mass 0.0010 g just barely dissolved in 100 mL of water. Chalk is made up of $CaCO_3$. What is the value of K_{sp} for $CaCO_3$? 1×10^{-8}

B-15. $K_{sp} = 5 \times 10^{-7}$ for $Zn(OH)_2$. What is the concentration of OH^- in a saturated solution of $Zn(OH)_2$?

B-16. What is the concentration of Cd^{2+} ions in a saturated solution of $Cd(OH)_2$? $K_{sp} = 2 \times 10^{-14}$ for $Cd(OH)_2$.

B-17. What mass of Hg is present in 1.0 L of a saturated Hg_2Cl_2 solution made by shaking Hg_2Cl_2 with water? $K_{sp} = 2 \times 10^{-18}$ for Hg_2Cl_2. Note that: $Hg_2Cl_2(s) \rightleftharpoons Hg_2^{2+} + 2\,Cl^-$.

C-18. The molar concentration of Co^{2+} in a solution in equilibrium with CoS(s) was found to be three times as great as the concentration of S^{2-}. $K_{sp} = 3 \times 10^{-26}$. What was the Co^{2+} concentration? $3 \times 10^{-26} = 3x^2$

C-19. A litre of solution which is in equilibrium with a precipitate of $Mn(OH)_2$ contains five times as many moles of OH^- as Mn^{2+}. How many moles of OH^- are present? $K_{sp} = 4.0 \times 10^{-14}$ for $Mn(OH)_2$. $4.\times 10^{-14} = x \cdot (5x)^2$

C-20. A solution in equilibrium with a precipitate of Ag_2CO_3 contains three times as many grams of CO_3^{2-} as Ag^+. How many grams of CO_3^{2-} are present per litre of solution? $K_{sp} = 6.2 \times 10^{-12}$ for Ag_2CO_3.

$$6.2 \times 10^{-12} = [2 \cdot 0.014 x]^2 [0.014]$$

589

32.

$\left[\dfrac{x}{215.6}\right]^2 \left[\dfrac{3x}{60}\right]$

$\dfrac{x^2 \quad 3x^3}{699840}$

$12.5 x^3 \times 10^{-5}$

7.9×10^{-3}

4.3×10^{-6}

5568

Section 7

Precipitation

The ION PRODUCT, K_{trial}, is just the value of the product of all the ionic concentrations in a solution (similar to the equilibrium expression). For example, for AgCl we have:

$$K_{trial} = [Ag^+][Cl^-].$$

When we have a *saturated* solution of AgCl, the ion product will be EXACTLY equal to the value of K_{sp}. For example,

$$K_{sp} = [Ag^+][Cl^-] = 1.6 \times 10^{-10}, \quad \text{at } 25°C$$

If we add only sufficient AgCl to water such that

$$K_{trial} < K_{sp}$$

then all the AgCl will dissolve, since there is insufficient AgCl to form a saturated solution. That is, the value of the ion product, $[Ag^+][Cl^-]$, is not sufficiently large to allow some AgCl(s) to stay undissolved and hence establish the equilibrium:

$$AgCl(s) \rightleftharpoons Ag^+(aq) + Cl^-(aq)$$

If we try to dissolve an amount of AgCl which would make

$$K_{trial} > K_{sp}$$

then some of the AgCl must remain undissolved since K_{sp} represents the maximum value of the ion product under normal circumstances. In this case an equilibrium situation DOES occur because some undissolved solid remains.

Similarly, assume we mix an $AgNO_3$ solution and a NaCl solution, such that in the resulting solution we expect:

$$K_{trial} > K_{sp}$$

45

In this case the solution will rid itself of the excess burden of Ag^+ and Cl^- by forming a *precipitate* of AgCl(s). The solution will *continue* producing precipitate until the value of K_{trial} has been *reduced* to *exactly* K_{sp}. That is, the *maximum* value of K_{trial} which will be able to exist in the solution will be the K_{sp} value.

Example: Predict whether a precipitate will form when 20 mL of 0.0020 kmol/m³ Ag^+ is added to 30 mL of 0.0020 kmol/m³ Cl^-.

When the Ag^+ solution and Cl^- solution are mixed, the two solutions dilute each other and hence we must calculate the new concentrations of Ag^+ and Cl^- in the mixed solution:

$$\text{moles } Ag^+ = 2.0 \times 10^{-3} \frac{mol}{L} \times 2.0 \times 10^{-2}\,L = 4.0 \times 10^{-5}\,mol$$

$$\text{moles } Cl^- = 2.0 \times 10^{-3} \frac{mol}{L} \times 3.0 \times 10^{-2}\,L = 6.0 \times 10^{-5}\,mol$$

$$\text{total volume} = 20\,mL + 30\,mL = 5.0 \times 10^{-2}\,L$$

$$[Ag^+] \text{ in mixture} = \frac{4.0 \times 10^{-5}\,mol}{5.0 \times 10^{-2}\,L} = 8.0 \times 10^{-4}\,kmol/m^3$$

$$[Cl^-] \text{ in mixture} = \frac{6.0 \times 10^{-5}\,mol}{5.0 \times 10^{-2}\,L} = 1.2 \times 10^{-3}\,kmol/m^3$$

We now check to see how the value of the ion product compares with K_{sp}:

$$K_{trial} = [Ag^+][Cl^-] = 8.0 \times 10^{-4} \times 1.2 \times 10^{-3} = 9.6 \times 10^{-7}$$

Since: $K_{trial} > K_{sp} = 1.6 \times 10^{-10}$, then a precipitate *will* form.

Note: We can use a short-cut to calculate $[Ag^+]$ and $[Cl^-]$ in the mixture.

Originally, all the Ag^+ was contained in a 20 mL volume. After dilution, the Ag^+ was contained in a total of 50 mL. Hence, the final $[Ag^+]$ will be only 20/50 of the original value, *i.e.*,

$$[Ag^+] \text{ (diluted)} = 2.0 \times 10^{-3}\,kmol/m^3 \times \frac{20\,mL}{50\,mL} = 8.0 \times 10^{-4}\,kmol/m^3$$

Similarly, the Cl^- which was in 30 mL has been diluted to 50 mL:

$$[Cl^-] \text{ (diluted)} = 2.0 \times 10^{-3}\,kmol/m^3 \times \frac{30\,mL}{50\,mL} = 1.2 \times 10^{-3}\,kmol/m^3$$

Example: Exactly 450 mL of 1.00×10^{-4} kmol/m³ $BaCl_2$ is placed in a beaker. In order to *just start* precipitation of $BaSO_4$ it is necessary to add, with constant stirring, exactly 350 mL of 2.00×10^{-4} kmol/m³ K_2SO_4. What is K_{sp} for $BaSO_4$?

46

First we calculate the concentration of Ba^{2+} and SO_4^{2-} in the mixed solution (before precipitation starts),

$$\text{total volume} = 450 \text{ mL} + 350 \text{ mL} = 0.800 \text{ L}$$

$$[Ba^{2+}] \text{ (mixture)} = 1.00 \times 10^{-4} \text{ kmol/m}^3 \times \frac{0.450 \text{ L}}{0.800 \text{ L}} = 5.63 \times 10^{-5} \text{ kmol/m}^3$$

$$[SO_4^{2-}] \text{ (mixture)} = 2.00 \times 10^{-4} \text{ kmol/m}^3 \times \frac{0.350 \text{ L}}{0.800 \text{ L}} = 8.75 \times 10^{-5} \text{ kmol/m}^3$$

When precipitation *just starts*, we have $K_{trial} = K_{sp}$, so that:

$$K_{sp} = [Ba^{2+}][SO_4^{2-}] = 5.63 \times 10^{-5} \times 8.75 \times 10^{-5} = \underline{\underline{4.93 \times 10^{-9}}}.$$

Example: What concentration of OH^-, in kilomoles per cubic metre, is required to just start precipitation of $Fe(OH)_3$ from a solution containing 2.0×10^{-6} kmol/m^3 Fe^{3+}? $K_{sp} = 6.0 \times 10^{-38}$ for $Fe(OH)_3$.

We have the situation:

$$Fe(OH)_3(s) \rightleftharpoons Fe^{3+}(aq) + 3\,OH^-(aq)$$

where: $K_{sp} = [Fe^{3+}][OH^-]^3$.

When precipitation just starts to occur we have $K_{trial} = K_{sp}$. Now, we know $[Fe^{3+}]$ and K_{sp} and hence we can solve directly for $[OH^-]$:

$$[OH^-]^3 = \frac{K_{sp}}{[Fe^{3+}]} = \frac{6.0 \times 10^{-38}}{2.0 \times 10^{-6}} = 3.0 \times 10^{-32}$$

and

$$[OH^-] = 3.1 \times 10^{-11} \text{ kmol/m}^3$$

ADDITIONAL COMMENTS FOR C-TYPE PROBLEMS

When two compounds can be precipitated from the same solution, such that the compounds have one ion in common, we proceed by considering both equilibrium expressions simultaneously.

Example: $K_{sp} = 7.7 \times 10^{-13}$ for AgBr, $K_{sp} = 1.6 \times 10^{-10}$ for AgCl. A solution is 0.0010 kmol/m^3 in Br^- and 0.010 kmol/m^3 in Cl^-. If Ag^+ ions are slowly added:
a) Which precipitate forms first?
The $[Ag^+]$ required to precipitate AgBr is:

$$[Ag^+] = \frac{K_{sp}}{[Br^-]} = \frac{7.7 \times 10^{-13}}{1.0 \times 10^{-3}} = 7.7 \times 10^{-10} \text{ kmol/m}^3$$

The [Ag$^+$] required to precipitate AgCl is:

$$[Ag^+] = \frac{K_{sp}}{[Cl^-]} = \frac{1.6 \times 10^{-10}}{1.0 \times 10^{-2}} = 1.6 \times 10^{-8} \text{ kmol/m}^3$$

Since AgBr requires the smallest [Ag$^+$] in solution before forming a precipitate, the AgBr precipitates first.

b) What is the concentration of the halide ion involved in the first precipitate that forms when the second halide ion starts to form a precipitate?

When the second precipitate just starts to form we have:

$$\left.\begin{array}{l} K_{sp}(1) = [Ag^+][Cl^-] \\ K_{sp}(2) = [Ag^+][Br^-] \end{array}\right\} \quad \begin{array}{l} \text{[Ag}^+] \text{ is the same in both of these since both} \\ \text{expressions hold true for the same solution.} \end{array}$$

From part (a) we found AgBr precipitates first. Now when AgCl starts to precipitate we require:

$$[Ag^+] = \frac{K_{sp}(1)}{[Cl^-]} = 1.6 \times 10^{-8} \text{ kmol/m}^3 \quad \text{(again, found in part (a))}$$

The [Br$^-$] in solution has been decreasing from the moment AgBr started to precipitate. By the time the Cl$^-$ starts to precipitate, the [Br$^-$] will be considerably reduced, due to precipitation losses:

$$[Br^-] = \frac{K_{sp}(2)}{[Ag^+]} = \frac{7.7 \times 10^{-13}}{1.6 \times 10^{-8}} = 4.8 \times 10^{-5} \text{ kmol/m}^3$$

The amount of precipitate formed in a reaction is rather tricky to calculate. We shall consider an example which illustrates several points.

Example: $K_{sp} = 1.6 \times 10^{-10}$ for AgCl. If 2.5×10^{-4} mol of Ag$^+$ and 4.0×10^{-4} mol of Cl$^-$ are mixed together in 1.0 L of water, what mass of AgCl is formed?

Let

$$\Delta[Ag^+] = \text{loss in [Ag}^+] \text{ due to precipitate formation}$$

$$\Delta[Cl^-] = \text{loss in [Cl}^-] \text{ due to precipitate formation}$$

Then:

$$[Ag^+]_{\text{EQUIL}} = [Ag^+]_{\text{START}} - \Delta[Ag^+]$$

$$[Cl^-]_{\text{EQUIL}} = [Cl^-]_{\text{START}} - \Delta[Cl^-]$$

But 1 mol of Ag$^+$ reacts with 1 mol of Cl$^-$ so that:

$$\Delta[Ag^+] = \Delta[Cl^-]$$

Let $s = \Delta[Ag^+] = \Delta[Cl^-]$. Substituting in the available data we have:

$$[Ag^+]_{EQUIL} = 2.5 \times 10^{-4} - s$$

$$[Cl^-]_{EQUIL} = 4.0 \times 10^{-4} - s.$$

But: $K_{sp} = [Ag^+]_{EQUIL} \times [Cl^-]_{EQUIL}$, so that:

$$1.6 \times 10^{-10} = (2.5 \times 10^{-4} - s) \times (4.0 \times 10^{-4} - s)$$

This equation is a quadratic in s which can be solved to give:

$$s = 2.49 \times 10^{-4} \text{ kmol/m}^3$$

Since we have 1.0 L of solution, we will then have 2.49×10^{-4} mol of Ag^+ lost from solution and hence 2.49×10^{-4} mol of AgCl will be formed. The mass of AgCl formed is then:

$$\text{mass AgCl} = 2.49 \times 10^{-4} \text{ mol} \times \frac{143.4 \text{ g}}{\text{mol}} = 0.036 \text{ g}$$

EXERCISES

A-1. $K_{sp} = 5.0 \times 10^{-22}$ for CoS. Will a precipitate form when 1.0 L of 3.0×10^{-10} kmol/m^3 Co^{2+} is added to 1.0 L of 2.0×10^{-11} kmol/m^3 S^{2-}?

A-2. $K_{sp} = 4.0 \times 10^{-17}$ for FeS. Will a precipitate form when 1.0 L of 5.0×10^{-9} kmol/m^3 Fe^{2+} is added to 1.0 L of 4.0×10^{-9} kmol/m^3 S^{2-}?

A-3. What concentration of S^{2-} must be present to just start precipitation of CuS from a 0.20 kmol/m^3 solution of $CuCl_2$? $K_{sp} = 4.0 \times 10^{-36}$ for CuS.

A-4. What concentration of F^- must be present to just start precipitation of CaF_2 from a 3.0×10^{-3} kmol/m^3 solution of $Ca(NO_3)_2$? $K_{sp} = 3.4 \times 10^{-11}$ for CaF_2.

A-5. K_{sp} for lead(II) sulphate, $PbSO_4$, is 1.06×10^{-8} at 18°C. Predict whether a precipitate will form when 10 mL of 1.0×10^{-3} kmol/m^3 lead(II) acetate is added to 40 mL of 1.5×10^{-4} kmol/m^3 Na_2SO_4.

A-6. A precipitate just starts to form when 20 mL of 1.0×10^{-2} kmol/m^3 Mg^{2+} is added to 60 mL of 2.0×10^{-2} kmol/m^3 CO_3^{2-}. What is K_{sp} for $MgCO_3$?

A-7. A precipitate just starts to form when 25 mL of 5.0×10^{-8} kmol/m^3 Ag^+ is added to 100 mL of 1.1×10^{-8} kmol/m^3 I^-. What is K_{sp} for AgI?

B-8. Predict whether a precipitate forms when 20 mL of 1.0×10^{-4} kmol/m^3 $Zn(NO_3)_2$ solution is added to 60 mL of 2.4×10^{-5} kmol/m^3 $Ca(OH)_2$. $K_{sp} = 1.8 \times 10^{-14}$ for $Zn(OH)_2$.

B-9. A precipitate just started to form under the following conditions: 5.0 mL of 1.0×10^{-7} kmol/m^3 Na$_2$S is diluted to 1.0 L and 10 mL of the resulting solution is added to 90 mL of 7.6×10^{-17} kmol/m^3 lead(II) acetate. What is K_{sp} for PbS?

B-10. When 100 mL of 2.5×10^{-5} kmol/m^3 ferrous chloride is added to 150 mL of 6.7×10^{-5} kmol/m^3 sodium hydroxide, a precipitate of ferrous hydroxide just starts to form. What is K_{sp} for Fe(OH)$_2$?

B-11. If Cu^{2+} is slowly added to a solution which is 0.020 kmol/m^3 in KIO$_3$:
  a) at what concentration of Cu^{2+} does a precipitate of Cu(IO$_3$)$_2$ start to form? $K_{sp} = 1.4 \times 10^{-7}$ for Cu(IO$_3$)$_2$.
  b) when [Cu^{2+}] = 5.0×10^{-4} kmol/m^3, what percentage of the IO$_3^-$ is left in solution?

B-12. If Ag$^+$ is slowly added to a solution which is 0.10 kmol/m^3 in Na$_2$CrO$_4$:
  a) at what concentration of Ag$^+$ does a precipitate of Ag$_2$CrO$_4$ start to form? $K_{sp} = 1.0 \times 10^{-12}$ for Ag$_2$CrO$_4$.
  b) when [Ag$^+$] = 1.0×10^{-4} kmol/m^3, what percentage of the CrO$_4^{2-}$ is left in solution?

B-13. Predict whether a precipitate will form when 1 drop (0.050 mL) of 5.0 kmol/m^3 Pb^{2+} is added to 100 mL of 3.0×10^{-5} kmol/m^3 I$^-$. $K_{sp} = 7.5 \times 10^{-9}$ for PbI$_2$.

B-14. Predict whether a precipitate will form when 20 mL of 5.0×10^{-5} kmol/m^3 Cu$^+$ is added to 35 mL of 2.5×10^{-4} kmol/m^3 Br$^-$ and the resulting solution is boiled down to a total volume of 25 mL. $K_{sp} = 4.2 \times 10^{-8}$ for CuBr.

B-15. The solubility product of Ag$_2$CO$_3$ is 6.2×10^{-12}. Assuming that a precipitate can be detected as soon as it begins to form, what is the minimum concentration of CO$_3^{2-}$ that can be detected in a solution having [Ag$^+$] = 0.050 kmol/m^3? Express your answer in grams per litre.

B-16. The solubility of Cu(IO$_3$)$_2$ in water is 3.3×10^{-3} kmol/m^3. What concentration of Cu^{2+} would be required to just start precipitation of Cu(IO$_3$)$_2$ from a 0.020 kmol/m^3 solution of KIO$_3$?

C-17. K_{sp} for AgBr is 1.0×10^{-13}, and K_{sp} for Ag$_2$CrO$_4$ is 1.0×10^{-12}. A solution is 0.10 kmol/m^3 in Br$^-$ and 0.010 kmol/m^3 in CrO$_4^{2-}$. If Ag$^+$ ions are slowly added:
  a) what precipitate forms first?
  b) what is the concentration of the negative ion involved in the first precipitate that forms when the second negative ion starts to form a precipitate?

C-18. K_{sp} for AgCl is 1.6×10^{-10}, and K_{sp} for Ag$_2$CrO$_4$ is 1.0×10^{-12}. A solution is 0.10 kmol/m^3 in Cl$^-$ and 0.010 kmol/m^3 in CrO$_4^{2-}$. If Ag$^+$ ions are slowly added:
  a) what precipitate forms first?
  b) what is the concentration of the negative ion involved in the first precipitate that forms when the second negative ion starts to form a precipitate?

C-19. A solution was made by mixing 0.0100 mol of Ag^+ and some Cl^- in 1.00 L of water. If 4.5×10^{-3} mol of AgCl(s) was formed, how much Cl^- remained in solution? $K_{sp} = 1.6 \times 10^{-10}$ for AgCl.

C-20. The solubility product of $SrCO_3$ is 1.6×10^{-9}. To a solution containing 0.175 g of Sr^{2+} per litre was added solid Na_2CO_3 until the concentration of CO_3^{2+} was 2.50×10^{-6} kmol/m³. What mass of $SrCO_3$ was precipitated?

C-21. A solution contains 5.07×10^{-5} g of Na_2SO_4 and 3.27 g of NaF in 1.00 L of water. When solid $BaCl_2$ is slowly added to the solution, both $BaSO_4$ and BaF_2 start to precipitate simultaneously. $K_{sp} = 1.0 \times 10^{-10}$ for $BaSO_4$. What is K_{sp} for BaF_2?

C-22. When an aqueous solution containing 0.401 g of Ca^{2+} in 500 mL was mixed with a solution containing 1.066 g of SO_4^{2-} in 500 mL, a precipitate of $CaSO_4$ formed and was separated by filtration. The solution remaining contained exactly three times as many grams of SO_4^{2-} as Ca^{2+}. Calculate K_{sp} for $CaSO_4$.

C-23. You are a physician in an emergency ward. A girl has entered respiratory collapse due to chewing on wood covered with lead based paint. Tests have shown $[Pb^{2+}]$ in her blood to be 1.0×10^{-5} kmol/m³. Reports have shown that $[Pb^{2+}] > 1.0 \times 10^{-7}$ kmol/m³ can be considered lethal. To quickly reduce $[Pb^{2+}]$ to 1.0×10^{-9} kmol/m³ you have decided to inject a Na_2CO_3 solution directly into her blood so as to cause a $PbCO_3$ precipitate to form ($K_{sp} = 3.3 \times 10^{-14}$), which can be filtered from the blood by her kidneys. If her body contains 1.7 L of blood, what mass of Na_2CO_3 is required to precipitate the Pb^{2+} from her blood and bring $[Pb^{2+}]$ down to 1.0×10^{-9} kmol/m³? Since Na_2CO_3 is lethal in large amounts you must not administer an overdose.

Section 8
Common Ion Effect

The equilibrium $CaSO_4(s) \rightleftharpoons Ca^{2+}(aq) + SO_4^{2-}(aq)$ has a solubility product of 2.45×10^{-5} at 25°C. This corresponds to a solubility of 0.674 g/L (*i.e.*, 4.95×10^{-3} kmol/m^3) for pure solid $CaSO_4$ in water. If we attempt to dissolve $CaSO_4$ in a solution which already contains some SO_4^{2-}, the solubility of $CaSO_4$ may be reduced considerably.

Example: Solid $CaSO_4$ is added to 1.00 L of a 0.100 kmol/m^3 solution of Na_2SO_4 until no more $CaSO_4$ will dissolve. If K_{sp} is 2.45×10^{-5} for $CaSO_4$, what is $[Ca^{2+}]$ in the saturated solution?

$$\left[\begin{array}{l} \text{The only source of } Ca^{2+} \text{ in the final solution is the } CaSO_4 \text{ which dissolves. The} \\ \text{solid } CaSO_4 \text{ and the } Na_2SO_4 \text{ both contribute to the } [SO_4^{2-}]. \text{ We will express} \\ K_{sp} = [Ca^{2+}][SO_4^{2-}] \text{ in terms of the known and unknown concentrations, and} \\ \text{solve for the unknown concentration.} \end{array} \right]$$

Let s = the concentration of dissolved $CaSO_4$. Then:

Na_2SO_4	$\rightarrow$	$2\,Na^+$	$+$
0.100 kmol/m^3		0.200 kmol/m^3	
$CaSO_4$		Ca^{2+}	
s		s	

By writing out both the equations representing the dissolving process and the resulting ion concentrations in this manner, we obtain a convenient table of values which frequently prevents errors in ion concentrations

SO_4^{2-}
0.100 kmol/m^3
SO_4^{2-}
s

Now:
$$[Ca^{2+}]_{total} = s$$
$$[SO_4^{2-}]_{total} = 0.100 + s$$

and:
$$K_{sp} = [Ca^{2+}]_{total} \times [SO_4^{2-}]_{total}$$

or:
$$2.45 \times 10^{-5} = s \times (0.100 + s)$$

This equation can be solved directly, but the solution process will be a little messy since the equation is a quadratic in s. Hence, we will simplify the solution process by making a simplifying assumption.

Since $(0.100 + s)$ is *at least* as big as 0.100, then s must be quite small in order to make $s \times (0.100 + s)$ sufficiently small enough to equal 2.45×10^{-5}. Now, if s is very small we can ASSUME that s is NEGLIGIBLE with respect to 0.100, and that: $0.100 + s \simeq 0.100$ ($\simeq$ means "approximately equal to"). Hence substitution into the K_{sp} expression gives:

$$s \times 0.100 = 2.45 \times 10^{-5}$$

and:

$$s = 2.45 \times 10^{-4} \text{ kmol/m}^3$$

> Check: 2.45×10^{-4} is indeed negligible with respect to 0.100, as we assumed.
> *Note:* We assume that one number is negligible with respect to another if one number is less than 5% of the other.

$$\therefore [Ca^{2+}] = 2.45 \times 10^{-4} \text{ kmol/m}^3$$

The solubility of $CaSO_4$ in our example (2.45×10^{-4} kmol/m^3) is reduced from the solubility of $CaSO_4$ in pure water (4.95×10^{-3} kmol/m^3), as a result of the Na_2SO_4 also present in the example. Since the solubility of $CaSO_4$ was reduced by the presence of the added SO_4^{2-} ion (which was *common* to both the $CaSO_4$ and the Na_2SO_4) we call this solubility reduction the *common ion effect*.

A variation on the above type of problem occurs when a known amount of a slightly soluble salt is dissolved in a solution containing a large, but unknown, concentration of a common ion.

Example: $K_{sp} = 1.8 \times 10^{-14}$ for $Zn(OH)_2$. The solubility of $Zn(OH)_2$ is 2.0×10^{-9} kmol/m^3 in a solution which already contains some NaOH. What is the concentration of NaOH in the solution?

We first list the known and unknown concentrations of the ions:

$$Zn(OH)_2 \rightarrow Zn^{2+} + 2\,OH^-$$
$$2.0 \times 10^{-9} \quad 2.0 \times 10^{-9} \quad 4.0 \times 10^{-9}$$

$$NaOH \rightarrow Na^+ + OH^-$$
$$s \qquad s \qquad s$$

Now:

$$[Zn^{2+}]_{total} = 2.0 \times 10^{-9}$$

$$[OH^-]_{total} = 4.0 \times 10^{-9} + s$$

so that: $$K_{sp} = [Zn^{2+}]_{total} \times [OH^-]^2_{total}$$

or: $$1.8 \times 10^{-14} = 2.0 \times 10^{-9} \times (4.0 \times 10^{-9} + s)^2$$

Since $[Zn^{2+}]$ is quite small, then $[OH^-]^2$ *cannot* be very small (or else $[Zn^{2+}][OH^-]^2$ would be much less than K_{sp}).

Let us *assume* 4.0×10^{-9} is negligibly small with respect to s, so that: $4.0 \times 10^{-9} + s \simeq s$ and hence substitution into the K_{sp} expression gives

$$2.0 \times 10^{-9} \times s^2 = 1.8 \times 10^{-14}$$

so that $$s = 3.0 \times 10^{-3} \, kmol/m^3$$

$$\left[\text{Check: } 4.0 \times 10^{-9} \text{ is indeed negligible with respect to } 3.0 \times 10^{-3}, \text{ as we assumed.} \right]$$

$$\therefore [NaOH] = 3.0 \times 10^{-3} \, kmol/m^3$$

The assumptions involved in common ion effect problems can be summed up as follows.

If we assume that one of the two ion concentrations involved in the K_{sp} expression is *known*, then the second concentration is assumed to be *unknown*.

More specifically, in the first example problem we made the assumption:

$$s \times (0.100 + s) \simeq s \times 0.100$$

unknown — assume other term is known

and in the second example problem we made the assumption:

$$2.0 \times 10^{-9} \times (4.0 \times 10^{-9} + s)^2 = 2.0 \times 10^{-9} \times s^2$$

known — assume other term is unknown

In both assumptions we dropped one of the terms INSIDE the brackets.

EXERCISES

A-1. K_{sp} for AgBr is 1.0×10^{-13}. How many moles of AgBr will dissolve in 1.0 L of $0.020 \, kmol/m^3$ KBr solution?

A-2. K_{sp} for AgCl is 1.6×10^{-10}. How many moles of AgCl will dissolve in 5.0 L of $0.10 \, kmol/m^3$ NaCl solution?

A-3. $K_{sp} = 1.1 \times 10^{-8}$ for $PbSO_4$. If 5.0×10^{-6} mol of $PbSO_4$ can dissolve in 1.0 L of a K_2SO_4 solution, what is the molar concentration of the K_2SO_4 solution?

A-4. $K_{sp} = 1.4 \times 10^{-7}$ for $Cu(IO_3)_2$. If 2.0×10^{-5} mol of $Cu(IO_3)_2$ can dissolve in 2.0 L of a $NaIO_3$ solution, what is the molar concentration of the $NaIO_3$ solution?

A-5. Powdered AgOH is slowly added to 2.0 L of a 0.020 kmol/m³ solution of NaOH until no more AgOH will dissolve. If $K_{sp} = 1.4 \times 10^{-8}$ for AgOH:
   a) what is $[Ag^+]$ in the saturated solution?
   b) what mass of AgOH had to be added to the solution to produce this concentration of Ag^+?

A-6. When excess Ag_2CO_3 is shaken with 1.00 L of 0.0100 kmol/m³ K_2CO_3, 6.84×10^{-3} g of Ag_2CO_3 dissolve. Calculate the solubility product of Ag_2CO_3.

A-7. K_{sp} for $BaSO_4$ is 1.5×10^{-9}. If $BaSO_4$ is added to a solution of K_2SO_4, the solubility of the $BaSO_4$ is 2.0×10^{-7} kmol/m³. What is the concentration of the K_2SO_4 solution?

B-8. A solution contains 0.020 mol of $(NH_4)_2S$. How many grams of MnS must be added to 1.0 L of the solution to just start forming a precipitate of MnS? $K_{sp} = 1.4 \times 10^{-15}$ for MnS.

B-9. Silver oxide dissolves according to the reaction:

$$Ag_2O + H_2O \rightleftharpoons 2\,Ag^+ + 2\,OH^-$$

If $K_{sp} = [Ag^+][OH^-] = 2.0 \times 10^{-8}$ for AgOH, how many moles of Ag_2O will dissolve in 2.0 L of a solution having $[OH^-] = 1.0 \times 10^{-3}$ kmol/m³?

B-10. $K_{sp} = 3.7 \times 10^{-15}$ for $Al(OH)_3$. A precipitate just began to form when 50.0 mL of 2.0×10^{-6} kmol/m³ $Al(OH)_3$ was mixed with 50.0 mL of NaOH solution. What was the concentration of the NaOH solution?

B-11. What is the solubility (expressed in grams per litre) of $Mg(OH)_2$ in 0.050 kmol/m³ $MgSO_4$. K_{sp} for $Mg(OH)_2$ is 1.2×10^{-12}.

C-12. $K_{sp} = 1.08 \times 10^{-10}$ for $BaSO_4$ and $K_{sp} = 1.73 \times 10^{-6}$ for BaF_2. Ba^{2+} ions are added to a solution which is 0.0100 kmol/m³ in Na_2SO_4 and 0.0100 kmol/m³ in NaF until 50% of the F^- has been precipitated. What is $[SO_4^{2-}]$ after the addition of the Ba^{2+}?

C-13. A 1.00 L solution contained a small amount of FeC_2O_4 and $Fe(OH)_2$ such that no undissolved solid was present. The concentration of OH^- in the solution was one-half that of the $C_2O_4^{2-}$. The addition of $Fe(ClO_4)_2(s)$ to the solution caused FeC_2O_4 and $Fe(OH)_2$ to precipitate simultaneously. What was the concentration of the FeC_2O_4 in the original solution? $K_{sp} = 2.10 \times 10^{-7}$ for FeC_2O_4; $K_{sp} = 1.64 \times 10^{-14}$ for $Fe(OH)_2$.

Section 9

Acid-Base Reactions

The reaction of an acid with a base is governed by the equilibrium:

$$H_2O(l) \rightleftharpoons H^+(aq) + OH^-(aq)$$

for which:

$$K_w = [H^+][OH^-] = 1.0 \times 10^{-14}$$

If we are given either $[H^+]$ or $[OH^-]$, then we can use the K_w expression to find the other concentration.

Example: What is $[OH^-]$ in a 0.010 kmol/m³ solution of HCl?
Since HCl is a strong acid (dissociates 100%) then:

$$[H^+] = [HCl] = 1.0 \times 10^{-2} \text{ kmol/m}^3$$

and
$$[OH^-] = \frac{K_w}{[H^+]} = \frac{1.0 \times 10^{-14}}{1.0 \times 10^{-2}} = \underline{\underline{1.0 \times 10^{-12} \text{ kmol/m}^3}}$$

If an acidic solution is added to a basic solution then *some* of the acid will react with *some* of the base until

$$K_{trial} = [H^+][OH^-] = 1.0 \times 10^{-14} = K_w$$

Example: 50 mL of 0.020 kmol/m³ H^+ is added to 50 mL of 0.030 kmol/m³ OH^-. What is $[H^+]$ in the final solution?
We start the problem by assuming the two solutions do not react when initially mixed, so that we first calculate the $[H^+]$ and $[OH^-]$ in the mixture:

$$\text{total volume} = 50 \text{ mL} + 50 \text{ mL} = 0.100 \text{ L}$$

$$[H^+] \text{(mixture)} = 0.020 \text{ kmol/m}^3 \times \frac{0.050 \text{ L}}{0.100 \text{ L}} = 0.010 \text{ kmol/m}^3$$

56

$$[\text{OH}^-]\,(\text{mixture}) = 0.030\ \text{kmol/m}^3 \times \frac{0.050\ \text{L}}{0.100\ \text{L}} = 0.015\ \text{kmol/m}^3$$

INITIAL METHOD OF FINISHING PROBLEM

We can set up the problem as follows.

		$[\text{H}^+]$	$[\text{OH}^-]$
	START	0.010	0.015
$+\,\Delta$		$-s$	$-s$
$=$	EQUIL	$0.010 - s$	$0.015 - s$

Then: $(0.010 - s)(0.015 - s) = 1.0 \times 10^{-14}$ at equilibrium or:

$$s^2 - 0.025s + 1.5 \times 10^{-4} - 1.0 \times 10^{-14} = 0$$

But: $\qquad\qquad 1.5 \times 10^{-4} - 1.0 \times 10^{-14} \simeq 1.5 \times 10^{-4}$

so that $\qquad\qquad s^2 - 0.025s + 1.5 \times 10^{-4} = 0$

and we solve to find:

$$s = 1.5 \times 10^{-2}\ \text{kmol/m}^3, \quad \text{or} \quad s = 1.0 \times 10^{-2}\ \text{kmol/m}^3$$

Now we only have $1.0 \times 10^{-2}\ \text{kmol/m}^3\ \text{H}^+$ originally, and hence the only allowable value is $1.0 \times 10^{-2}\ \text{kmol/m}^3$. This means:

$$[\text{H}^+]_{\text{EQUIL}} = 0.010 - 0.010 = 0!$$

and $\qquad\qquad [\text{OH}^-]_{\text{EQUIL}} = 0.015 - 0.010 = \underline{\underline{0.005\ \text{kmol/m}^3}}$

However, we cannot *actually* have $[\text{H}^+]_{\text{EQUIL}} = 0$. This "zero" value must have resulted from the rounding-off approximation above. We can find the correct value from:

$$[\text{H}^+] = \frac{1.0 \times 10^{-14}}{[\text{OH}^-]} = \frac{1.0 \times 10^{-14}}{5 \times 10^{-3}} = \underline{\underline{2 \times 10^{-12}}}\ \text{kmol/m}^3 \ (\text{which is } close \text{ to zero!})$$

REFINED METHOD OF FINISHING PROBLEM

Since $[\text{H}^+][\text{OH}^-] = 1.0 \times 10^{-14}$, then one or both of $[\text{H}^+]$ or $[\text{OH}^-]$ *must* be small at equilibrium. The initial method, above, shows that the $[\text{OH}^-]$ was originally in excess and that *effectively all* of the original amount of H^+ reacted (thus reducing $[\text{H}^+]$ to a small number, as required). Since $[\text{OH}^-] > [\text{H}^+]$, originally, we can write:

$$[\text{OH}^-]_{\text{EXCESS}} = [\text{OH}^-]_{\text{START}} - [\text{OH}^-]_{\text{REACTED}}$$

57

But we can assume that:

$$[OH^-]_{REACTED} = [H^+]_{REACTED} \simeq [H^+]_{START}$$

and substitution gives us:

$$[OH^-]_{EXCESS} = [OH^-]_{START} - [H^+]_{START}$$

If, in a different problem, we knew that H^+ was originally in excess then we could write:

$$[H^+]_{EXCESS} = [H^+]_{START} - [OH^-]_{START}$$

Continuing, we now have:

$$[OH^-]_{EXCESS} = 0.015 - 0.010 = \underline{0.005 \text{ kmol/m}^3}$$

and

$$[H^+] = \frac{K_w}{[OH^-]} = \frac{1.0 \times 10^{-14}}{5 \times 10^{-3}} = \underline{\underline{2 \times 10^{-12} \text{ kmol/m}^3}}$$

Example: How many moles of OH^- must be added to 100 mL of 0.20 kmol/m³ H^+ to produce a solution having 0.30 kmol/m³ OH^-? Assume no change in volume occurs.
We want to end up with an excess of OH^-:

$$[OH^-]_{EXCESS} = [OH^-]_{START} - [H^+]_{START}$$
$$0.30 \text{ kmol/m}^3 = [OH^-]_{START} - 0.20 \text{ kmol/m}^3$$

and $[OH^-]_{START} = 0.50 \text{ kmol/m}^3$
= the concentration of OH^- needed at the start (before the reaction begins)

$$\therefore \text{ moles } OH^- \text{ required} = 0.50 \frac{\text{mol}}{\text{L}} \times 0.100 \text{ L} = \underline{\underline{0.050 \text{ mol}}}$$

EXERCISES

A-1. Calculate both $[H^+]$ and $[OH^-]$ in the following solutions.
a) 0.0010 kmol/m³ HCl   b) 4.0 kmol/m³ NaOH
c) 6.00×10^{-3} kmol/m³ $Ca(OH)_2$ d) 2.5×10^{-4} kmol/m³ HNO_3
A-2. Calculate $[OH^-]$ and $[H^+]$ which results when 50.0 mL of 0.150 kmol/m³ NaOH are added to 50.0 mL of 0.200 kmol/m³ HCl.

A-3. Calculate $[H^+]$ and $[OH^-]$ which results when 75.0 mL of 0.200 $kmol/m^3$ HBr are mixed with 225.0 mL of 0.150 $kmol/m^3$ KOH.

A-4. Calculate $[H^+]$ and $[OH^-]$ which results when 60.0 mL of 0.380 $kmol/m^3$ HNO_3 are mixed with 150.0 mL of 0.0700 $kmol/m^3$ $Ca(OH)_2$.

A-5. Calculate $[OH^-]$ and $[H^+]$ which results when 25.0 mL of 0.0420 $kmol/m^3$ $Mg(OH)_2$ are mixed with 125.0 mL of 0.0120 $kmol/m^3$ HCl.

A-6. Calculate $[H^+]$ and $[OH^-]$ which results when 50.0 g of KOH are added to 200 mL of water containing 60.0 g of HCl.

A-7. Calculate $[H^+]$ and $[OH^-]$ which results when 5.00 g of NaOH are added to 100 mL of 1.00 $kmol/m^3$ HCl.

A-8. How many moles of hydrobromic acid must be added to 250 mL of 0.200 $kmol/m^3$ NaOH to produce a solution having $[H^+] = 4.0 \times 10^{-2}\, kmol/m^3$? Assume no volume change.

A-9. How many moles of NaOH must be added to 3.500 L of $1.75 \times 10^{-3}\, kmol/m^3$ $HClO_4$ to produce a solution having $[OH^-] = 3.600 \times 10^{-2}\, kmol/m^3$? Assume no volume change.

B-10. How many grams of KOH must be added to 150 mL of 0.250 $kmol/m^3$ HNO_3 to produce a solution having $[OH^-] = 0.0100\, kmol/m^3$?

B-11. How many grams of HCl(g) must be added to 2.5 L of a 0.30 $kmol/m^3$ solution of KOH to produce a solution having $[H^+] = 0.70\, kmol/m^3$?

B-12. How many grams of $Ca(OH)_2$ must be added to 100 mL of a 0.10 $kmol/m^3$ solution of HNO_3 to produce a solution having $[OH^-] = 0.010\, kmol/m^3$?

C-13. How many mL of 0.25 $kmol/m^3$ KOH must be added to 100 mL of 0.10 $kmol/m^3$ HCl to produce a solution having $[OH^-] = 0.010\, kmol/m^3$?

> *Hint:* The volumes are different in the initial and final solutions, so that $[OH^-]_{EXCESS} = [OH^-]_{START} - [H^+]_{START}$ *cannot* be used. This equation is based on moles and assumes that subtracting concentrations is *exactly* equivalent to subtracting moles (which is not so if the volumes containing the moles are unequal). You should find how much base must be added to neutralize the acid and *then* how much base must be added to the neutral solution to give the required $[OH^-]$.

C-14. How many mL of 0.030 $kmol/m^3$ HCl must be added to 50 mL of 0.080 $kmol/m^3$ NaOH to produce a solution having $[H^+] = 0.010\, kmol/m^3$?

C-15. How many mL of 0.10 $kmol/m^3$ HCl must be added to a solution made from 1.0 g of $Ca(OH)_2$ and 2.0 L of water to produce a solution having $[H^+] = 0.030\, kmol/m^3$?

C-16. A solution is made by adding 50 mL of 0.10 $kmol/m^3$ HNO_3 and 20 mL of 0.060 $kmol/m^3$ NaOH to 100 mL of water. How much of this solution would have to be added to 50 mL of 0.10 $kmol/m^3$ KOH to make $[OH^-] = 0.090$ $kmol/m^3$ in the final solution?

Section 10
pH and pOH

We define:

$$pH = -\log_{10}[H^+]$$
$$pOH = -\log_{10}[OH^-]$$

The process of calculating pH or pOH is straightforward.

Example: If $[H^+] = 2.00 \times 10^{-4}$ kmol/m³, what is pH?

$$[H^+] = 2.00 \times 10^{-4} = 10^{0.3010} \times 10^{-4}$$
$$\log[H^+] = 0.3010 + (-4) = -3.699$$
$$pH = -\log[H^+] = \underline{\underline{3.699}}$$

Note: If a number has 3 significant figures, then the *fractional* part of the logarithm of the number should also contain 3 significant figures.

$$\left[\quad \textit{i.e.,} \qquad \log(2.00 \times 10^{-4}) = -3.699 \qquad\qquad\qquad\qquad\quad \text{3 significant figures} \qquad \right]$$

Conversion from pH to $[H^+]$, or pOH to $[OH^-]$ is accomplished by REVERSING the order of the steps in the previous example.

Example: If pH = 3.699, what is $[H^+]$?

$$pH = -\log[H^+] = 3.699$$
$$\log[H^+] = -3.699$$

Since we cannot look up the antilog of a negative number in most log tables, we perform the following little trick: when confronted with a negative logarithm, we add 1 to the fractional part and add -1 to the whole number part, *e.g.*,

$$-3.699 = (-0.699 + 1) + (-3 - 1) = 0.301 + (-4)$$

Hence: $$\log[H^+] = 0.301 + (-4)$$

and: $$[H^+] = 10^{0.301} \times 10^{-4} = \underline{2.00 \times 10^{-4} \, \text{kmol/m}^3}$$

If we are asked to calculate *both* pH and pOH, we can use the following:

$$K_w = 1.0 \times 10^{-14} = [H^+][OH^-]$$

and taking logs:

$$-14 = \log[H^+] + \log[OH^-]$$

or $$\boxed{14 = \text{pH} + \text{pOH}}$$

Example: The pH of a solution is 3.50. What is pOH?

$$\text{pOH} = 14 - \text{pH}$$
$$= 14 - 3.50 = \underline{\underline{10.50}}$$

When dealing with neutralization problems involving pH and pOH, we *MUST* first convert to $[H^+]$ and $[OH^-]$.

Example: What is the pH of the solution resulting from the addition of 50.0 mL of a solution having pH $= 3.500$ to 50.0 mL of a solution having pH $= 11.500$?
We first convert to concentration units.

$$\text{pH} = -\log[H^+] = 3.500$$
$$\log[H^+] = -3.500 = 0.500 + (-4)$$
$$[H^+] = 10^{0.500} \times 10^{-4} = 3.16 \times 10^{-4} \, \text{kmol/m}^3$$

Note that a solution having pH $= 11.500$ is actually *BASIC*, so that we should give our attention to the concentration of OH^- rather than the concentration of H^+. Hence our next step should be:

$$\text{pOH} = 14 - \text{pH} = 14 - 11.500 = 2.500 = -\log[OH^-]$$
$$\log[OH^-] = -2.500 = 0.500 + (-3)$$
$$[OH^-] = 10^{0.500} \times 10^{-3} = 3.16 \times 10^{-3} \, \text{kmol/m}^3$$

Now:

$$\text{total volume} = 50.0 \text{ mL} + 50.0 \text{ mL} = 0.1000 \text{ L}$$

$$\therefore [H^+]_{\text{START}} = 3.16 \times 10^{-4} \text{ kmol/m}^3 \times \frac{0.0500}{0.1000} = 1.58 \times 10^{-4} \text{ kmol/m}^3$$

$$[OH^-]_{\text{START}} = 3.16 \times 10^{-3} \text{ kmol/m}^3 \times \frac{0.0500}{0.1000} = 1.58 \times 10^{-3} \text{ kmol/m}^3$$

Hence:

$$[OH^-]_{\text{EXCESS}} = [OH^-]_{\text{START}} - [H^+]_{\text{START}}$$
$$= 1.58 \times 10^{-3} - 1.58 \times 10^{-4}$$
$$= 1.42 \times 10^{-3} \text{ kmol/m}^3$$
$$pOH = -\log(1.42 \times 10^{-3}) = -\log(10^{0.152} \times 10^{-3})$$
$$= -(0.152 - 3) = 2.848$$
$$pH = 14 - 2.848 = \underline{\underline{11.152}}$$

EXERCISES

A-1. Calculate pH *and* pOH for the following.
   a) $[H^+] = 1.0 \times 10^{-5} \text{ kmol/m}^3$
   b) $[OH^-] = 3.0 \times 10^{-8} \text{ kmol/m}^3$
   c) $[H^+] = 2.5 \times 10^{-2} \text{ kmol/m}^3$
   d) $[OH^-] = 7.53 \times 10^{-3} \text{ kmol/m}^3$
   e) $[H^+] = 1.25 \times 10^{-14} \text{ kmol/m}^3$
   f) $[H^+] = 10.0 \text{ kmol/m}^3$
   g) $[OH^-] = 12.5 \text{ kmol/m}^3$
   h) $[H^+] = 1.00 \text{ kmol/m}^3$
   i) $[H^+] = 4.93 \times 10^{-6} \text{ kmol/m}^3$
   j) $[OH^-] = 3.15 \times 10^{-11} \text{ kmol/m}^3$
   k) $[OH^-] = 6.45 \times 10^{-4} \text{ kmol/m}^3$
   l) $[H^+] = 7.04 \times 10^{-6} \text{ kmol/m}^3$
   m) $[OH^-] = 3.14 \times 10^{-1} \text{ kmol/m}^3$
   n) $[H^+] = 1.05 \text{ kmol/m}^3$
   o) $[H^+] = 0.0123 \text{ kmol/m}^3$
   p) $[OH^-] = 9.76 \times 10^{-9} \text{ kmol/m}^3$
   q) $[H^+] = 5.22 \times 10^{-3} \text{ kmol/m}^3$
   r) $[OH^-] = 4.76 \times 10^{-6} \text{ kmol/m}^3$

s) $[OH^-] = 9.50 \times 10^{-4}$ kmol/m³
t) $[H^+] = 8.52 \times 10^{-10}$ kmol/m³

A-2. Calculate $[H^+]$ and $[OH^-]$ for the following.

a) pH = 3.0   b) pOH = 2.60
c) pOH = 5.633   d) pH = 7.519
e) pOH = −1.132   f) pH = 0.031
g) pH = 6.413   h) pOH = 4.947
i) pH = −0.356   j) pOH = 11.542
k) pOH = −0.020   l) pH = 5.755
m) pH = 12.612   n) pOH = 9.437
o) pH = 7.814   p) pOH = 10.050
q) pOH = −1.009   r) pH = 7.232
s) pH = 3.176   t) pOH = 9.561

B-3. What is the pH of the solution resulting from the addition of 25.0 mL of a solution having pH = 3.550 to 25.0 mL of a solution having pH = 11.250?

B-4. What is the pH of the solution resulting from the addition of 50.0 mL of a solution having pH = 6.350 to 100 mL of a solution having pH = 6.600?

B-5. What is the pH of the solution resulting from the addition of 100 mL of a solution having pH = 5.716 to 250 mL of a solution having pOH = 5.042?

B-6. What is the pH of the solution resulting from the addition of 50.0 mL of a solution having pH = 5.137 to 30.0 mL of a solution having pH = 8.941?

B-7. What is the pH of the solution resulting from the addition of 25.0 mL of a solution having pOH = 12.433 to 15.0 mL of a solution having pH = 12.556?

?. What is the pOH of the solution resulting from the addition of 120.0 mL of a solution having pOH = 8.754 to 50.0 mL of a solution having pOH = 9.021?

B-9. What is the pH of the solution resulting from the addition of 85.0 mL of a solution having pH = 3.893 to 75.0 mL of a solution having pOH = 4.077?

B-10. What is the pOH of the solution resulting from the addition of 20.0 mL of a solution having pH = 10.751 to 400 mL of a solution having pOH = 9.507?

B-11. What is the pH of the solution resulting from the addition of 135.0 mL of a solution having pH = 8.655 to 70.0 mL of a solution having pOH = 5.136?

B-12. What is the pH of the solution resulting from the addition of 95.0 mL of a solution having pOH = 9.008 to 15.0 mL of a solution having pH = 4.636?

B-13. How many litres of stomach acid (pH = 4.000) will be neutralized by a 1.50 g tablet of "Bicar", a commercial indigestion remedy which is 50.0% flavoured filler and 50.0% $NaHCO_3$? Note that: $NaHCO_3(s) \rightarrow Na^+(aq) + HCO_3^-(aq)$ and: $H^+(aq) + HCO_3^-(aq) \rightarrow H_2O(l) + CO_2(g)$

C-14. How many millilitres of a solution having pH = 1.398 must be added to 50.0 mL of a solution having pH = 12.845 to produce a solution having pH = 2.000?

C-15. How many millilitres of a solution having pOH = 2.850 must be added to 100 mL of a solution having pH = 2.715 to produce a solution having pH = 10.000?

Section 11

Calculations Based on Brönsted–Lowry Theory

A. THE BRÖNSTED–LOWRY THEORY OF ACIDS AND BASES

In the Brönsted–Lowry theory of acids and bases we define:

> An *ACID* is any substance which can *donate* a proton to another substance.
> A *BASE* is any substance which can *accept* a proton from another substance.

Unlike the situation for Arrhenius acids and bases, we shall find that:

a) A Brönsted–Lowry acid DOES NOT NECESSARILY give rise to significant amounts of H^+ in solution.
b) A Brönsted–Lowry base DOES NOT NECESSARILY give rise to significant amounts of OH^- in solution.
c) A Brönsted–Lowry base may also be able to act as a Brönsted–Lowry acid, and vice-versa.

Consider the following equilibria.

$$NH_3 + H_2O \rightleftharpoons NH_4^+ + OH^-$$
$$\text{base} \quad \text{acid}$$

$$CH_3COOH + H_2O \rightleftharpoons CH_3COO^- + H_3O^+$$
$$\text{acid} \quad \text{base}$$

Note that the *base* reacts by *accepting* a proton, and the *acid* reacts by *donating* a proton.

As can be seen, a substance (H_2O in this case) may act as an acid or a base, depending on the circumstances in which it finds itself.

64

Notes

1. The molecule H_3O^+ is called the "hydronium ion" or the "hydrated proton". A bare proton, H^+, cannot actually exist as such in aqueous solution, so that the proton is always found combined with H_2O in the form of H_3O^+ (or a more extensively hydrated form such as $H_5O_2^+$, $H_7O_3^+$, $H_9O_4^+$, etc.).

2. If we reverse the above two equilibria we have:

$$\underset{\text{acid}}{NH_4^+} + \underset{\text{base}}{OH^-} \rightleftharpoons NH_3 + H_2O$$

$$\underset{\text{base}}{CH_3COO^-} + \underset{\text{acid}}{H_3O^+} \rightleftharpoons CH_3COOH + H_2O$$

Overall we then have:

$$\underset{\text{base}}{NH_3} + \underset{\text{acid}}{H_2O} \rightleftharpoons \underset{\text{acid}}{NH_4^+} + \underset{\text{base}}{OH^-}$$

$$\underset{\text{acid}}{CH_3COOH} + \underset{\text{base}}{H_2O} \rightleftharpoons \underset{\text{base}}{CH_3COO^-} + \underset{\text{acid}}{H_3O^+}$$

In general, a Brönsted–Lowry acid-base reaction just involves a PROTON TRANSFER:

$$\left(\begin{matrix} \text{ACID FORM} \\ \text{of A} \end{matrix} \right) + \left(\begin{matrix} \text{BASE FORM} \\ \text{of B} \end{matrix} \right) \rightleftharpoons \left(\begin{matrix} \text{BASE FORM} \\ \text{of A} \end{matrix} \right) + \left(\begin{matrix} \text{ACID FORM} \\ \text{of B} \end{matrix} \right)$$

We should notice that NH_3 and NH_4^+ differ only by a proton, as do CH_3COOH and CH_3COO^-, H_2O and OH^-, and H_2O and H_3O^+.

A pair of molecules which differ only by an easily removable proton are said to be a *CONJUGATE PAIR*.

The molecule which has the extra proton attached is defined to be the CONJUGATE ACID. That is, the molecule is the member of the conjugate pair which can act as an acid (*i.e.*, donate the extra proton). For example, CH_3COOH is the conjugate acid of CH_3COO^-.

The molecule which lacks the removable proton is defined to be the CONJUGATE BASE. That is, the molecule is the member of the conjugate pair which can act as a base (*i.e.*, accept a proton). For example, CH_3COO^- is the conjugate base of CH_3COOH.

B. K_A AND K_B

Acetic acid, CH_3COOH, dissolves easily in water, but, being a weak acid, does not dissociate completely:

$$CH_3COOH + H_2O \rightleftharpoons CH_3COO^- + H_3O^+$$

Hence, for such an *acid dissociation* we can write

$$K_A = \frac{[CH_3COO^-][H_3O^+]}{[CH_3COOH]} \qquad \begin{pmatrix} \text{Note that we omit } [H_2O] \text{ since} \\ \text{the concentration of the solvent is} \\ \text{a constant.} \end{pmatrix}$$

Experimentally it is found that $K_A = 1.76 \times 10^{-5}$ at 25°C for acetic acid.
Similarly we have: $NH_4^+ + H_2O \rightleftharpoons NH_3 + H_3O^+$

$$K_A = \frac{[NH_3][H_3O^+]}{[NH_4^+]} = 5.59 \times 10^{-10}$$

Now, recall that: $NH_3 + H_2O \rightleftharpoons NH_4^+ + OH^-$. For such a *base dissociation* we can write

$$K_B = \frac{[NH_4^+][OH^-]}{[NH_3]} = 1.79 \times 10^{-5}$$

C. THE RELATIONSHIP BETWEEN K_A AND K_B FOR A CONJUGATE PAIR

Recall from Section B that:

$$NH_4^+ + H_2O \rightleftharpoons NH_3 + H_3O^+ ; \qquad K_A = \frac{[NH_3][H_3O^+]}{[NH_4^+]} = 5.59 \times 10^{-10}$$

and:

$$NH_3 + H_2O \rightleftharpoons NH_4^+ + OH^- ; \qquad K_B = \frac{[NH_4^+][OH^-]}{[NH_3]} = 1.79 \times 10^{-5}$$

Since NH_4^+ and NH_3 form a conjugate pair, we might suspect that K_A and K_B are related for this pair. In fact:

$$K_A \cdot K_B = \frac{[NH_3][H_3O^+]}{[NH_4^+]} \times \frac{[NH_4^+][OH^-]}{[NH_3]} = [H_3O^+][OH^-] = K_w$$

∴ for a conjugate pair we have:

$$\boxed{K_A \cdot K_B = K_w}$$

Example: If $K_A = 1.76 \times 10^{-5}$ for CH_3COOH, what is K_B for CH_3COO^-?

$$K_B(CH_3COO^-) = \frac{K_w}{K_A(CH_3COOH)} = \frac{1.00 \times 10^{-14}}{1.76 \times 10^{-5}} = 5.68 \times 10^{-10}$$

$$\left[\begin{array}{l} \text{Note that } K_A(CH_3COOH) \text{ refers to:} \\[4pt] \qquad CH_3COOH + H_2O \rightleftharpoons CH_3COO^- + H_3O^+ \\[4pt] \text{and } K_B(CH_3COO^-) \text{ refers to:} \\[4pt] \qquad CH_3COO^- + H_2O \rightleftharpoons CH_3COOH + OH^- \\[4pt] \textit{i.e., } K_A \text{ and } K_B \textit{ must} \text{ refer to a conjugate pair in order to be related.} \end{array} \right]$$

D. HYDROLYSIS

Recall that $CH_3COO^- + H_2O \rightleftharpoons CH_3COOH + OH^-$.

We define *HYDROLYSIS* to be a reaction between an aqueous substance and the water in which it is dissolved.

We say that CH_3COO^- is HYDROLYZED in water to form CH_3COOH and OH^-. For practical purposes, we can think of hydrolysis as a reaction in which water is "ripped apart".

$$\left[\begin{array}{l} \text{Note that two conjugate pairs are involved in a hydrolysis reaction } (\textit{e.g.,} \\[4pt] CH_3COO^-, CH_3COOH \text{ and } H_2O, OH^- \text{ above).} \end{array} \right]$$

A hydrolysis reaction actually involves two equilibria operating simultaneously.

$$\begin{array}{rl} \text{first:} & H_2O \rightleftharpoons H^+ + OH^- \\ \text{followed by:} & CH_3COO^- + H^+ \rightleftharpoons CH_3COOH \\ \hline \text{overall:} & CH_3COO^- + H_2O \rightleftharpoons CH_3COOH + OH^- \end{array}$$

We can also show this as:

$$\begin{array}{c} H_2O \\ \Updownarrow \\ CH_3COO^- + \; H^+ \; \rightleftharpoons CH_3COOH \\ + \\ OH^- \end{array}$$

Since CH_3COOH is a weak acid, then in the reaction

$$CH_3COO^- + H^+ \rightleftharpoons CH_3COOH$$

most of the H^+ present reacts with the available CH_3COO^- to form CH_3COOH. That is, once the CH_3COOH is formed only a very small amount of CH_3COOH dissociates to give H^+ again (*i.e.*, CH_3COOH is a *weak* acid). As H_2O continues to dissociate, the H^+ produced by the dissociation is "gobbled up" by the CH_3COO^- present. The OH^- which also result from the dissociation of the H_2O remains un-reacted, so that the $[OH^-]$ continues to build up as the H_2O dissociates.

General Rules for the Hydrolysis of Salts

1. Unless there is information to the contrary (*e.g.*, a solubility product constant), assume that all salts are soluble in water and 100% ionized when in solution.

2. If we let BA(s) be the general formula of a salt, such that $BA(s) \rightleftharpoons B^+(aq) + A^-(aq)$, then the positive ion (cation) is considered to result from a base, BOH, and the negative ion (anion) is considered to result from an acid, HA, so that:

$$BOH + HA \rightleftharpoons BA + H_2O$$

Example:

$$NaOH + HNO_3 \rightarrow NaNO_3 + H_2O$$

and $NaNO_3$ is a SALT.

3. "Spectator ions" can be thought of as being the result of dissolving a strong base or a strong acid.

Example:

$$HNO_3(l) \rightarrow H^+(aq) + NO_3^-(aq)$$

does not react further
$\therefore$ is a spectator ion

$$NaOH(s) \rightarrow Na^+(aq) + OH^-(aq)$$

4. If a salt dissolves to form one spectator ion and one non-spectator ion, the non-spectator ion undergoes hydrolysis or dissociation.

Example:

$$NH_4Cl(s) \rightarrow NH_4^+(aq) + Cl^-(aq)$$

spectator

The NH_4^+ undergoes dissociation (is a weak acid):

$$NH_4^+(aq) \rightleftharpoons NH_3(aq) + H^+(aq)$$

$\therefore NH_4Cl$ is ACIDIC when dissolved in water.

Example:

$$NaNO_2(s) \rightarrow Na^+(aq) + NO_2^-(aq)$$
$$\underset{\text{spectator}}{\longleftarrow}$$

The NO_2^- under goes hydrolysis (NO_2^- is derived from the weak acid HNO_2):

$$NO_2^-(aq) + H_2O(l) \rightleftharpoons HNO_2(aq) + OH^-(aq)$$

∴ $NaNO_2$ is BASIC when dissolved in water.

5. If a salt dissolves to form only spectator ions, the solution of the salt will be *neutral*.

Example:

$$NaCl(s) \rightarrow Na^+(aq) + Cl^-(aq)$$

Both Na^+ and Cl^- are spectator ions and hence will not react further. Since no reaction occurs after the dissolving process, the solution remains neutral.

E. CALCULATIONS INVOLVING K_A AND K_B

Example: If $K_A = 1.8 \times 10^{-5}$ for an acid HA, what is $[H^+]$ in a 0.20 kmol/m^3 solution of HA?

> *Note:* We shall use "H^+" and "H_3O^+" interchangeably. Furthermore, we shall frequently omit the solvent, H_2O, in equations dealing with acid dissociation (*e.g.*, $HA \rightleftharpoons H^+ + A^-$, instead of $HA + H_2O \rightleftharpoons A^- + H_3O^+$, even though this latter form is more correct).

We shall assume that s kmol/m³ of HA dissociate:

	HA	⇌	H^+	+	A^-
START	0.20		0		0
+ Δ	$-s$		$+s$		$+s$
= EQUIL	$0.20 - s$		s		s

If we assume that only a very small percentage of the HA actually dissociates, then:

$$0.20 - s \simeq 0.20$$

$$\therefore K_A = \frac{[H^+][A^-]}{[HA]} = \frac{s^2}{0.20} = 1.8 \times 10^{-5}$$

and

$$s^2 = 3.6 \times 10^{-6}$$

or

$$s = 1.9 \times 10^{-3} \text{ kmol/m}^3 = [H^+]$$

69

Note that 1.9×10^{-3} kmol/m³ is indeed negligible with respect to 0.20 kmol/m³, as we assumed.

Example: Calculate the percentage dissociation of the 0.20 kmol/m³ solution of HA in the previous example.

By "percentage dissociation" we mean the percentage of the original amount of undissociated acid which is dissociated at equilibrium.

$$\% \text{ dissociation} = \frac{\text{moles dissociated}}{\text{original number of moles}} \times 100\%$$

or, since "moles dissociated" and "original number of moles" are contained in the same volume (so that we can directly compare the molar concentrations), then:

$$\% \text{ dissociation} = \frac{[\text{dissociated species}]}{[\text{undissociated species}]_{\text{original}}} \times 100\%$$

Since in the previous example we found that 1.9×10^{-3} kmol of HA dissociates per cubic metre of 0.20 kmol/m³ solution, then:

$$\% \text{ dissociation} = \frac{1.9 \times 10^{-3}}{0.20} \times 100\% = 0.95\%$$

As can be seen from the % dissociation, the term "weak acid" is well deserved for HA since very little of the acid actually dissociates to form H^+.

Rule of Thumb: When adding or subtracting two quantities in dissociation problems, we can neglect the smaller quantity if it is less than 5% of the larger quantity. The % dissociation should always be checked in K_A problems (*e.g.*, in the above problem we found the % dissociation to be 0.95% and hence it was said to be negligible).

In this course you should ALWAYS ASSUME that the amount dissociated IS negligible. If a subsequent check of the % dissociation shows that the amount is *not* negligible, the K_A expression will have to be solved as a quadratic equation, *e.g.*, in the first example the K_A expression will be

$$K_A = \frac{s^2}{0.20 - s}$$

Example: The pH of a 0.10 kmol/m^3 solution of an acid HA is 5.500. What is K_A for the acid HA?

First we find $[H^+]$

$$pH = -\log[H^+] = 5.500$$

$$\log[H^+] = -5.500 = 0.500 + (-6)$$

$$[H^+] = 3.16 \times 10^{-6} \text{ kmol/m}^3$$

Now we can set up the problem as follows:

	HA	$\rightleftharpoons$	H^+	+	A^-
START	0.10		0		0
$+ \Delta$					
$=$ EQUIL			3.16×10^{-6}		

and complete the table:

	HA	$\rightleftharpoons$	H^+	+	A^-
START	0.10		0		0
$+ \Delta$	-3.16×10^{-6}		$+3.16 \times 10^{-6}$		$+3.16 \times 10^{-6}$
$=$ EQUIL	$0.10 - 3.16 \times 10^{-6}$		3.16×10^{-6}		3.16×10^{-6}

Assume $0.10 - 3.16 \times 10^{-6} \simeq 0.10$. Then:

$$K_A = \frac{[H^+][A^-]}{[HA]} = \frac{(3.16 \times 10^{-6})^2}{0.10} = 1.0 \times 10^{-10}$$

Example: Calculate the pH of a 0.10 kmol/m^3 solution of NH_4Cl. $K_A = 5.59 \times 10^{-10}$ for NH_4^+.

Since NH_4Cl is 100% ionized in solution (is a salt), then:

$$NH_4Cl(s) \rightarrow NH_4^+(aq) + Cl^-(aq)$$

The NH_4^+ is acidic in solution (Cl^- is a spectator ion):

$$NH_4^+ \rightleftharpoons NH_3 + H^+$$

We solve for $[H^+]$ at equilibrium as follows:

	NH_4^+	$\rightleftharpoons$	NH_3	+	H^+
START	0.10		0		0
$+ \Delta$	$-s$		$+s$		$+s$
$=$ EQUIL	$0.10 - s$		s		s

Assume $0.10 - s \simeq 0.1$ Then:

$$K_A = \frac{[NH_3][H^+]}{[NH_4^+]} = \frac{s^2}{0.10} = 5.59 \times 10^{-10}$$

Solving for s we find:

$$s = [H^+] = 7.48 \times 10^{-6} \text{ kmol/m}^3$$

$$= 10^{0.8739} \times 10^{-6} \quad \text{(preparing to take the log)}$$

$$\log[H^+] = 0.8739 + (-6)$$

$$pH = -\log[H^+] = \underline{\underline{5.126}}$$

Example: Calculate the pH of a 0.10 kmol/m^3 solution·of CH_3COONa. $K_A = 1.76 \times 10^{-5}$ for CH_3COOH.

Since CH_3COONa is 100% ionized in solution (is a salt), then:

$$CH_3COONa(s) \rightarrow Na^+(aq) + CH_3COO^-(aq).$$

The Na^+ is a spectator ion but the CH_3COO^- now undergoes hydrolysis:

$$CH_3COO^-(aq) + H_2O(l) \rightleftharpoons CH_3COOH(aq) + OH^-(aq)$$

Next:

	CH_3COO^-	$+ H_2O \rightleftharpoons$	CH_3COOH	$+ OH^-$
START	0.10		0	0
$+ \Delta$	$-s$		$+s$	$+s$
$= $ EQUIL	$0.10 - s$		s	s

Assume $0.10 - s \simeq 0.10$. We can now write:

$$K_B = \frac{[CH_3COOH][OH^-]}{[CH_3COO^-]} = \frac{K_w}{K_A} = \frac{1.00 \times 10^{-14}}{1.76 \times 10^{-5}} = 5.68 \times 10^{-10}$$

$$\therefore \frac{s^2}{0.10} = 5.68 \times 10^{-10}$$

and

$$s = [OH^-] = 7.54 \times 10^{-6} \text{ kmol/m}^3$$

which gives

$$pOH = 5.123 \text{ and } pH = \underline{\underline{8.877}}$$

F. CALCULATING TOTAL DISSOCIATION CONSTANTS

Consider the equilibrium equation:

$$H_2Te + 2 H_2O \rightleftharpoons 2 H_3O^+ + Te^{2-}$$

The value of K_A for the expression

$$K_A = \frac{[H_3O^+]^2[Te^{2-}]}{[H_2Te]}$$

72

normally is not listed in a table. On the other hand we can readily find that

$$K_A(1) = \frac{[H_3O^+][HTe^-]}{[H_2Te]} = 2.3 \times 10^{-3}$$

for $H_2Te + H_2O \rightleftharpoons H_3O^+ + HTe^-$ (*i.e.*, first H^+ dissociates)

$$K_A(2) = \frac{[H_3O^+][Te^{2-}]}{[HTe^-]} = 1.0 \times 10^{-11}$$

for $HTe^- + H_2O \rightleftharpoons H_3O^+ + Te^{2-}$ (*i.e.*, second H^+ dissociates). But:

$$\frac{[H_3O^+][HTe^-]}{[H_2Te]} \times \frac{[H_3O^+][Te^{2-}]}{[HTe^-]} = \frac{[H_3O^+]^2[Te^{2-}]}{[H_2Te]}$$

So that:

$$K_{total} = K_A(1) \times K_A(2)$$
$$= 2.3 \times 10^{-3} \times 1.0 \times 10^{-11} = \underline{\underline{2.3 \times 10^{-14}}}$$

Note: When the acid H_2A dissociates, the first H^+ only has to overcome the attraction by a single negative charge in order to stay ionized: $H_2A + H_2O \rightleftharpoons HA^- + H_3O^+$. When the acid HA^- dissociates, the H^+ has to overcome the attraction by *two* negative charges to stay ionized: $HA^- + H_2O \rightleftharpoons A^{2-} + H_3O^+$. Since it is more difficult to remove a second proton we therefore normally find $K_A(1) > K_A(2)$. (A few exceptions to this rule exist as a result of special circumstances, but we need not concern ourselves with these exceptions at this time.)

G. COMPETITION BETWEEN EQUILIBRIA

Consider the following table of relative acid and base strengths.

increasing
acid strength

K_A		K_B
K_A = very large	$HCl \rightleftharpoons H^+ + Cl^-$	K_B = very small
$K_A = 7.1 \times 10^{-3}$	$H_3PO_4 \rightleftharpoons H^+ + H_2PO_4^-$	$K_B = 1.4 \times 10^{-12}$
$K_A = 5.1 \times 10^{-4}$	$HNO_2 \rightleftharpoons H^+ + NO_2^-$	$K_B = 2.0 \times 10^{-11}$
$K_A = 1.0 \times 10^{-7}$	$H_2S \rightleftharpoons H^+ + HS^-$	$K_B = 1.0 \times 10^{-7}$
$K_A = 6.3 \times 10^{-8}$	$H_2PO_4^- \rightleftharpoons H^+ + HPO_4^{2-}$	$K_B = 1.6 \times 10^{-7}$
$K_A = 4.7 \times 10^{-11}$	$HCO_3^- \rightleftharpoons H^+ + CO_3^{2-}$	$K_B = 2.1 \times 10^{-4}$
$K_A = 4.4 \times 10^{-13}$	$HPO_4^{2-} \rightleftharpoons H^+ + PO_4^{3-}$	$K_B = 2.3 \times 10^{-2}$
$K_A = 1.3 \times 10^{-13}$	$HS^- \rightleftharpoons H^+ + S^{2-}$	$K_B = 7.7 \times 10^{-2}$
$K_A = 1.0 \times 10^{-14}$	$H_2O \rightleftharpoons H^+ + OH^-$	$K_B = 1.0$
K_A = very small	$NH_3 \rightleftharpoons H^+ + NH_2^-$	K_B = very large

increasing
base strength

We shall first examine the pair of equilibria:

$$H_2PO_4^- \rightleftharpoons H^+ + HPO_4^{2-}; \qquad K_A = 6.3 \times 10^{-8}$$

$$HCO_3^- \rightleftharpoons H^+ + CO_3^{2-}; \qquad K_A = 4.7 \times 10^{-11}$$

According to the K_A values, $H_2PO_4^-$ is a stronger acid than HCO_3^- (*i.e.*, $H_2PO_4^-$ dissociates to a greater extent than does HCO_3^-). That is, $H_2PO_4^-$ releases protons more readily than does HCO_3^-, or conversely, HCO_3^- has a greater attraction for protons than does $H_2PO_4^-$. We can generalize this argument as follows:

> The greater the value of K_A for an acid, the stronger the strength of the acid.

This statement is illustrated on the table of acid strengths above by means of an arrow pointing up the left-hand side (forward reactions increase in strength as we go up the table).

We may look at the previous argument from a reversed point of view. Since K_A (for $H_2PO_4^-$) $>$ K_A (for HCO_3^-) then $H_2PO_4^-$ has a greater tendency to dissociate and act as a proton donor than does HCO_3^-; that is, CO_3^{2-} has a greater tendency to accept protons than does HPO_4^{2-}. Hence CO_3^{2-} is a stronger base than HPO_4^{2-}. We can generalize this argument as follows:

> The smaller the value of K_A for an acid, the stronger the base strength of the conjugate base resulting from the acid dissociation.

This statement is illustrated on the table of base strengths on the previous page by means of an arrow pointing down the right-hand side (reverse, *i.e.*, hydrolysis, reactions increase in base strength as we go down the table).

Now, if we let the $H_2PO_4^-/HPO_4^{2-}$ and HCO_3^-/CO_3^{2-} equilibria exist in the same solution, a competition for protons will arise. For example, if we mix Na_2CO_3 and NaH_2PO_4 then initially we have

$$Na_2CO_3 \rightarrow 2\,Na^+ + CO_3^{2-} \quad \text{and} \quad NaH_2PO_4 \rightarrow Na^+ + H_2PO_4^-$$

74

and the anions establish an equilibrium as follows:

$$H_2PO_4^- + CO_3^{2-} \rightleftharpoons HPO_4^{2-} + HCO_3^-$$

Since HCO_3^- is a weaker acid than $H_2PO_4^-$, the dissociation reaction of $H_2PO_4^-$ occurs to a greater extent than the dissociation reaction of HCO_3^{2-}, causing the production of products to be favoured, *i.e.*,

$$
\begin{array}{ll}
H_2PO_4^- & \rightarrow H^+ + HPO_4^{2-} \\
H^+ + CO_3^{2-} & \leftarrow HCO_3^- \\
\hline
H_2PO_4^- + CO_3^{2-} & \rightleftharpoons HPO_4^{2-} + HCO_3^-
\end{array}
\left. \begin{array}{l} HCO_3^- \text{ dissociates less} \\ \text{than } H_2PO_4^- \end{array} \right\}
$$

} products favoured

We can also demonstrate mathematically that the products are favoured. The equilibrium constant for the reaction

$$H_2PO_4^- + CO_3^{2-} \rightleftharpoons HPO_4^{2-} + HCO_3^-$$

is given by:

$$K_{eq} = \frac{[HPO_4^{2-}][HCO_3^-]}{[H_2PO_4^-][CO_3^{2-}]} = \frac{[H^+][HPO_4^{2-}]}{[H_2PO_4^-]} \times \frac{[HCO_3^-]}{[H^+][CO_3^{2-}]}$$

But:

$$\frac{[H^+][HPO_4^{2-}]}{[H_2PO_4^-]} \times \frac{[HCO_3^-]}{[H^+][CO_3^{2-}]} = K_A(H_2PO_4^-) \times \frac{1}{K_A(HCO_3^-)}$$

so that:

$$K_{eq} = \frac{K_A(H_2PO_4^-)}{K_A(HCO_3^-)} = \frac{6.3 \times 10^{-8}}{4.7 \times 10^{-11}} = 1.3 \times 10^3$$

and since $K_{eq} > 1$, the products are favoured.

We can generalize the results of the proton competition between $H_2PO_4^-$ and HCO_3^- as follows:

---

1. In a Brönsted–Lowry acid-base equilibrium, the side of the equilibrium having the weaker acid will be favoured.
2. In the equilibrium: $HA + B^- \rightleftharpoons A^- + HB$ the equilibrium constant for the reaction is given by

$$K_{eq} = \frac{K_A \text{ (reactant acid)}}{K_A \text{ (product acid)}}$$

Example: If a solution is made by mixing equal numbers of moles of $H_2PO_4^-$ and NO_2^-,

a) what is the equilibrium expression?

According to the problem statement, the *reactants* are $H_2PO_4^-$ and NO_2^- and hence the equilibrium is:

$$H_2PO_4^- + NO_2^- \rightleftharpoons HPO_4^{2-} + HNO_2$$

b) are products or reactants favoured by the equilibrium?
From the table of acid strengths we find

$$HNO_2 \rightleftharpoons H^+ + NO_2^-; \qquad K_A = 5.1 \times 10^{-4}$$

$$H_2PO_4^- \rightleftharpoons H^+ + HPO_4^{2-}; \qquad K_A = 6.3 \times 10^{-8}$$

and since $H_2PO_4^-$ is the weaker acid and hence has less tendency to dissociate then there will be more $H_2PO_4^-$ than HNO_2 at equilibrium, *i.e.*,

$$
\begin{array}{ll}
H_2PO_4^- & \rightarrow H^+ + HPO_4^{2-} \\
H^+ + NO_2^- & \leftarrow HNO_2
\end{array}
\left.\begin{array}{l} \\ \\ \end{array}\right\}
\begin{array}{l} H_2PO_4^- \text{ dissociates less} \\ \text{than } HNO_2 \end{array}
$$

$$\overline{H_2PO_4^- + NO_2^- \rightleftarrows HPO_4^{2-} + HNO_2\} \text{ reactants favoured}}$$

Alternatively: The equilibrium constant for the combined equation is given by

$$K_{eq} = \frac{K_A(H_2PO_4^-)}{K_A(HNO_2)} = \frac{6.3 \times 10^{-8}}{5.1 \times 10^{-4}} = 1.2 \times 10^{-4} \left(= \frac{[\text{Products}]}{[\text{Reactants}]} \right)$$

and since $K_{eq} < 1$ then the reaction favours the reactants.

Notes

1. Hydrolysis is just an example of proton competition between H_2O and another acid.

Example: Since

$$HNO_2 \rightleftharpoons H^+ + NO_2^-; \qquad K_A = 5.1 \times 10^{-4}$$

$$H_2O \rightleftharpoons H^+ + OH^-; \qquad K_A = 1.0 \times 10^{-14}$$

then if we add NO_2^- to H_2O we have

$$
\begin{array}{ll}
H^+ + NO_2^- & \leftarrow HNO_2 \\
H_2O & \rightarrow H^+ + OH^-
\end{array}
\left.\begin{array}{l} \\ \\ \end{array}\right\}
\begin{array}{l} H_2O \text{ dissociates less} \\ \text{than } HNO_2 \end{array}
$$

$$\overline{NO_2^- + H_2O \rightleftarrows HNO_2 + OH^- \} \text{ reactants favoured}}$$

or mathematically:

$$K_{eq} = \frac{K_A(H_2O)}{K_A(HNO_2)} = \frac{1.0 \times 10^{-14}}{5.1 \times 10^{-4}} = 2.0 \times 10^{-11}$$

and this value, 2.0×10^{-11}, agrees with the conclusion that reactants are favoured in the reaction between NO_2^- and H_2O. *Note* that the expression $K_{eq} = K_A(H_2O)/K_A(HNO_2)$ is exactly equivalent to the expression

$$K_B(NO_2^-) = K_w/K_A(HNO_2)$$

2. If a substance can act as either an acid (*i.e.*, dissociation) or a base (*i.e.*, hydrolysis) the value of K_A and K_B must be checked to determine whether the substance acts primarily as an acid (by undergoing dissociation) or as a base (by undergoing hydrolysis).

Example: $H_2PO_4^-$ can either gain or lose a proton.
   a) *$H_2PO_4^-$ acting as an acid:*
$$H_2PO_4^- \rightleftharpoons H^+ + HPO_4^{2-}; \qquad K_A = 6.3 \times 10^{-8}$$
   b) *$H_2PO_4^-$ acting as a base:*

   Since $\qquad H_3PO_4 \rightleftharpoons H^+ + H_2PO_4^-; \qquad K_A = 7.1 \times 10^{-3}$

   then if hydrolysis of $H_2PO_4^-$ occurs we have
$$H_2PO_4^- + H_2O \rightleftharpoons H_3PO_4 + OH^-; \qquad K_B = K_w/K_A = 1.4 \times 10^{-12}$$
$\therefore$ $H_2PO_4^-$ is a stronger acid ($K_A = 6.3 \times 10^{-8}$) than it is a base ($K_B = 1.4 \times 10^{-12}$) and hence an aqueous solution of $H_2PO_4^-$ will be acidic.

Example: HS^- can either gain or lose a proton,
   a) *HS^- acting as an acid:*
$$HS^- \rightleftharpoons H^+ + S^{2-}; \qquad K_A = 1.3 \times 10^{-13}$$
   b) *HS^- acting as a base:*

   Since $\qquad H_2S \rightleftharpoons H^+ + HS^-; \qquad K_A = 1.0 \times 10^{-7}$

   then if hydrolysis of HS^- occurs we have
$$HS^- + H_2O \rightleftharpoons H_2S + OH^-; \qquad K_B = K_w/K_A = 1.0 \times 10^{-7}$$
$\therefore$ HS^- is a stronger base ($K_B = 1.0 \times 10^{-7}$) than it is an acid ($K_A = 1.3 \times 10^{-13}$) and hence an aqueous solution of HS^- will be basic.

H. ACID SALTS

An acid able to donate only *ONE* proton is called a *MONO*PROTIC ACID (*e.g.*, HCl). An acid able to donate exactly *TWO* protons is called a *DI*PROTIC ACID (*e.g.*, H_2SO_4). An acid able to donate *THREE* protons is called a *TRI*PROTIC ACID (*e.g.*, H_3PO_4).

The conjugate base of a weak monoprotic acid such as HF will always act as a base in solution: $F^- + H_2O \rightleftharpoons HF + OH^-$.

Partial neutralization of a diprotic acid such as H_2S or a triprotic acid such as

H_3PO_4 will result in salts such as NaHS, NaH_2PO_4 or Na_2HPO_4. Since these salts still have protons available to be donated, we call such salts *"acid salts"*.

An acid salt can act as either an acid or a base, depending on circumstances.

Example: If HCO_3^- ($K_A = 4.7 \times 10^{-11}$) is mixed with a stronger acid, such as CH_3COOH ($K_A = 1.8 \times 10^{-5}$), then HCO_3^- will accept a proton from the stronger acid and act as a base:

$$CH_3COOH + HCO_3^- \rightleftharpoons CH_3COO^- + H_2CO_3$$

If HCO_3^- ($K_A = 4.7 \times 10^{-11}$) is mixed with a weaker acid, such as H_2O_2 ($K_A = 2.4 \times 10^{-12}$) then HCO_3^- can donate a proton to the conjugate base of H_2O_2 and act as an acid:

$$HCO_3^- + HO_2^- \rightleftharpoons CO_3^{2-} + H_2O_2$$

When two acid salts are mixed, we must compare the K_A values for the acidic ions produced in order to determine which ion is able to donate a proton to the other.

Example: If HS^- and $H_2PO_4^-$ are mixed
a) what are the dominant products formed? We have for HS^-:

$$HS^- \rightleftharpoons H^+ + S^{2-}; \qquad K_A = 1.3 \times 10^{-13}$$

and for $H_2PO_4^-$:

$$H_2PO_4^- \rightleftharpoons H^+ + HPO_4^{2-}; \qquad K_A = 6.3 \times 10^{-8}$$

Since $H_2PO_4^-$ is the stronger acid, it will donate a proton to HS^- rather than vice versa:

$$H_2PO_4^- + HS^- \rightleftharpoons HPO_4^{2-} + H_2S$$

Note: There will be a *very small* tendency for HS^- to act as an acid:

$$H_2PO_4^- + HS^- \rightleftharpoons H_3PO_4 + S^{2-}$$

Enough H_3PO_4 and S^{2-} *MUST* be formed to satisfy the equilibria:

$$H_2PO_4^- + H_2O \rightleftharpoons H_3PO_4 + OH^-; \qquad K_B = 1.4 \times 10^{-12}$$

$$HS^- \rightleftharpoons H^+ + S^{2-}; \qquad\qquad\qquad K_A = 1.3 \times 10^{-13}$$

since specific amounts of H_3PO_4, $H_2PO_4^-$, HPO_4^{2-}, PO_4^{3-}, H_2S, HS^-, S^{2-}, H^+ and OH^- must be present in order to satisfy all possible equilibrium expressions before a true equilibrium can exist in solution. On the other hand, so little S^{2-} and H_3PO_4 will be formed (as a result of the small K_A value for HS^- and K_B value for $H_2PO_4^-$) that we can regard HPO_4^{2-} and H_2S as the dominant products and H_3PO_4 and S^{2-} as minor products.

b) will the reaction favour products or reactants? Since:

$$K_{eq} = \frac{K_A \text{ (reactant acid)}}{K_A \text{ (product acid)}} = \frac{K_A(H_2PO_4^-)}{K_A(H_2S)}$$

then

$$K_{eq} = \frac{6.3 \times 10^{-8}}{1.0 \times 10^{-7}} = 0.63 < 1.$$

Hence, the equilibrium has a *slight* tendency to favour reactants since $K_{eq} =$ [Products]/[Reactants].

EXERCISES

A-1. Write the conjugate acid of the following
    a) NO_2^- b) HCO_3^-
    c) HPO_4^{2-} d) OH^-
    e) H_2SO_4 f) CH_3NH_2
A-2. Write the conjugate base of the following:
    a) HF b) HCO_3^-
    c) NH_3 d) $N_2H_5^+$
    e) HPO_4^{2-} f) $(CH_3)_2NH_2^+$
A-3. Write the Brönsted–Lowry acid-base equilibria which occur when the following pairs of substances are mixed in solution. Identify the conjugate pairs formed.
    a) HNO_2 and NH_3 b) CO_3^{2-} and HF
    c) HTe^- and H_3PO_4 d) HCO_3^- and S^{2-}
    e) H^- and H_2O f) H_2Se and HO_2^-
    g) O^{2-} and H_2O h) H_2O and H_2SO_3
A-4. Calculate the value of K_A (or K_B) for the following equilibria.
    a) $Te^{2-} + H_2O \rightleftharpoons HTe^- + OH^-$; $K_A = 1.0 \times 10^{-11}$ for HTe^-
    b) $N_2H_5^+ + H_2O \rightleftharpoons N_2H_4 + H_3O^+$; $K_B = 1.7 \times 10^{-6}$ for N_2H_4
    c) $HS^- + H_2O \rightleftharpoons H_2S + OH^-$; $K_A = 1.0 \times 10^{-7}$ for H_2S
    d) $SO_4^{2-} + H_2O \rightleftharpoons HSO_4^- + OH^-$; $K_A = 1.3 \times 10^{-2}$ for HSO_4^-
    e) $Be^{2+} + 2 H_2O \rightleftharpoons BeOH^+ + H_3O^+$; $K_B = 5 \times 10^{-11}$ for $BeOH^+$
A-5. Which member of each of the following pairs is the stronger acid?
    a) H_2Te or CH_3COOH b) H_2O_2 or HSO_3^-
    c) $H_2PO_4^-$ or HS^-
A-6. Which member of each of the following pairs is the stronger base?
    a) HCO_3^- or Te^{2-} b) HPO_4^{2-} or HS^-
    c) OH^- or NH_3 d) HSe^- or HSO_3^-
A-7. Write the hydrolysis reaction occurring when the following substances are added to water.
    a) Na_2SO_3 b) K_2Te

c) $Al(H_2O)_5(OH)Cl_2$ d) Na_2HPO_4

e) $LiHCO_3$ f) K_2O

g) $LiBr$ h) $K_2C_2O_4$

A-8. State whether the following salts are acidic or basic in solution. Assume all salts given are soluble and 100% ionized in solution.

     a) $NaNO_2$ b) NH_4Br

     c) $Cr(H_2O)_6Cl_3$ d) KBr

     e) Na_2CO_3 f) KF

A-9. Calculate K_{total} for the following.

     a) $H_2S \rightleftharpoons 2\,H^+ + S^{2-}$, given:

$$H_2S \rightleftharpoons H^+ + HS^-; \qquad K_A = 1.0 \times 10^{-7}$$

$$HS^- \rightleftharpoons H^+ + S^{2-}; \qquad K_A = 1.3 \times 10^{-13}$$

     b) $H_3BO_3 \rightleftharpoons 3\,H^+ + BO_3{}^{3-}$, given:

$$H_3BO_3 \rightleftharpoons H^+ + H_2BO_3{}^-; \qquad K_A = 7.3 \times 10^{-10}$$

$$H_2BO_3{}^- \rightleftharpoons H^+ + HBO_3{}^{2-}; \qquad K_A = 1.8 \times 10^{-13}$$

$$HBO_3{}^{2-} \rightleftharpoons H^+ + BO_3{}^{3-}; \qquad K_A = 1.6 \times 10^{-14}$$

     c) $H_2SeO_3 \rightleftharpoons 2\,H^+ + SeO_3{}^{2-}$, given:

$$H_2SeO_3 \rightleftharpoons H^+ + HSeO_3{}^-; \qquad K_A = 3.5 \times 10^{-3}$$

$$HSeO_3{}^- \rightleftharpoons H^+ + SeO_3{}^{2-}; \qquad K_A = 5.0 \times 10^{-8}$$

A-10. Calculate K_{eq} for the following.

     a) $H_2S + NH_3 \rightleftharpoons HS^- + NH_4{}^+$

     b) $H_2PO_4{}^- + HS^- \rightleftharpoons HPO_4{}^{2-} + H_2S$

     c) $NH_4{}^+ + OH^- \rightleftharpoons NH_3 + H_2O$

     d) $H_2O_2 + SO_3{}^{2-} \rightleftharpoons HO_2{}^- + HSO_3{}^-$

     e) $CH_3COOH + PO_4{}^{3-} \rightleftharpoons CH_3COO^- + HPO_4{}^{2-}$

     f) $CO_3{}^{2-} + 2\,H_2O \rightleftharpoons H_2CO_3 + 2\,OH^-$

A-11. When the following substances are introduced into water do the resulting equilibria favour products or reactants?

     a) $NaHSO_4$ and $NaNO_2$ b) NH_4F

     c) H_3PO_4 and Na_2HPO_4 d) H_2O_2 and KHS

     e) $(NH_4)_2S$ f) MgO

     g) H_2S and $LiNO_2$ h) $NaHCO_3$ and $NaHSO_3$

A-12. The value of K_A for $H_2S \rightleftharpoons H^+ + HS^-$ is 1.0×10^{-7}. What is the value of $[H^+]$ in a $0.050\ kmol/m^3$ solution of H_2S?

A-13. What is the percentage dissociation of H_2S in problem 12?

A-14. The value of K_A for $H_2O_2 \rightleftharpoons H^+ + HO_2{}^-$ is 2.4×10^{-12}. What is the pH of a $0.20\ kmol/m^3$ solution of H_2O_2?

A-15. What is the percentage dissociation of H_2O_2 in problem 14?

B-16. What concentration of $H_2Se(aq)$ is required to produce a pH of 1.93?

B-17. What concentration of $CO_2(aq)$ (*i.e.*, "H_2CO_3") is required to produce a pH of 4.178?

B-18. Calculate the pH of a 0.30 kmol/m³ solution of the following.
   a) NH_4NO_3 b) NaF
   c) CH_3COOK d) Na_2S
   e) Na_2CO_3 f) $Fe(H_2O)_6Cl_3$

B-19. The pH of a 0.010 kmol/m³ solution of HBr is 2.00. What is K_A for HBr?

B-20. a) A 0.010 kmol/m³ solution of HCN is 0.020% ionized. What is K_A for HCN?

   b) A 0.40 kmol/m³ solution of HClO is 0.027% ionized. What is K_A for HClO?

B-21. What concentration of $SO_3^{2-}(aq)$ is required to produce a pH of 9.691?

B-22. A 0.0100 kmol/m³ solution of HOBr has a pH of 5.343. What is K_A for HOBr?

B-23. K_B for NH_3 is 1.8×10^{-5}. Calculate $[H^+]$, $[OH^-]$, pH, pOH and the percentage hydrolysis of a 0.0200 kmol/m³ NH_3 solution.

B-24. K_A for HNO_2 is 5.1×10^{-4}. What is the pH of a 0.400 kmol/m³ HNO_2 solution?

B-25. $K_B = 1.7 \times 10^{-6}$ for N_2H_4, hydrazine. If a solution of N_2H_4 has a pH of 10.50, what is the $[N_2H_4]$ in the solution? Note: $N_2H_4 + H_2O \rightleftharpoons N_2H_5^+ + OH^-$

B-26. The pH of a 0.10 kmol/m³ solution of HA is 5.75. What is K_A for HA?

B-27. Red blood cells undergo "hemolysis" (rupture of the cell walls) at a pH of 3.00. In an effort to cause the minimum amount of damage to the cell contents, a biochemist added acetic acid (CH_3COOH, $K_A = 1.8 \times 10^{-5}$) to 100 mL of an aqueous suspension of red blood cells in an effort to gently rupture the cell walls. What mass of acetic acid was required?

B-28. If HCl is added to a 0.20 kmol/m³ solution of acetic acid until the pH of the solution is 2.00, what is the concentration of CH_3COO^- in the final solution?

C-29. Calculate the pH of a 0.10 kmol/m³ solution of H_2SO_4. Be sure to check the percentage dissociation of HSO_4^-.

C-30. K_A for HF is 6.7×10^{-4}. Calculate both the pH and percentage dissociation of a 0.0100 kmol/m³ HF solution.

C-31. The ionization constant, K_B, for NH_3 is 1.8×10^{-5}. Calculate the original molar concentration of the NH_3 in a solution in which 1.30% of the NH_3 is hydrolyzed, and also calculate $[OH^-]$ in the final solution.

C-32. Calculate the pH of a solution made by adding 1.000 mol of CH_3COONa and 0.500 mol of HCl to water and diluting to 1.000 L. K_A for CH_3COOH is 1.8×10^{-5}. Hint: if we mix the CH_3COO^- and H^+ how much CH_3COOH do we produce?

C-33. a) What is the new pH if we add 0.020 mol of HCl to the solution in problem 32?

b) What is the new pH if we add 0.020 mol of NaOH to the solution in problem 32?

c) What would be the pH for parts (a) and (b) of this problem if no CH_3COONa were used in problem 32? Notice the rather substantial difference in pH depending on whether or not the CH_3COONa was present.

Section 12
Buffers

A BUFFER solution is a solution containg a weak acid and a weak base

We shall restrict ourselves primarily to buffer solutions containing substantial amounts of both a weak acid and its conjugate base.

A buffer solution will be of interest to us because of the ability to NEUTRALIZE BOTH strong acids and strong bases without appreciably altering the pH of the solution.

Consider the following three examples.

Example 1: What is the pH of a buffer containing 0.100 mol of CH_3COOH and 0.100 mol of CH_3COO^- in 1.00 L?

We are dealing with the equilibrium:

$$CH_3COOH \rightleftharpoons CH_3COO^- + H^+$$

for which:

$$K_A = \frac{[CH_3COO^-][H^+]}{[CH_3COOH]} = 1.76 \times 10^{-5}$$

But in the buffer we have:

$$[CH_3COOH] = [CH_3COO^-] = 0.100 \text{ kmol/m}^3$$

so that:

$$[H^+] = 1.76 \times 10^{-5} \text{ kmol/m}^3$$

and:

$$pH = \underline{4.754}$$

Example 2: If we add 1.00 mL of 1.00 kmol/m³ H⁺ to the buffer solution in example 1, what is the resulting pH? (Ignore any volume change.)

A preliminary calculation shows that when adding 1.00 mL of 1.00 kmol/m³ H^+ or OH^- to 1.000 L of solution we have:

$$\text{moles } H^+ \text{ or } OH^- = 1.00 \, \frac{\text{mol}}{\text{L}} \times 1.00 \times 10^{-3} \, L$$

$$= 1.00 \times 10^{-3} \, \text{mol}$$

$$[H^+ \text{ or } OH^-] = \frac{1.00 \times 10^{-3} \, \text{mol}}{1.000 \, L} = 1.00 \times 10^{-3} \, \text{kmol/m}^3$$

The added H^+ will be removed by reaction with the base, CH_3COO^-:

$$CH_3COO^- + H^+ \rightarrow CH_3COOH$$

We therefore set up the calculation as follows:

	CH_3COOH	$\rightleftharpoons$ CH_3COO^- +	H^+
START	0.100	0.100	0.001
+ Δ	+0.001	−0.001	−0.001
EQUIL	0.101	0.099	≃0

We can now solve for the *actual* value of $[H^+]$

$$K_A = \frac{[CH_3COO^-][H^+]}{[CH_3COOH]} = 1.76 \times 10^{-5}$$

so that:
$$[H^+] = \frac{[CH_3COOH]}{[CH_3COO^-]} \times K_A = \frac{0.101}{0.099} \times 1.76 \times 10^{-5}$$

$$= 1.80 \times 10^{-5} \, \text{kmol/m}^3$$

$$pH = \underline{\underline{4.746}}$$

(Compare this pH to the original pH of the buffer, 4.754.)

Example 3: If we add 1.00 mL of 1.00 kmol/m³ OH^- to the buffer solution in example 1, what is the resulting pH? (Ignore any volume change.)

The OH^- added will be removed by reaction with the acid, CH_3COOH:

$$CH_3COOH + OH^- \rightarrow CH_3COO^- + H_2O$$

We set up the calculation as follows (note that we turn the equation around and treat the reaction as a hydrolysis):

$$CH_3COO^- + H_2O \rightleftharpoons CH_3COOH + OH^-$$

START	0.100	0.100	0.001
$+\Delta$	$+0.001$	-0.001	-0.001
$=$ EQUIL	0.101	0.099	$\simeq 0$

and we now solve for the *actual* value of $[OH^-]$

$$K_B = \frac{[CH_3COOH][OH^-]}{[CH_3COO^-]} = \frac{K_w}{K_A} = \frac{1.00 \times 10^{-14}}{1.76 \times 10^{-5}} = 5.68 \times 10^{-10}$$

so that:
$$[OH^-] = \frac{[CH_3COO^-]}{[CH_3COOH]} \times K_B = \frac{0.101}{0.099} \times 5.68 \times 10^{-10}$$

$$= 5.79 \times 10^{-10} \text{ kmol/m}^3$$

$$pOH = 9.237$$

and
$$pH = \underline{4.763}$$

(Compare this pH to the original pH of the buffer, 4.754)

Note: The addition of 1 mL of 1 kmol/m^3 OH$^-$ or H$^+$ changes the pH of the buffer by only ± 0.009. We can contrast this small pH change with the following situations.

a) *Pure water:* addition of 1 mL of 1 kmol/m^3 OH$^-$ or H$^+$ to 1 L of pure water will change the pH of the water by ± 4.00.

b) *Weak acid:* addition of 1 mL of 1 kmol/m^3 OH$^-$ or H$^+$ to 1 L of 0.1 kmol/m^3 CH$_3$COOH will change the pH of the solution by ± 0.16.

c) *Weak base:* addition of 1 mL of 1 kmol/m^3 OH$^-$ or H$^+$ to 1 L of 0.1 kmol/m^3 CH$_3$COO$^-$ will change the pH of the solution by ± 2.13.

Hence the pH change in the buffer is much smaller than that which occurs in any of the other solutions.

A non-chemical definition of the word "buffer" states that a buffer is an object which cushions or deadens the effect of some action or tendency. As we saw in examples 2 and 3, above, a solution containing substantial amounts of a weak acid and its conjugate base will "gobble up" both H$^+$ and OH$^-$, so as to prevent a sudden build-up of H$^+$ or OH$^-$. That is, the conjugate pair in solution will "buffer" the effect of changing the amount of H$^+$ and OH$^-$ present.

The basis of the buffer effect can be seen by comparing the following situations.

1. For the acid dissociation: $CH_3COOH \rightleftharpoons CH_3COO^- + H^+$ we have

$$K_A = \frac{[CH_3COO^-][H^+]}{[CH_3COOH]}$$

85

and:

$$[H^+] = \frac{[CH_3COOH]}{[CH_3COO^-]} \times K_A \qquad (1)$$

If a solution is made by adding CH_3COONa to water, then the only source of CH_3COOH in the solution is the hydrolysis of the CH_3COO^- present. Since CH_3COO^- is a weak base only a small amount of CH_3COOH will be formed. The addition of H^+ will cause some of the CH_3COO^- to be used up:

$$CH_3COO^- + H^+ \rightarrow CH_3COOH$$

leading to an increase in the $[CH_3COOH]$. Although only a small amount of the CH_3COO^- originally present may be used up by reaction with the H^+, the amount of CH_3COOH produced will often be several times larger than the original amount of CH_3COOH present. Hence the ratio $[CH_3COOH]/[CH_3COO^-]$ may be greatly altered (see equation 1) and therefore the value of $[H^+]$ may be greatly altered.

On the other hand, if substantial amounts of both CH_3COOH and CH_3COO^- are present in solution, then by using up a small amount of the CH_3COO^- present by reaction with H^+ we only increase the amount of CH_3COOH by a similar small amount (see example 2). As a result, the ratio $[CH_3COOH]/[CH_3COO^-]$ will not be greatly altered and the value of $[H^+]$ will not be greatly altered.

2. For the hydrolysis: $CH_3COO^- + H_2O \rightleftharpoons CH_3COOH + OH^-$ we have

$$K_B = \frac{[CH_3COOH][OH^-]}{[CH_3COO^-]}$$

and

$$[OH^-] = \frac{[CH_3COO^-]}{[CH_3COOH]} \times K_B \qquad (2)$$

Similar to the above arguments, we can see that the addition of CH_3COOH to water produces only a small amount of CH_3COO^-. Subsequent addition of OH^- will use up some of the CH_3COOH present to produce more CH_3COO^-:

$$CH_3COOH + OH^- \rightarrow CH_3COO^- + H_2O.$$

The loss in the amount of CH_3COOH will not necessarily be large but the final amount of CH_3COO^- produced may be several times larger than the original amount. Hence both the ratio $[CH_3COO^-]/[CH_3COOH]$ and the OH^- concentration may be greatly altered.

On the other hand, if both CH_3COOH and CH_3COO^- are present in substantial quantities then a small loss in the amount of CH_3COOH will only lead to a small gain in CH_3COO^-. Hence the ratio $[CH_3COO^-]/[CH_3COOH]$ and the OH^- concentration will not be greatly altered.

The K_A value of the weak acid will be the major factor determining the pH of a buffer solution. By carefully selecting a particular conjugate pair we can pre-set the pH of a buffered solution to any value we wish.

Example: 2-aminobenzoic acid, $C_6H_4(NH_2)COOH$, has a K_A value of 1.07×10^{-7}. If a buffer solution has $[C_6H_4(NH_2)COOH] = [C_6H_4(NH_2)COO^-] = 0.10$ kmol/m³ then

$$K_A = 1.07 \times 10^{-7} = \frac{[C_6H_4(NH_2)COO^-][H^+]}{[C_6H_4(NH_2)COOH]} = [H^+]$$

and

$$pH = -\log(1.07 \times 10^{-7}) = \underline{\underline{6.971}}$$

that is, almost exactly neutral.

Example: A buffer solution contains 1.000 mol of $C_6H_4(NH_2)COOH$ and 1.500 mol of $C_6H_4(NH_2)COO^-$ ion in 1.000 L. K_A is 1.07×10^{-7} for $C_6H_4(NH_2)COOH$.
  a) What is the pH of the buffer solution?

$$K_A = \frac{[C_6H_4(NH_2)COO^-][H^+]}{[C_6H_4(NH_2)COOH]} = 1.07 \times 10^{-7} = \frac{1.500\,[H^+]}{1.000}$$

$$[H^+] = 7.13 \times 10^{-7} \text{ kmol/m}^3$$

$$pH = \underline{\underline{7.146}}$$

  b) How many moles of H^+ must be added to the buffer solution to reduce the pH to 7.000? Ignore any volume change.
    Since we require pH = 7.000, then we require

$$[H^+] = 1.00 \times 10^{-7} \text{ kmol/m}^3.$$

Let s = the number of moles of H^+ added at the start:

	$C_6H_4(NH_2)COO^-$	$+ H^+ \rightleftharpoons$	$C_6H_4(NH_2)COOH$	
START	1.500	s	1.000	we assume almost all
$+ \Delta$	$-s$	$-s$	$+s$	of the
$=$ EQUIL	$1.500 - s$	$\simeq 0$	$1.000 + s$	added H^+ reacts

Now:

$$K_A = \frac{[C_6H_4(NH_2)COO^-][H^+]}{[C_6H_4(NH_2)COOH]} = 1.07 \times 10^{-7}$$

and:

$$\frac{(1.500 - s) \times 1.00 \times 10^{-7}}{1.000 + s} = 1.07 \times 10^{-7}$$

Solving for s we find: $\quad s = 0.208$ kmol/m³

$$\therefore \text{ we must add } \underline{\underline{0.208 \text{ mol}}} \text{ of } H^+$$

  c) How many moles of $C_6H_4(NH_2)COOH$ must be added to 1.000 L of the original buffer solution to reduce the pH to 7.000?

Again, a pH of 7.000 requires $[H^+] = 1.00 \times 10^{-7}$ kmol/m^3. Let s = the number of moles of $C_6H_4(NH_2)COOH$ added.

	$C_6H_4(NH_2)COOH \rightleftharpoons$	$C_6H_4(NH_2)COO^- +$	H^+
START	$1.000 + s$	1.500	0
$+ \Delta$	-1.00×10^{-7}	$+1.00 \times 10^{-7}$	$+1.00 \times 10^{-7}$
$=$ EQUIL	$\simeq 1.000 + s$	$\simeq 1.500$	1.00×10^{-7}

(We assume that no H^+ was present originally. Note that adding to the amount of $C_6H_4(NH_2)COOH$ has a negligible effect on the amount of $C_6H_4(NH_2)COO^-$ present.)

Now:
$$K_A = \frac{[C_6H_4(NH_2)COO^-][H^+]}{[C_6H_4(NH_2)COOH]} = 1.07 \times 10^{-7}$$

and:
$$\frac{1.500 \times 1.00 \times 10^{-7}}{1.000 + s} = 1.07 \times 10^{-7}$$

Solving for s we find: $\quad s = 0.402$ kmol/m^3

$\therefore$ we must add $\underline{\underline{0.402 \text{ mol}}}$ of $C_6H_4(NH_2)COOH$.

d) What would the pH be if 1.550 mol of H^+ were added to 1.00 L of the buffer solution?

> Since the buffer contains only 1.500 mol of the base per litre, we will EXCEED THE CAPACITY of the buffer. That is, we will exceed the amount of H^+ which can be neutralized, and some of the H^+ will remain in excess.

$$[H^+]_{EXCESS} = [H^+]_{START} - [Base]_{START}$$
$$= 1.550 - 1.500 = 0.050 \text{ kmol/m}^3$$
$$pH = -\log(0.050) = \underline{\underline{1.301}}$$

e) How many moles of H^+ must be added to 1.00 L of the buffer to change the pH to 2.000?

Since pH = 2.000, then $[H^+] = 1.00 \times 10^{-2}$ kmol/m^3. Because this concentration is rather large, compared to the starting value of 7.13×10^{-7} kmol/m^3, we will not assume that it is negligible with respect to the original amount of H^+ added. Let s = the molar concentration of the added H^+ in the buffer.

	$C_6H_4(NH_2)COO^- +$	H^+	$\rightleftharpoons C_6H_4(NH_2)COOH$
START	1.500	s	1.000
$+ \Delta$	$-s + 0.010$	$-s + 0.010$	$s - 0.010$
$=$ EQUIL	$1.510 - s$	0.010	$0.990 + s$

Now:
$$K_A = \frac{[C_6H_4(NH_2)COO^-][H^+]}{[C_6H_4(NH_2)COOH]} = 1.07 \times 10^{-7}$$

or:
$$\frac{(1.510 - s) \times 1.0 \times 10^{-2}}{(0.990 + s)} = 1.07 \times 10^{-7}$$

Solving for s we find: $s = 1.51$ kmol/m^3
and moles of H$^+$ added = $\underline{1.51 \text{ mol}}$

> *Note:* Since $[C_6H_4(NH_2)COO^-]_{EQ} = 1.51 - 1.51 = 0$, then we have effectively used up all the base present and exceeded the capacity of the buffer. The fact that we have exceeded the buffer capacity does not change the answer we obtained for the number of moles of H$^+$ added, since we did *not* assume $[H^+]_{EQ} \simeq 0$ (*i.e.*, we allowed for the presence of an excess).

EXERCISES

A-1. $K_A = 5.00 \times 10^{-5}$ for HA(aq) $\rightleftharpoons$ H$^+$(aq) + A$^-$(aq). Determine the pH of the following buffer solutions.
  a) [HA] = [A$^-$] = 0.100 kmol/m^3
  b) [HA] = [A$^-$] = 0.500 kmol/m^3
  c) [HA] = 0.200 kmol/m^3, [A$^-$] = 0.400 kmol/m^3
  d) [HA] = 0.400 kmol/m^3, [A$^-$] = 0.200 kmol/m^3
  e) [HA] = 0.100 kmol/m^3, [A$^-$] = 0.800 kmol/m^3
  f) [A$^-$]/[HA] = 0.300
  g) [A$^-$]/[HA] = 2.50
  h) [A$^-$]/[HA] = 9.00
A-2. $K_A = 3.53 \times 10^{-4}$ for HF. What ratio of [F$^-$]/[HF] must be present to give pH = 4.327?
A-3. $K_A = 5.59 \times 10^{-10}$ for NH$_4$$^+$. What ratio of [NH$_3$]/[NH$_4$$^+$] must be present to give pH = 8.810?
A-4. Determine the pH of the following buffer solutions.
  a) 100 mL of 0.300 kmol/m^3 CH$_3$COOH is mixed with 100 mL of 0.400 kmol/m^3 CH$_3$COONa. ($K_A = 1.76 \times 10^{-5}$).
  b) 250 mL of 0.200 kmol/m^3 NH$_3$ is mixed with 400 mL of 0.150 kmol/m^3 NH$_4$Cl. ($K_A = 5.59 \times 10^{-10}$).
  c) 50.0 mL of 0.600 kmol/m^3 N$_2$H$_4$ is mixed with 100 mL of 0.400 kmol/m^3 N$_2$H$_5$Cl. ($K_A = 1.7 \times 10^{-6}$).
  d) 25.0 mL of 0.100 kmol/m^3 HCOOH is added to 35.0 mL of 0.0500 kmol/m^3 HCOONa. ($K_A = 1.77 \times 10^{-4}$).

B-5. How many grams of NH_4Cl must be added to 0.700 mol of NH_3 in order to prepare 1.00 L of a buffer having pH $= 9.120$? ($K_A = 5.59 \times 10^{-10}$).

B-6. A buffer solution contains $0.500 \ kmol/m^3 \ CH_3COOH$ and $0.500 \ kmol/m^3$ CH_3COONa. ($K_A = 1.76 \times 10^{-5}$). What is the pH of the buffer:
a) before any further acid or base is added?
b) after adding 0.050 mol of HCl to 1.00 L of the buffer?
c) after adding 0.050 mol of NaOH to 1.00 L of the buffer?

B-7. A buffer solution contains $0.0300 \ kmol/m^3 \ NaH_2PO_4$ and $0.0250 \ kmol/m^3$ Na_2HPO_4 ($K_A = 6.23 \times 10^{-8}$ for $H_2PO_4^-$. Ignore the amount of HPO_4^{2-} which undergoes acid dissociation and the amount of $H_2PO_4^-$ which undergoes hydrolysis). Calculate the pH of a solution:
a) containing only the NaH_2PO_4—Na_2HPO_4 buffer.
b) made by mixing 0.005 00 mol of NaOH with 1.00 L of the buffer.
c) made by mixing 0.001 00 mol of HCl with 0.500 L of the buffer.

B-8. What concentration of CH_3COOH exists in a CH_3COOH—CH_3COO^- buffer having $[CH_3COO^-] = 0.250 \ kmol/m^3$ and a pH of 4.608?

B-9. What concentration of HCO_3^- exists in a H_2CO_3—HCO_3^- buffer having $[CO_2(aq)] = 0.0250 \ kmol/m^3$ and pH $= 6.923$? Note: "H_2CO_3" is the name given to $CO_2(aq)$. Ignore the further dissociation of HCO_3^-. $K_A = 4.30 \times 10^{-7}$

B-10. A buffer solution contained $0.300 \ kmol/m^3 \ NH_3$ and $0.250 \ kmol/m^3 \ NH_4Cl$. How many moles of NH_4Cl must be added to 1.00 L of the buffer to change the pH to 8.989? $K_A = 5.59 \times 10^{-10}$.

B-11. A buffer solution contained $0.0750 \ kmol/m^3 \ CH_3COOH$ and $0.0470 \ kmol/m^3$ CH_3COOK. How many moles of CH_3COOK must be added to 1.00 L of the buffer to change the pH to 4.679? $K_A = 1.76 \times 10^{-5}$.

B-12. How much would the pH change if 0.0350 mol of HCl were added to 1.00 L of a solution containing 0.0700 mol of formic acid, HCOOH, and 0.0650 mol of sodium formate, HCOONa? $K_A = 1.77 \times 10^{-4}$.

B-13. How much would the pH change if 0.0900 mol of HCl were used instead of the 0.0350 mol in problem 12?

B-14. How much would the pH change if 0.125 mol of NaOH were added to 1.00 L of a solution containing 0.350 mol of hydrazine, N_2H_4, and 0.280 mol of hydrazine hydrochloride, N_2H_5Cl? $K_B = 1.7 \times 10^{-6}$ for N_2H_4.

B-15. How much would the pH change if 0.400 mol of NaOH were used instead of 0.125 mol in problem 14?

B-16. How many moles of HCl must be added to 1.00 L of a buffer solution containing 0.130 mol of CH_3COOH ($K_A = 1.76 \times 10^{-5}$) and 0.200 mol of CH_3COO^- to change the pH to:

a) 4.675   b) 4.430
c) 4.101   d) 0.824

B-17. How many moles of NaOH must be added to 1.00 L of a buffer solution containing 0.0950 mol of NH_3 ($K_B = 1.79 \times 10^{-5}$) and 0.125 mol of NH_4Br to change the pH to:

    a) 9.332   b) 9.654

    c) 9.906   d) 12.301

Section 13

Titration and Indicators

Consider what happens when we add NaOH(s) to 1 L of 1 kmol/m³ HCl:

Moles mixed at start		Equilibrium concentrations	
H^+	OH^-	$[H^+]$	$[OH^-]$
1	0	1	10^{-14}
1	0.9	10^{-1}	10^{-13}
1	0.99	10^{-2}	10^{-12}
1	0.999	10^{-3}	10^{-11}
1	1	10^{-7}	10^{-7}
1	1.001	10^{-11}	10^{-3}
1	1.01	10^{-12}	10^{-2}
1	1.1	10^{-13}	10^{-1}
1	2	10^{-14}	1

This table is shown graphically at the top of the page opposite. The curves on the graph are called "titration curves". Note that as the curve for H^+ approaches the "1 mol of NaOH added" point, the $[H^+]$ is *very rapidly* decreasing: to go from a situation having $[H^+] = 10^{-6}$ to $[H^+] = 10^{-8}$ only requires 2×10^{-6} mol of NaOH (*i.e.*, 0.000 08 g!).

In order to indicate the point at which the number of moles of NaOH exactly equals the number of moles of HCl, we take advantage of an organic dye which has one colour in an acidic solution and a different colour in a basic solution. These dyes, called *INDICATORS*, are actually organic *acids*:

$$HIn \rightleftharpoons H^+ + In^- \qquad \begin{bmatrix} \text{Example colours. Colours are} \\ \text{different for different dyes.} \end{bmatrix}$$
$$\text{yellow} \qquad\qquad \text{blue}$$

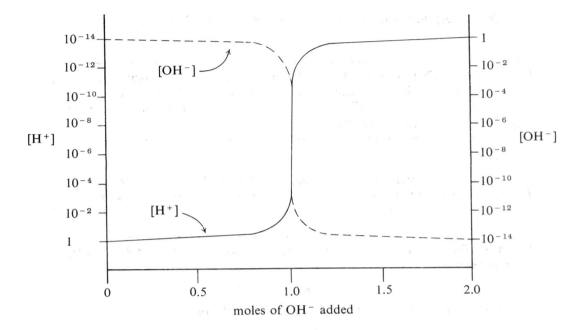

When conditions are acidic, most of the dye is in the HIn form (recall Le Chatelier). When conditions are basic (*i.e.*, [H$^+$] is small) most of the dye is in the In$^-$ form. Hence in acidic conditions the dye colours the solution yellow, and in basic conditions the dye colours the solution blue.

   Now, when the dye is *changing* colour we have: [HIn] = [In$^-$] (*i.e.*, neither HIn nor In$^-$ is in excess half-way through the change), and:

$$K_A = \frac{[H^+][In^-]}{[HIn]} = [H^+], \quad (\text{since } [In^-] = [HIn])$$

Not all indicators change colour at the same value of [H$^+$]. Therefore, we can determine K_A for an indicating acid by simply measuring the [H$^+$] at which the colour change occurs.

Example: The indicator methyl red changes from red (at pH = 4.8) to yellow (at pH = 6.0). At pH = 5.4 the colour is an intermediate orange. When is K_A for methyl red?

   At pH = 5.4 we have [HMe] = [Me$^-$], and $K_A = [H^+]$. Now:

$$-\log[H^+] = 5.4 \quad \text{and} \quad [H^+] = 3.89 \times 10^{-6} \, \text{kmol/m}^3$$

$$\therefore K_A = \underline{\underline{3.89 \times 10^{-6}}}$$

93

The process illustrated in the previous graph is called a *titration*.

A TITRATION is a process by which measured amounts of a solution with a known concentration are reacted with a known volume of a solution with an unknown concentration until a desired END POINT, such as a colour change or a predetermined pH, is reached.

[Although the previous graph involved the addition of a solid to a solution of known concentration, most titrations occur as noted in the above definition.]

The END POINT of a titration involving the reaction between A and B according to the equation:

$$a A + b B \rightarrow c C + d D$$

will be the point at which A and B are present in the ratio:

$$\frac{\text{moles of A}}{\text{moles of B}} = \frac{a}{b}$$

i.e., the reaction equation has been *exactly* satisfied.

Example:

a) The titration of HCl with NaOH will reach an end point in the reaction $HCl + NaOH \rightarrow NaCl + H_2O$ when:

$$\text{moles HCl} = \text{moles NaOH}.$$

b) The titration of H_2SO_4 with OH^- will have *two* end points, depending on the extent of reaction required.

　　i) If we are interested in the reaction:

$$H_2SO_4 + OH^- \rightarrow HSO_4^- + H_2O$$

　then the end point occurs when:

$$\text{moles } OH^- = \text{moles } H_2SO_4$$

　　ii) If we are interested in the reaction:

$$H_2SO_4 + 2 OH^- \rightarrow SO_4^{2-} + 2 H_2O$$

94

then the end point occurs when:

$$\frac{\text{moles OH}^-}{\text{moles H}_2\text{SO}_4} = 2$$

or: moles OH$^-$ = 2 × moles H$_2$SO$_4$

Example: A drop of bromothymol blue, which changes colour at pH = 7, was added to 25.0 mL of a HCl solution of unknown concentration. When exactly 44.0 mL of a 0.200 kmol/m³ NaOH solution had been added dropwise to the HCl solution, the indicator abruptly changed colour. What was the concentration of the acid?

$$\text{moles of OH}^- = 0.200 \frac{\text{mol}}{\text{L}} \times 0.0440 \text{ L}$$

$$= 0.008\,80 \text{ mol}$$

but, at end point: moles of H$^+$ = moles of OH$^-$

$$\therefore \text{ molar concentration of HCl} = \frac{0.008\,80 \text{ mol}}{0.0250 \text{ L}} = \underline{\underline{0.352 \text{ kmol/m}^3}}$$

Example: A drop of para nitrophenol, which changes from colourless to yellow at pH = 6, was used as an indicator for the titration of H$_2$SO$_4$ with NaOH. An end point was observed corresponding to the completion of the reaction

$$\text{H}_2\text{SO}_4 + 2\,\text{OH}^- \rightarrow \text{SO}_4{}^{2-} + 2\,\text{H}_2\text{O},$$

when 38.3 mL of 0.0750 kmol/m³ NaOH was added to a 50.0 mL sample of an H$_2$SO$_4$ solution of unknown concentration. What was the concentration of the H$_2$SO$_4$?

> Note that we are assuming that
> $$\text{H}_2\text{SO}_4 \rightarrow 2\,\text{H}^+ + \text{SO}_4^{2-}$$
> and that the titration involves the reaction:
> $$\text{H}^+ + \text{OH}^- \rightarrow \text{H}_2\text{O}$$

$$\text{moles of OH}^- = 0.0750 \frac{\text{mol}}{\text{L}} \times 0.0383 \text{ L}$$

$$= 0.002\,87 \text{ mol}$$

and: moles of H$^+$ = moles of OH$^-$ = 0.002 87 mol

But: 1 mol H$_2$SO$_4$ produces 2 mol H$^+$

$$\therefore \text{ molar concentration of H}_2\text{SO}_4 = \frac{0.002\,87 \text{ mol H}^+}{0.0500 \text{ L}} \times \frac{1 \text{ mol H}_2\text{SO}_4}{2 \text{ mol H}^+}$$

$$= \underline{\underline{0.0287 \text{ kmol/m}^3}}$$

To determine the pH of a solution at end point, we initially assume that the reaction is *not* an equilibrium reaction (*i.e.*, the reaction is 100% complete) and *then* allow the products to dissociate or hydrolyze.

Example: In the titration of CH_3COOH with NaOH we initially assume that:

$$CH_3COOH + OH^- \xrightarrow{100\%} CH_3COO^- + H_2O$$

We then assume that the resulting solution of CH_3COO^- undergoes hydrolysis.

Example: A solution contains CH_3COOH. The molar concentration of the CH_3COOH is known to be about 0.1 kmol/m³. Calculate the final pH of the titration when NaOH solution is added to reach an end point.

> A titration of the 0.1 kmol/m³ CH_3COOH solution with NaOH will produce a solution of CH_3COO^- which is also about 0.1 kmol/m³. (We will ignore the dilution effect due to the added NaOH solution since even a 50% reduction in the final $[H^+]$ as a result of the dilution will only change the pH by 0.3. Since we require only a crude approximation to the final pH, say ± 1, then we need not worry about introducing the small pH change due to the dilution. Most indicators change colour over a broad interval of about 1 to 2 pH units and hence an accurate estimation of the final pH of the titrated solution is unnecessary.)

Since the CH_3COO^- solution will undergo hydrolysis:

$$CH_3COO^- + H_2O \rightleftharpoons CH_3COOH + OH^-; \qquad K_B = 5.56 \times 10^{-10}$$

then: $\qquad K_B = \dfrac{[CH_3COOH][OH^-]}{[CH_3COO^-]} = 5.56 \times 10^{-10}$

Let $s = [CH_3COOH] = [OH^-]$ (both formed by same reaction) and $[CH_3COO^-]_{EQ} \simeq [CH_3COO^-]_{START}$ (small amount of hydrolysis) Then:

$$\frac{s^2}{0.1} = 5.56 \times 10^{-10}$$

which can be solved to give:

$$s = [OH^-] = 7.46 \times 10^{-6} \text{ kmol/m}^3$$

so that

$$pOH = 5.127, \quad \text{and} \quad pH \simeq 8.9.$$

$\therefore$ we require an indicator which changes colour at about pH = 9 (Phenolphthalein, which changes colour in the pH range 8.2 to 10.0, would be a suitable choice.)

EXERCISES

A-1. An acidic dye, HIn, is red in acids and blue in bases. What is the colour of the anion, In$^-$?

A-2. Bromocresol purple is yellow in its acid form and purple in its base form. If the colour change occurs in the pH range 5.2 to 6.8, what will be the colour of bromocresol purple in 0.01 kmol/m³ HCl?

A-3. An indicator named Clayton Yellow changes colour from yellow to amber at about pH $=$ 12.7. What is K_A for the indicator?

A-4. The indicator 2,4-dinitrophenol undergoes a colour change in the pH range 2.8 to 4.0, such that it is half-way through the change at pH $=$ 3.4. Estimate the K_A value of the indicator.

A-5. A NaOH solution of unknown concentration was titrated with 0.125 kmol/m³ HCl using bromothymol blue ($K_A = 10^{-7}$) as an indicator. The indicator changed colour after 15.3 mL of HCl had been added to a 25.0 mL portion of the base. What was the concentration of the base?

A-6. If an indicator which turned colour at pH $=$ 9 was used in place of the bromothymol blue in the previous problem, would the volume of HCl required to reach an end point have been significantly different? Why? (Refer to the graph at the beginning of this section when answering this problem.)

A-7. Phenolphthalein indicator ($K_A = 8 \times 10^{-10}$) was used to titrate a CH$_3$COOH solution of unknown concentration with 0.0635 kmol/m³ NaOH. At the end point 14.1 mL of NaOH had been added to 25.0 mL portion of CH$_3$COOH. What was the concentration of the CH$_3$COOH?

A-8. What volume of 0.0350 kmol/m³ NH$_3$ will be required to reach an end point in the titration of 50.0 mL of 0.0275 kmol/m³ HCl?

B-9. You wish to titrate an NH$_3$ solution to an end point using HCl. You know that the molar concentration of the NH$_3$ is about 0.3 kmol/m³.

    a) What is the approximate pH expected for the titrated solution at end point? (Neglect the volume of HCl added.)

    b) Based on your answer to part (a), which of the following indicators would be best to use in the titration?
      i) Methyl green ($K_A = 3 \times 10^{-2}$)
      ii) Methyl orange ($K_A = 2 \times 10^{-4}$)
      iii) Methyl red ($K_A = 4 \times 10^{-6}$)
      iv) Bromothymol blue ($K_A = 2 \times 10^{-7}$)
      v) Cresol red ($K_A = 1 \times 10^{-8}$)
      vi) Thymolphthalein ($K_A = 1 \times 10^{-10}$)

B-10. What is the pH expected for the end point occurring when 25.0 mL of benzoic acid ($K_A = 6.46 \times 10^{-5}$) having an approximate molar concentration of 0.1 kmol/m³ is titrated with 0.100 kmol/m³ NaOH? Which of the indicators listed in problem 9(b) would be most suitable for this titration?

B-11. An indicator named Alizarin turns from yellow to red at about pH $= 6.4$ and turns from red to purple at about pH $= 11.7$. What can you conclude about the number of acidic groups in the Alizarin molecule and their acidic strength?

B-12. Ethyl red, HEth ($K_A = 1 \times 10^{-5}$), undergoes a colour change from colourless to red. If Eth$^-$ is red, what colour is a solution of ethyl red in pure water?

B-13. What volume of 0.230 kmol/m^3 NaOH is required to exactly neutralize 25.0 mL of 0.175 kmol/m^3 H_2SO_4?

B-14. A 50.0 mL portion of 0.0735 kmol/m^3 NaOH was exactly neutralized by 39.2 mL of H_2SO_4 solution. What was the concentration of the H_2SO_4?

B-15. A 35.0 mL portion of 0.0475 kmol/m^3 citric acid, H_3Cit, was titrated to a certain end point with 27.8 mL of 0.120 kmol/m^3 NaOH. How many protons (on the average) had been neutralized on H_3Cit at the end point?

B-16. A 28.7 mL portion of 0.0136 kmol/m^3 pyrophosphoric acid, $H_4P_2O_7$, was titrated to a certain end point with 40.3 mL of 0.0387 kmol/m^3 KOH. How many protons (on the average) had been neutralized on $H_4P_2O_7$ at the end point?

B-17. A solution of chloride ion of unknown concentration was titrated with a 0.250 kmol/m^3 solution of silver ion. To indicate the end point, a set of electrodes was connected to an electrical circuit which included a small light bulb, and the electrodes were immersed in the chloride solution. After 17.5 mL of silver solution had been added to a 20.0 mL portion of chloride solution the light bulb went out. $K_{sp}(AgCl) = 10^{-10}$.
a) Why did the light bulb go out, and why was this point used as an end point?
b) What was the concentration of the chloride solution?

B-18. A solution of Fe^{2+} of unknown concentration was titrated with a 0.125 kmol/m^3 solution of MnO_4^- according to the reaction:

$$5\ Fe^{2+} + MnO_4^- + 8\ H^+ \rightarrow 5\ Fe^{3+} + Mn^{2+} + 4\ H_2O$$

If 50.0 mL of acidified Fe^{2+} required 16.8 mL of the MnO_4^- solution, what was the concentration of the Fe^{2+} solution? (The end point of the reaction is indicated when the purple coloured MnO_4^- can no longer be converted to the colourless Mn^{2+} ion, so that when all the Fe^{2+} is used up the MnO_4^- colour will suddenly persist, rather than disappearing.)

B-19. A student performed a "back-titration" as follows. To 25.0 mL of a solution of $NaHCO_3$ was added 75.0 mL of 0.230 kmol/m^3 HCl. The reaction $HCO_3^-(aq) + H^+(aq) \rightleftharpoons CO_2(g) + H_2O(l)$ was then boiled to drive off all the $CO_2(g)$. The resulting solution required the addition of 36.4 mL of 0.105 kmol/m^3 NaOH to neutralize the excess HCl. What was the molar concentration of the $NaHCO_3$ solution?

B-20. A sample of aspirin (acetylsalicylic acid, $C_6H_4(OCOCH_3)COOH$) was analyzed as follows. A 0.341 g aspirin tablet was dissolved, with heating, in 50.0 mL of

0.112 kmol/m³ NaOH according to the reaction:

$$C_6H_4(OCOCH_3)COOH + 2\,NaOH \rightarrow$$
$$C_6H_4(OH)COONa + CH_3COONa + H_2O$$

The excess NaOH in the resulting solution was back-titrated with 15.7 mL of 0.127 kmol/m³ HCl to reach an end point indicated by phenolphthalein. What was the percentage purity of the aspirin tablet?

Section 14

Electrochemical Cells and Half-Cell Potentials

PART A: ELECTROCHEMICAL CELLS

A chemical reaction which involves a net loss or gain of electrons is called a HALF-CELL REACTION. For example,

$$Cu(s) \rightleftharpoons Cu^{2+}(aq) + 2\,e^-$$

and
$$Ag^+(aq) + e^- \rightleftharpoons Ag(s)$$

are half-cell reactions. We define:

OXIDATION = a reaction involving the *loss* of electrons.
REDUCTION = a reaction involving the *gain* of electrons.

MEMORY AID: "LEO the lion says GER"
LEO ⇒ *L*oss of *E*lectrons is *O*xidation
GER ⇒ *G*ain of *E*lectrons is *R*eduction

The combination of a *reduction* half-cell and an *oxidation* half-cell is called an *ELECTROCHEMICAL CELL*. For example, when Cu(s) and Ag⁺(aq) are contained in the same system,

$$Cu(s) + 2\,Ag^+(aq) \rightarrow Cu^{2+}(aq) + 2\,Ag(s)$$

the result is an electrochemical cell.

The overall reaction between Cu(s) and Ag⁺(aq) is called a *REDUCTION-OXIDATION REACTION*, or simply a "*REDOX*" *REACTION*.

Consider the cell

$$Cu(s) + 2\,Ag^+(aq) \rightarrow Cu^{2+}(aq) + 2\,Ag(s),$$

made up of the half-cells:

$$Cu(s) \rightleftharpoons Cu^{2+}(aq) + 2e^- \quad \text{(Cu is OXIDIZED)}$$

and

$$Ag^+(aq) + e^- \rightleftharpoons Ag(s) \quad \text{(Ag}^+ \text{ is REDUCED)}.$$

Since the Cu causes the Ag^+ to become reduced, that is, Cu is the *agent* which causes Ag^+ to become reduced, we say that Cu is the *REDUCING AGENT*. Similarly, since Ag^+ is the *agent* which causes the Cu to become *oxidized*, we say that Ag^+ is the *OXIDIZING AGENT*.

The Operation of an Electrochemical Cell

The following vocabulary is required to describe an electrochemical cell.

ANION = a negatively charged ion
CATION = a positively charged ion
ELECTRODE = a conductor at which a half-cell reaction occurs

ANODE: All the following definitions are effectively equivalent.
  a) the electrode at which oxidation occurs
  b) the electrode which receives the electrons given off by a substance undergoing oxidation
  c) the electrode toward which anions travel

CATHODE: All the following definitions are effectively equivalent.
  a) the electrode at which reduction occurs
  b) the electrode which supplies electrons to a substance undergoing reduction
  c) the electrode toward which cations travel

[
MEMORY AID:
        *O*xidation at *A*node (both start with vowels)
        *R*eduction at *C*athode (both start with consonants)
]

Consider the typical electrochemical cell shown in Figure 14.1. The following comments apply in particular to Figure 14.1, and in general to every electrochemical cell.

[
Note: The porous barrier serves only to keep the contents of one half-cell from freely mixing with the contents of the other half-cell. Separating the half-cells makes it easier for us to understand the processes occurring in a cell. Ions are still able to pass through the barrier, although at a slower rate.
]

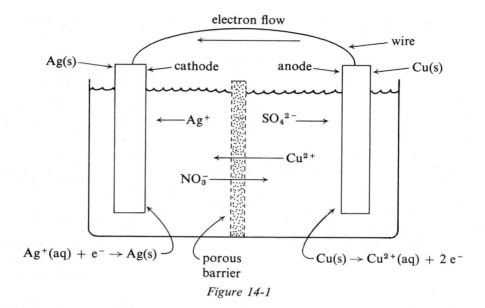

electron flow

wire

Ag(s) — cathode   anode — Cu(s)

← Ag^+ SO_4^{2-} →

← Cu^{2+}

NO_3^- →

$Ag^+(aq) + e^- \rightarrow Ag(s)$ porous barrier $Cu(s) \rightarrow Cu^{2+}(aq) + 2\,e^-$

Figure 14-1

1. A strip of Ag(s) in 1 kmol/m³ $Ag^+(aq)$ will quickly set up an equilibrium: that is, Ag(s) has a very small but non-zero tendency to produce $Ag^+(aq)$. (See Figure 14-2.) Similarly, Cu(s) has a small tendency to form $Cu^{2+}(aq)$ and build up an excess negative charge on the copper strip. Experimentally, Cu(s) is found to have a greater tendency to form ions than does Ag(s), and hence a somewhat greater number of electrons "pile up" on the Cu strip.

2. When an electrochemical cell is set up by connecting a silver half-cell to a copper half-cell, as shown in Figure 14-1, the greater tendency of Cu(s) to "pile up"

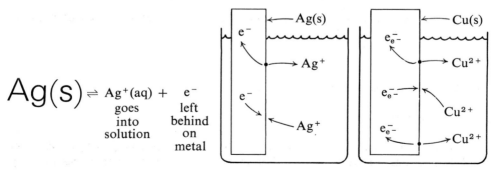

$Ag(s) \rightleftharpoons Ag^+(aq) + e^-$
goes into solution — left behind on metal

Figure 14-2

electrons causes some of the excess electrons to flow from Cu to Ag along the wire which is external to the solutions. We then have

$$Cu(s) \rightarrow Cu^{2+}(aq) + 2\,e^- \qquad (OXIDATION\ occurs\ at\ the\ ANODE)$$

$$2\,e^- + 2\,Ag^+(aq) \rightarrow 2\,Ag(s) \quad (REDUCTION\ occurs\ at\ the\ CATHODE)$$

3. After Cu(s) gives up its electrons, the resulting Cu^{2+} drifts away from the anode. (The oxidation of Cu increases the $[Cu^{2+}]$ around the anode. Since the direction of movement of the ions in solution is random, the greater numbers of Cu^{2+} ions around the anode permit more Cu^{2+} to move away from the anode than toward it.)

4. As $Ag^+(aq)$ is reduced to Ag(s) at the cathode, more Ag^+ ions drift toward the cathode. (As the $[Ag^+]$ is depleted around the cathode, random movement of ions ensures that more Ag^+ will move toward the cathode than away from it.)

5. The migration of ions serves an extremely important function, namely, maintaining electrical neutrality in every region of the solutions.

    a) *migration of ions around the anode.* As oxidation occurs, the net positive charge tends to increase around the anode. Two processes counteract this trend: positive ions move away from the anode AND negative ions move toward the anode.

    b) *migration of ions around the cathode.* As reduction occurs, the net positive charge tends to decrease around the anode. Again, two processes counteract this trend: positive ions move toward the cathode and negative ions move away.

6. There is *NO* flow of electrons in the solution, only a flow of negatively and positively charged ions.

7. The number of electrons *given up to* the *anode* by the oxidation reaction must equal the number of electrons *supplied to* the reduction reaction by the *cathode*, so as to maintain electrical neutrality. In other words, *two* Ag^+ ions must be *reduced* to Ag atoms for every Cu atom oxidized to a Cu^{2+} ion:

$$Cu + 2\,Ag^+ \rightarrow Cu^{2+} + 2\,Ag$$

8. A half-cell reaction cannot occur in isolation; there must be a second half-cell reaction to accept or donate electrons.

PART B: HALF-CELL POTENTIALS

I. Introduction

All half-cell reactions operate according to the principles governing equilibrium reactions. In common with other equilibrium reactions, half-cells can be described by an equilibrium equation and an equilibrium constant.

Since a cell at equilibrium will exhibit *no observable macroscopic changes*, including no net flow of electrons, we have little interest in cells at equilibrium. Instead, we shall concern ourselves with systems which are not yet at equilibrium, but which operate according to the principles of dynamic equilibria. To summarize, we will treat *half-cells* as equilibrium reactions, but will treat *cells* (*i.e.*, combinations of half-cells) as non-equilibrium reactions.

Rather than characterizing a half-cell by its equilibrium constant, we will describe instead the half-cell's *tendency to acquire a flow of electrons*. All the following definitions are *equivalent*.

The tendency of electrons to flow in an electrochemical reaction:

1) is called the VOLTAGE.
2) is called the ELECTRICAL PRESSURE.
3) is called the ELECTRICAL POTENTIAL TO DO WORK, or more simply, the ELECTRICAL POTENTIAL.
4) is the WORK DONE PER ELECTRON TRANSFERRED.

The symbol "E" is given to the electrical potential, where E is measured in "volts" (V).

Since we cannot have electron flow to or from an isolated half-cell, we cannot actually measure the voltage of an individual half-cell. We can only measure the difference in voltage between two half-cells. To establish a definite scale, we ARBITRARILY define a "zero-point" voltage:

$$2\,H^+(aq) + 2\,e^- \rightleftharpoons H_2(g); \qquad E^\circ = 0.00\ V$$

Notes

1. The "$\circ$" in E° means that the value of the electrical potential, E, refers to a STANDARD STATE. We say that E° is the STANDARD REDUCTION POTENTIAL. The standard state conditions are 25°C and a 1 kmol/m^3 solution of *all* soluble reactants AND products (or 101.3 kPa pressure if the reaction involves a gas).

2. The E° values ONLY apply to FRESHLY MADE 1 kmol/m^3 solutions. As the reaction proceeds, the voltage steadily drops and eventually goes to zero at equilibrium. At equilibrium, no observable macroscopic change such as a flow of electrons will occur.

II. Calculating the Potential of a Cell

The reaction $Cu + Hg^{2+} \rightarrow Cu^{2+} + Hg$ heavily favours the products. This means that in the half-cells

$$Hg^{2+} + 2\,e^- \rightleftharpoons Hg$$

$$Cu^{2+} + 2\,e^- \rightleftharpoons Cu,$$

Hg^{2+} has a greater tendency to acquire electrons than does Cu^{2+}. Hence the Cu is forced to give electrons to Hg^{2+}:

$$Hg^{2+} + 2\,e^- \rightarrow Hg$$
$$\underline{Cu \rightarrow Cu^{2+} + 2\,e^-}$$
$$Hg^{2+} + Cu \rightarrow Hg + Cu^{2+}$$

Since this reaction is equally random on both sides of the equation, the forward reaction must be driven by a tendency to attain *minimum energy.*

The *overall tendency* for the reaction

$$Hg^{2+} + Cu \rightarrow Hg + Cu^{2+}$$

to occur will depend on the *difference* between the *individual half-cell potentials.* The greater the difference in the half-cell potentials, the greater the reaction tendency.

Example:

$Hg^{2+} + 2\,e^- \rightleftharpoons Hg; \; E^\circ = 0.85$ V $Cu^{2+} + 2\,e^- \rightleftharpoons Cu; \; E^\circ = 0.34$ V

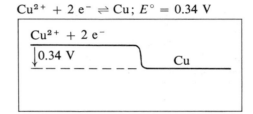

Overall, for $Hg^{2+} + Cu \rightarrow Hg + Cu^{2+}$, we have:

that is:

$$Hg^{2+} + 2\,e^- \rightarrow Hg; \qquad E_1^\circ = 0.85 \text{ V} \quad \text{(reduction)}$$
$$\underline{Cu \rightarrow Cu^{2+} + 2\,e^-; \quad -E_2^\circ = -0.34 \text{ V} \quad \text{(oxidation)}}$$
$$Hg^{2+} + Cu \rightarrow Hg + Cu^{2+}; \qquad E_{cell}^\circ = E_1^\circ + (-E_2^\circ) = 0.51 \text{ V}$$

Note that the energy given off by the reduction half-cell will cause the other half-cell to be *turned around* and hence become an oxidation half-cell (give off electrons). The large amount of energy given off by the reduction of Hg^{2+} will supply Cu with enough energy to force the reaction to go backwards up the energy "hill". The half-cell having the smaller tendency to reduce (smaller E° value) will become an oxidation half-cell.

Now consider the following half-cells.

$$Ag^+ + e^- \rightleftharpoons Ag; \; E^\circ = 0.80 \text{ V}$$
$$Cu^{2+} + 2\,e^- \rightleftharpoons Cu; \; E^\circ = 0.34 \text{ V}$$
$$Pb^{2+} + 2\,e^- \rightleftharpoons Pb; \; E^\circ = -0.13 \text{ V}$$
$$Co^{2+} + 2\,e^- \rightleftharpoons Co; \; E^\circ = -0.28 \text{ V}$$

negative tendency to acquire electrons with respect to:
$$2\,H^+ + 2\,e^- \rightleftharpoons H_2$$

We can calculate the potential of a cell if we recall that the half-cell having the larger E° value will represent a reduction, while the half-cell having the smaller E° will represent an oxidation.

Examples:

1.
$$Pb^{2+} + 2\,e^- \rightarrow Pb; \quad E_1^\circ = -0.13 \text{ V}$$
$$Co \rightarrow Co^{2+} + 2\,e^-; \quad -E_2^\circ = 0.28 \text{ V}$$
$$\overline{Co + Pb^{2+} \rightarrow Co^{2+} + Pb; \quad E_{cell}^\circ = E_1^\circ + (-E_2^\circ) = 0.15 \text{ V}}$$

2.
$$Cu^{2+} + 2\,e^- \rightarrow Cu; \quad E_1^\circ = 0.34 \text{ V}$$
$$Co \rightarrow Co^{2+} + 2\,e^-; \quad -E_2^\circ = 0.28 \text{ V}$$
$$\overline{Co + Cu^{2+} \rightarrow Co^{2+} + Cu; \quad E_{cell}^\circ = E_1^\circ + (-E_2^\circ) = 0.62 \text{ V}}$$

3.
$$Co^{2+} + 2\,e^- \rightarrow Co; \quad E_1^\circ = -0.28 \text{ V}$$
$$Cu \rightarrow Cu^{2+} + 2\,e^-; \quad -E_2^\circ = -0.34 \text{ V}$$
$$\overline{Cu + Co^{2+} \rightarrow Cu^{2+} + Co; \quad E_{cell}^\circ = E_1^\circ + (-E_2^\circ) = -0.62 \text{ V}}$$

4.
$$2\,Ag^+ + 2\,e^- \rightarrow 2\,Ag; \quad E_1^\circ = 0.80 \text{ V}$$
$$Cu \rightarrow Cu^{2+} + 2\,e^-; \quad -E_2^\circ = -0.34 \text{ V}$$
$$\overline{Cu + 2\,Ag^+ \rightarrow Cu^{2+} + 2\,Ag; \quad E_{cell}^\circ = E_1^\circ + (-E_2^\circ) = 0.46 \text{ V}}$$

Notes

1. If an overall reaction has a NEGATIVE VOLTAGE (*e.g.*, 3, above), then the electrical potential to *do work* is negative. This means that work must be *done on the system* to make the reaction proceed as written. The reverse reaction (*e.g.*, 2, above) will, of course, be *spontaneous*.

2. As stated previously, electrochemical reactions operate according to the principles governing equilibrium reactions. However, in the same way that the value of K_{eq} gives no information on the *rate* of an equilibrium reaction, the value of E° gives no information on the *rate* of an electrochemical reaction (*e.g.*, E° may be very large, but the rate might be very small).

3. Doubling the number of moles of Ag^+ in the reaction $2\,Ag^+ + 2\,e^- \rightleftharpoons 2\,Ag$ DOES NOT ALTER THE VOLTAGE. The reason is that (as previously mentioned) the voltage is a measure of the AMOUNT OF WORK DONE *PER ELECTRON*. Hence:

$$\frac{2 \times \text{work}}{2 \times \text{electrons}} = \frac{\text{work}}{\text{electrons}}$$

that is, when we double the number of electrons transferred we double the amount of work done, so that the voltage (*i.e.*, the ratio of work/electron) is unchanged.

Using the ideas developed so far, we can summarize the table of standard reduction potentials as follows:

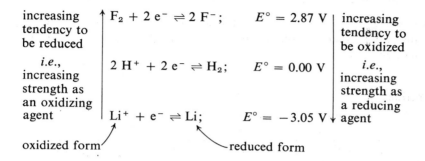

increasing tendency to be reduced *i.e.*, increasing strength as an oxidizing agent

$F_2 + 2\,e^- \rightleftharpoons 2\,F^-;$ $E° = 2.87\text{ V}$

$2\,H^+ + 2\,e^- \rightleftharpoons H_2;$ $E° = 0.00\text{ V}$

$Li^+ + e^- \rightleftharpoons Li;$ $E° = -3.05\text{ V}$

increasing tendency to be oxidized *i.e.*, increasing strength as a reducing agent

oxidized form   reduced form

Example: Consider the following half-cells.

$Cl_2 + 2\,e^- \rightleftharpoons 2\,Cl^-;$ $E° = 1.36\text{ V}$ ←—Cl_2 has strongest tendency to reduce (in this group)

$Br_2 + 2\,e^- \rightleftharpoons 2\,Br^-;$ $E° = 1.07\text{ V}$

$Hg^{2+} + 2\,e^- \rightleftharpoons Hg;$ $E° = 0.85\text{ V}$

$I_2 + 2\,e^- \rightleftharpoons 2\,I^-;$ $E° = 0.54\text{ V}$ Cu has strongest tendency to oxidize (in this group)

$Cu^{2+} + 2\,e^- \rightleftharpoons Cu;$ $E° = 0.34\text{ V}$

We can make the following statements.

1. Cl_2 can be *reduced* by any of Br^-, Hg, I^- and Cu (since Cl_2 has highest $E°$ value in group)

2. Hg^{2+} can be *reduced* by I^- and Cu, but NOT by Cl^- or Br^- ($E°$ for Hg^{2+} is above $E°$ for I_2 and Cu^{2+}, but is below $E°$ for Cl_2 and Br_2).

3. Cu can be *oxidized* by any of Cl_2, Br_2, Hg^{2+} and I_2 (Cu^{2+} has lowest $E°$ value).

4. Br^- can be *oxidized* by Cl_2, but NOT by Hg^{2+}, I_2 or Cu^{2+} ($E°$ for Br_2 is below $E°$ for Cl_2, but above $E°$ for Hg^{2+}, I_2 and Cu^{2+}).

5. Hg^{2+} can act as an *oxidizing agent* for I^- and Cu, but NOT for Cl^- and Br^-.

6. I^- can act as a *reducing agent* for Cl_2, Br_2 and Hg^{2+}, but NOT for Cu^{2+}.

7. Cl_2 *can* oxidize I^-, but *cannot* oxidize I_2 (I_2 is already in its oxidized form).

8. Cu *can* reduce Br_2, but *cannot* reduce Br^- (Br^- is already in its reduced form).

We can summarize all the above statements by a diagram.

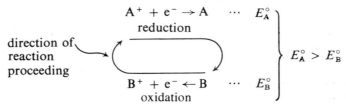

A reaction $A^+ + B \rightarrow A + B^+$ will procede spontaneously if we can trace out a *clockwise* curve as follows:

$$A^+ + e^- \rightarrow A \quad \cdots \quad E_A^\circ$$
reduction

direction of reaction proceeding

$$B^+ + e^- \leftarrow B \quad \cdots \quad E_B^\circ$$
oxidation

$$E_A^\circ > E_B^\circ$$

If we cannot trace out such a curve, the reaction is *not* spontaneous.

Examples: The reaction between Hg^{2+} and I^- can be written as

$$Hg^{2+} + 2\,e^- \rightarrow Hg$$
$$I_2 + 2\,e^- \leftarrow 2\,I^-$$

and hence these reactants form a spontaneous cell:

$$
\begin{array}{ll}
Hg^{2+} + 2\,e^- \rightarrow Hg; & E^\circ = 0.85 \text{ V} \\
2\,I^- \rightarrow I_2 + 2\,e^-; & -E^\circ = -0.54 \text{ V} \\
\hline
Hg^{2+} + 2\,I^- \rightarrow Hg + I_2; & E_{cell}^\circ = 0.31 \text{ V}
\end{array}
$$

On the other hand, the reaction between Hg and I_2 can be written as:

$$Hg^{2+} + 2\,e^- \leftarrow Hg$$
$$I_2 + 2\,e^- \rightarrow 2\,I^-$$

and hence these reactants form a *non-spontaneous* cell:

$$
\begin{array}{ll}
Hg \rightarrow Hg^{2+} + 2\,e^-; & -E^\circ = -0.85 \text{ V} \\
I_2 + 2\,e^- \rightarrow 2\,I^-; & E^\circ = 0.54 \text{ V} \\
\hline
Hg + I_2 \rightarrow Hg^{2+} + 2\,I^-; & E_{cell}^\circ = -0.31 \text{ V}
\end{array}
$$

II. Selecting Preferred Reactions

On occasion we may be faced with a situation in which several different reactions appear to be possible simultaneously.

For example:

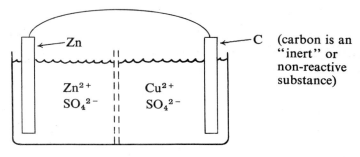

Both $\qquad\qquad$ $Cu^{2+} + 2\,e^- \rightleftharpoons Cu$; $\qquad E° = 0.34$ V

and $\qquad\qquad$ $Cu^{2+} + e^- \rightleftharpoons Cu^+$; $\qquad E° = 0.16$ V

appear to be possible reduction half-cells. However, the half-cell $Cu^{2+} + 2\,e^- \rightleftharpoons Cu$ has the higher $E°$ value, that is, the stronger tendency to occur as a reduction, and hence the cell:

$$Cu^{2+} + Zn \rightarrow Cu + Zn^{2+}; \qquad E°_{cell} = 1.10 \text{ V}$$

has a greater drive to minimum energy than does the cell:

$$2\,Cu^{2+} + Zn \rightarrow 2\,Cu^+ + Zn^{2+}; \qquad E°_{cell} = 0.92 \text{ V}$$

Therefore, the reduction $Cu^{2+} + 2\,e^- \rightleftharpoons Cu$ will occur preferentially.

When several possible reduction half-cells can occur, the half-cell having the highest tendency to accept electrons (highest reduction potential) will occur preferentially.

Similarly, consider the cell:

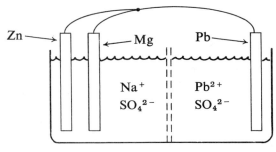

Both $\qquad\qquad$ $Zn^{2+} + 2\,e^- \rightleftharpoons Zn$; $\qquad E° = -0.76$ V

and $\qquad\qquad$ $Mg^{2+} + 2\,e^- \rightleftharpoons Mg$; $\qquad E° = -2.38$ V can be turned around to serve as oxidation half-cells. Since the reduction potential for Mg^{2+} is less than that for Zn^{2+}, Mg^{2+} has a lower tendency to be reduced. That is, *Mg has a higher tendency to be oxidized.*

When several possible oxidation half-cells can occur, the half-cell having the highest tendency to give off electrons (*i.e.*, lowest reduction potential) will occur preferentially.

Hence, the fact that the Mg electrode acts as the anode (Mg is oxidized) will *force* the Zn electrode to act as a *cathode* (RELATIVE TO Mg). The presence of the Mg therefore *protects* the Zn from being oxidized.

$$\begin{array}{l} Zn^{2+} + 2\,e^- \rightarrow Zn \\ \underline{Mg \rightarrow Mg^{2+} + 2\,e^-} \\ Zn^{2+} + Mg \rightarrow Zn + Mg^{2+} \end{array}$$

$$\left[\begin{array}{l} \text{Note that the Mg and Zn electrodes} \\ \text{are joined by a wire. Mg will} \\ \text{oxidize preferentially and force} \\ \text{Zn to } \textit{remain} \text{ in reduced form.} \\ (\textit{i.e.}, Zn^{2+} \text{ gets little or no chance} \\ \text{to form.)} \end{array} \right]$$

The term CATHODIC PROTECTION is applied to the process in which a substance having a higher oxidation potential (*i.e.*, a lower reduction potential) is preferentially sacrificed by oxidation, rather than allowing an unwanted oxidation reaction with a lower oxidation potential (*i.e.*, higher reduction potential) to occur.

Example: A strip of zinc attached by a wire to a buried oil tank made of iron will protect the iron drum from corrosion (*i.e.*, oxidation):

$$Fe^{2+} + 2\,e^- \rightarrow Fe$$

$$Zn \rightarrow Zn^{2+} + 2\,e^-$$

The Zn is sacrificed so as to keep the Fe in its reduced form. That is, by periodically replacing the strip of Zn as it oxidizes and corrodes, we prevent the buried iron tank from corroding.

Further example of selection of preferred reactions

What is the overall reaction occurring when

$$1 \text{ kmol/m}^3 \text{ HCl and } 1 \text{ kmol/m}^3 \text{ HNO}_3 \text{ are added to Cr(s)?}$$

Our mixture contains H^+, Cl^-, NO_3^- and Cr.

First we look *down* the *left*-hand side of the table of reduction potentials until we find a reduction half-cell made up *only* of one or more of H^+, Cl^-, NO_3^- and Cr. The first suitable reduction we find is

$$NO_3^- + 4\,H^+ + 3\,e^- \rightleftharpoons NO + 2\,H_2O; \qquad E° = 0.96 \text{ V}$$

Since we are looking *down* the table, this first-encountered reduction will have the highest possible reduction potential and hence is the preferred reduction.

Next, we look *up* the *right*-hand side of the table to find a suitable oxidation reaction. The first suitable reaction we find is

$$Cr \rightleftharpoons Cr^{3+} + 3\,e^-; \qquad -E° = 0.74 \text{ V}$$

and hence this oxidation will be preferred.

Overall we have

$$\begin{array}{l} NO_3^- + 4\,H^+ + 3\,e^- \rightarrow NO + 2\,H_2O \\ \underline{\hspace{4em} Cr \rightarrow Cr^{3+} + 3\,e^-} \\ Cr + NO_3^- + 4\,H^+ \rightarrow Cr^{3+} + NO + 2\,H_2O \end{array}$$

Note that Cl^- will not enter the reaction since $2\,Cl^- \rightleftharpoons Cl_2 + 2\,e^-$ is an oxidation, and Cl^- has less tendency to be oxidized than does Cr.

IV. Disproportionation

The cuprous ion, Cu^+, is relatively unstable in aqueous solution. When Cu^+ is in solution, the following reactions occur.

$$\begin{array}{lll} Cu^+ + e^- \rightarrow Cu; & E° = 0.52 \text{ V} & (Cu^+ \text{ is reduced}) \\ \underline{Cu^+ \rightarrow Cu^{2+} + e^-;} & \underline{-E° = -0.16 \text{ V}} & (Cu^+ \text{ is oxidized}) \\ 2\,Cu^+ \rightarrow Cu^{2+} + Cu; & E°_{cell} = 0.36 \text{ V} & \end{array}$$

Copper is stable in solution as Cu or as Cu^{2+}, but not as Cu^+; hence part of the Cu^+ is oxidized to Cu^{2+}, while part of the Cu^+ is reduced to Cu, *without the aid of another oxidizing or reducing agent*. This process of SELF OXIDATION-REDUCTION is called DISPROPORTIONATION.

Some disproportionation reactions occur only in the presence of acidic or basic solutions.

Example:

$$\begin{array}{lll} \tfrac{1}{2}\,Br_2 + e^- \rightarrow Br^-; & E° = 1.07 \text{ V} & (\text{reduction}) \\ \underline{\tfrac{1}{2}\,Br_2 + 2\,OH^- \rightarrow BrO^- + H_2O + e^-;} & \underline{-E° = -0.33 \text{ V}} & (\text{oxidation}) \\ Br_2 + 2\,OH^- \rightarrow BrO^- + Br^- + H_2O; & E°_{cell} = 0.74 \text{ V} & \end{array}$$

V. The Effect of Concentration of $E°$

The half-cell $2 H^+(aq) + 2 e^- \rightleftharpoons H_2(g)$; $E° = 0.00$ V, refers to a situation in which $[H^+] = 1.0$ kmol/m³ and the pressure of $H_2(g)$ equals 101.3 kPa. If we raise the $[H^+]$ by adding HCl to the solution, then by Le Chatelier's principle the equilibrium will be shifted to the product side so as to lower the $[H^+]$ again: $2 H^+ + 2 e^- \rightarrow H_2$. As a result of this shift, $[H^+]$ has an *increased* overall tendency to accept electrons (*i.e.*, to become reduced) and hence its reduction potential increases; that is, E increases. (Note that the reduction potential, E, is written as $E°$ only when the half-cell is at standard state.)

Example: Which half-cell has the greater E value: a 0.2 kmol/m³ solution of NaCl, through which is bubbled $Cl_2(g)$ at 101.3 kPa pressure, or a 0.5 kmol/m³ solution of NaCl, through which is bubbled $Cl_2(g)$ at 101.3 kPa pressure?

> The equation with which we are dealing is: $Cl_2(g) + 2 e^- \rightleftharpoons 2 Cl^-$. The two half-cells differ only in their $[Cl^-]$ and hence we must examine the effect of $[Cl^-]$ on the E value.

We can argue backwards from the final result as follows: to have the largest E value we require the greatest tendency to accept electrons (*i.e.*, to form products), and hence by Le Chatelier's principle the smaller the $[Cl^-]$ the more the equilibrium will favour the formation of products.

∴ the $Cl_2(g)$ in 0.2 kmol/m³ NaCl will give the greater E value.

VI. Calculating $E°$ for a Half-Cell Using $E°$ Values of Other Half-Cells

We have seen that the voltage of a *complete* cell is just the difference of the reduction potentials of the two half-cells involved. Let us now consider the following half-cells.

a) $Cu^{2+} + e^- \rightleftharpoons Cu^+$; $E° = 0.158$ V
b) $Cu^+ + e^- \rightleftharpoons Cu$; $E° = 0.522$ V
c) $Cu^{2+} + 2 e^- \rightleftharpoons Cu$; $E° = 0.340$ V

We can see that the addition of half-cells (a) and (b) gives us half-cell (c). On the other hand, when we add the $E°$ values for (a) and (b) we DO NOT get the $E°$ value for (c)!

Let us re-examine what an $E°$ value means. We stated previously that voltage is a measure of the amount of work done per electron:

$$\text{voltage} = \frac{\text{work}}{\text{number of electrons}}$$

112

and $\qquad$ work = (number of volts) × (number of electrons)

> *Note:* The units of work in this case will be ELECTRON-VOLTS, symbol "eV". (1 eV is the work required to pass 1 electron through a potential of 1 V.)

Now, let us add up the *work* done in the previous case.

HALF-CELL	$E°$	WORK
$Cu^{2+} + e^- \rightleftharpoons Cu^+$	0.158 V	0.158 V × 1 e⁻ = 0.158 eV
$Cu^+ + e^- \rightleftharpoons Cu$	0.522 V	0.522 V × 1 e⁻ = 0.522 eV
$Cu^{2+} + 2 e^- \rightleftharpoons Cu$		total work = 0.680 eV

Since: $$\text{volts} = \frac{\text{work}}{\text{number of electrons}}$$

then we expect: $$E°(\text{volts}) = \frac{0.680 \text{ eV}}{2 \text{ e}^-} = 0.340 \text{ V}$$

for the half-cell: $$Cu^{2+} + \boxed{2 \text{ e}^-} \rightleftharpoons Cu$$

and the half-cell voltage for (c) is indeed found to be 0.340 V.

Example:

Given $\qquad BrO_3^- + 3 H_2O + 6 e^- \rightleftharpoons 6 OH^- + Br^-; \quad E° = 0.61 \text{ V}$

and $\qquad BrO^- + H_2O + 2 e^- \rightleftharpoons 2 OH^- + Br^-; \quad E° = 0.76 \text{ V}$

predict $E°$ for: $BrO_3^- + 2 H_2O + 4 e^- \rightleftharpoons 4 OH^- + BrO^-$.

HALF-CELL	$E°$	WORK
$BrO_3^- + 3H_2O + 6e^- \rightleftharpoons 6OH^- + Br^-$	0.61 V	0.61 V × 6 e⁻ = 3.66 eV
$2OH^- + Br^- \rightleftharpoons BrO^- + H_2O + 2e^-$	−0.76 V	−0.76 V × 2 e⁻ = −1.53 eV
$BrO_3^- + 2H_2O + 4e^- \rightleftharpoons 4OH^- + BrO^-$		total work = 2.14 eV

and: $$E° = \frac{2.14 \text{ eV}}{4 \text{ e}^-} = 0.54 \text{ V}$$

EXERCISES

A-1. In the following reactions, indicate: (i) the species oxidized, (ii) the species reduced, (iii) the oxidizing agent, and (iv) the reducing agent.
   a) $Hg^{2+} + Mn \rightarrow Hg + Mn^{2+}$
   b) $H_2 + Sn^{4+} \rightarrow 2 H^+ + Sn^{2+}$
   c) $2 Li + F_2 \rightarrow 2 Li^+ + 2 F^-$
   d) $Br_2 + 2 Cr^{2+} \rightarrow 2 Br^- + 2 Cr^{3+}$
   e) $2 Fe^{2+} + Sn^{4+} \rightarrow Sn^{2+} + 2 Fe^{3+}$

A-2. When a solution containing iodide ion is mixed with manganese dioxide (MnO_2) and acid, a cloud of purple $I_2(g)$ is given off. Use the table of half-reactions at the back of this book to:
   a) write the half-reactions which occur.
   b) write the net ionic equation.
   c) identify the reducing agent.

A-3. When hot cesium metal is exposed to chlorine gas, a bright flash occurs as the elements react. The product is a white solid composed of cesium ions and chloride ions.
   a) Write the half-reactions which occur.
   b) Write the net ionic equation.
   c) Identify the oxidizing and reducing agents.

A-4. A cell is made up as follows. A piece of Ni foil is immersed in a beaker of $NiCl_2$ solution, and a strip of Cu foil is immersed in a beaker of $CuSO_4$ solution. The metal electrodes are then connected by a wire and the beakers connected by a salt bridge. The net ionic equation for the reaction is:

$$Ni + Cu^{2+} \rightarrow Ni^{2+} + Cu$$

   a) Which electrode is the anode?
   b) Toward which electrode do the $SO_4{}^{2-}$ ions migrate?
   c) Which way do the electrons flow in the wire?
   d) If 0.025 mol of Cu(s) is produced in the reaction, how many moles of electrons flow through the wire?
   e) Toward which electrode do the Ni^{2+} ions migrate after being formed?

A-5. An electrochemical cell was made as follows. A weighed strip of Sn was immersed in a beaker of 1 kmol/m³ $SnSO_4$ and a weighed strip of Ag was immersed in a second beaker containing 1 kmol/m³ $AgNO_3$. The metal strips were then connected by a wire and the beakers connected by a salt bridge. After several hours the mass of the Sn electrode was found to have decreased.
   a) What is the net ionic equation for the reaction?
   b) Which electrode is the cathode?
   c) Toward which electrode do the Ag^+ ions migrate?
   d) Which way do the electrons flow in the wire?
   e) Did the Ag electrode gain or lose mass?
   f) If 0.010 mol of Sn(s) goes into solution, how many moles of electrons flow through the wire?
   g) If 0.020 mol of Sn(s) goes into solution, how many moles of Ag are involved in the reaction?
   h) How many moles of electrons flow through the salt bridge in part (g)?

A-6. Calculate the potential of the following cells and indicate whether the reaction is expected to be spontaneous.
   a) $Cr + 3 Ag^+ \rightarrow Cr^{3+} + 3 Ag$

b) $Cu^+ + Fe^{3+} \rightarrow Cu^{2+} + Fe^{2+}$

c) $Mn^{2+} + 2\,H_2O + I_2 \rightarrow MnO_2 + 4\,H^+ + 2\,I^-$

d) $3\,Cu + 2\,NO_3^- + 8\,H^+ \rightarrow 3\,Cu^{2+} + 4\,H_2O + 2\,NO$

e) $2\,Cr^{3+} + 7\,H_2O + 3\,Pb^{2+} \rightarrow Cr_2O_7^{2-} + 14\,H^+ + 3\,Pb$

A-7. You have six half-cells available (all solutions are 1 kmol/m³):

    i) a Cu electrode in a $CuSO_4$ solution

    ii) a Cr electrode in a $Cr_2(SO_4)_3$ solution

    iii) a Mg electrode in a $MgSO_4$ solution

    iv) a Zn electrode in a $ZnSO_4$ solution

    v) a Ag electrode in a $AgNO_3$ solution

    vi) an Fe electrode in a $FeSO_4$ solution

a) Which pair of half-cells will form the cell with the highest voltage?

b) Which pair of half-cells will form the cell with the lowest voltage?

A-8. Predict whether a reaction will occur to an appreciable extent when the following are mixed, and state the products of the reaction.

a) $Zn(s)$ and H_2 (101.3 kPa)

b) $Sn(s)$ and Sn^{4+} (1 kmol/m³)

c) 1 kmol/m³ H^+ is added to a metal, M, having $E° = -1.20$ V for the reaction: $M^+ + e^- \rightleftharpoons M$

d) 1 kmol/m³ H^+ is added to a metal, X, having $E° = 0.030$ V for the reaction: $X^{3+} + 3\,e^- \rightleftharpoons X$

e) $Cu(s)$ and HCl (1 kmol/m³)

f) $MnO_2(s)$ in 1 kmol/m³ H^+ is added to 1 kmol/m³ I^-

A-9. Which is the stronger oxidizing agent:

a) Zn^{2+} or Ca^{2+}?

b) Cr^{3+} or Cu^{2+}?

c) Br_2 or I_2?

A-10. Which is the stronger reducing agent?

a) Mn or Pb?

b) $N_2O_4(aq)$ or $SO_2(aq)$?

c) $Hg(l)$ immersed in 1 kmol/m³ $Hg^{2+}(aq)$ or $Hg(l)$ immersed in 1 kmol/m³ $Hg_2^{2+}(aq)$?

B-11. For a hypothetical metal, A, we have

$$A^+ + e^- \rightleftharpoons A; \qquad E° = -0.29 \text{ V}$$

and $\qquad A^{2+} + 2\,e^- \rightleftharpoons A; \qquad E° = 0.31 \text{ V.}$

a) Can metal A dissolve in pure water ($[H^+] = 10^{-7}$ kmol/m³) to produce H_2 gas? If so, is the A^+ or A^{2+} ion produced?

b) Can metal A dissolve in 1 kmol/m³ H^+ to produce H_2 gas? If so, is the A^+ or A^{2+} ion produced?

B-12. Given: $\qquad Ag^+ + e^- \rightleftharpoons Ag; \qquad\qquad E° = 0.80 \text{ V}$

$$AgI + e^- \rightleftharpoons Ag + I^-; \qquad E° = -0.15 \text{ V}$$

a) Will Ag dissolve in 1 kmol/m³ H^+ to liberate H_2? If so, what is the cell potential?

b) Will Ag dissolve in 1 kmol/m³ HI, a strong acid, to produce H_2? If so, what is the cell potential?

B-13. a) Which of Cr, I_2, Al and Fe^{3+} will oxidize Co?

b) Which of H_2, Cl_2, Hg^{2+} and H_2O_2 will reduce Ag^+?

c) Which of I^-, Pb, Br_2 and Sn^{2+} will act as reducing agents for Sn^{4+}?

d) Which of Cu^{2+}, Zn, acidic NO_3^- and Cl^- will act as oxidizing agents for aqueous SO_2?

e) Which substance(s) can be oxidized by I_2 but not by an acidic solution of SO_4^{2-}?

f) Which substance(s) can be reduced by Cu but not by Fe^{2+}?

g) Which substance(s) can act as an oxidizing agent for Pb but not for Sn^{2+}?

h) Which substance(s) will oxidize Co and reduce 1 kmol/m³ H^+?

B-14. Predict the reaction which will be favoured in the following cells.

a) A mixture of Br_2(aq) and Cl_2(aq) is added to a beaker containing $CuSO_4$ and a copper rod.

b) A mixture of powdered Al and Fe is added to a beaker of Cr^{3+} solution.

c) A tin strip is immersed in 1 kmol/m³ HNO_3.

d) A copper strip is immersed in 1 kmol/m³ HNO_3.

e) A copper rod is immersed in a 1 kmol/m³ solution of HCl, through which is bubbled O_2 at 101.3 kPa pressure.

f) A few drops of Hg(l) are dropped into a solution which is 1 kmol/m³ in both H_2SO_4 and $KMnO_4$.

g) 1 kmol/m³ H_2O_2 is mixed with 1 kmol/m³ HCl.

B-15. A small strip of magnesium was attached to the outside of an aluminum outboard motor casing below the water line. What was the purpose of the strip?

B-16. Write the net equation and predict the cell potential of the following reactions.

a) In^{2+} disproportionates in aqueous solution.

$$In^{2+} + e^- \rightleftharpoons In^+; \qquad E° = -0.40 \text{ V}$$

$$In^{3+} + e^- \rightleftharpoons In^{2+}; \qquad E° = -0.49 \text{ V}$$

b) H_2SO_3 disproportionates in acidic solution.

$$S + 3 H_2O \rightleftharpoons H_2SO_3 + 4 H^+ + 4 e^-; \qquad -E° = -0.45 \text{ V}$$

$$SO_4^{2-} + 4 H^+ + 2 e^- \rightleftharpoons H_2SO_3 + H_2O; \qquad E° = 0.20 \text{ V}$$

c) HNO_2 disproportionates in acidic solution.

$$NO_3^- + 3 H^+ + 2 e^- \rightleftharpoons HNO_2 + H_2O; \qquad E° = 0.94 \text{ V}$$

$$2 HNO_2 + 4 H^+ + 4 e^- \rightleftharpoons N_2O + 3 H_2O; \qquad E° = 1.27 \text{ V}$$

116

B-17. Predict whether the reduction potential of the following half-cells will increase or decrease under the conditions stated.
  a) H_2O_2 is made 1 kmol/m³ in OH^-
  b) $NO_3^- + H_2O + 2 e^- \rightleftharpoons NO_2^- + 2 OH^-$; $E° = 0.01$ V. The solution is made 1 kmol/m³ in H^+.
  c) $TeO_4^- + 8 H^+ + 7 e^- \rightleftharpoons Te + 4 H_2O$; $E° = 0.472$ V. The pH in the half-cell is adjusted to 7.0.
  d) $2 NO_3^- + 4 H^+ + 2 e^- \rightleftharpoons N_2O_4 + 2 H_2O$; $E° = 0.81$ V. This solution is made basic.
  e) $U^{4+} + 2 H_2O \rightleftharpoons UO_2^{2+} + 4 H^+ + 2 e^-$; $E° = -0.33$ V. The $[H^+]$ is set to 0.5 kmol/m³.
  f) $O_2 + 2 OH^- \rightleftharpoons O_3 + H_2O + 2 e^-$; $E° = -1.24$ V. The $[OH^-]$ is set to 2.0 kmol/m³.

B-18. Which is the stronger oxidizing agent:
  a) O_2 bubbled through 1 kmol/m³ Na_2SO_4 or O_2 bubbled through 1 kmol/m³ H_2SO_4?
  b) $KMnO_4$ in 1 kmol/m³ HCl or $KMnO_4$ in 2 kmol/m³ HCl?
  c) 1 kmol/m³ Pb^{2+} or 2 kmol/m³ Pb^{2+}?
  d) $Cr_2O_7^{2-}$ in 0.1 kmol/m³ H^+ or $Cr_2O_7^{2-}$ in 0.2 kmol/m³ H^+?

B-19. Which is the stronger reducing agent:
  a) H_2 in 1 kmol/m³ HCl or H_2 in 1 kmol/m³ NaCl?
  b) SO_2 bubbled through 1 kmol/m³ NaOH or SO_2 bubbled through 1 kmol/m³ HCl?
  c) N_2O_4 bubbled through 1 kmol/m³ $NaNO_3$ or N_2O_4 bubbled through 1 kmol/m³ HNO_3?
  d) 0.5 kmol/m³ Sn^{2+} or 0.2 kmol/m³ Sn^{2+}?

B-20. Half-cell A consists of a Zn electrode in a solution of Zn^{2+} having a concentration less than 1 kmol/m³. Half-cell B consists of a Cu electrode in a solution of Cu^{2+} having a concentration greater than 1 kmol/m³. Would the potential of the cell formed by joining half-cells A and B be greater than, equal to, or less than 1.10 V?

B-21. Calculate $E°$ for the following half-cells.
  a) $\frac{1}{2} O_2 + 2 H^+ + 2 e^- \rightleftharpoons H_2O$, given:

$$H_2O_2 + 2 H^+ + 2 e^- \rightleftharpoons 2 H_2O; \qquad E° = 1.77 \text{ V}$$

$$O_2 + 2 H^+ + 2 e^- \rightleftharpoons H_2O_2; \qquad E° = 0.68 \text{ V}$$

  b) $AsO_4^{3-} + 4 H_2O + 5 e^- \rightleftharpoons As + 8 OH^-$, given:

$$AsO_4^{3-} + 2 H_2O + 2 e^- \rightleftharpoons AsO_2^- + 4 OH^-; \qquad E° = -0.71 \text{ V}$$

$$AsO_2^- + 2 H_2O + 3 e \rightleftharpoons As + 4 OH^-; \qquad E° = -0.68 \text{ V}$$

  c) $N_2O_4(g) + e^- \rightleftharpoons NO(g) + NO_3^-$, using your table of reduction potentials.

d) $ClO_3^- + 6\,H^+ + 5\,e^- \rightleftharpoons \tfrac{1}{2}\,Cl_2 + 3\,H_2O$, given:

$$ClO_3^- + 6\,H^+ + 6\,e^- \rightleftharpoons Cl^- + 3\,H_2O; \qquad E^\circ = 1.45\ V$$

and your table of reduction potentials.

e) $U^{3+} + 3\,e^- \rightleftharpoons U$, given:

$$UO_2^{2+} + 4\,H^+ + 6\,e^- \rightleftharpoons U + 2\,H_2O; \qquad E^\circ = -0.82\ V$$

$$U^{4+} + e^- \rightleftharpoons U^{3+}; \qquad E^\circ = -0.61\ V$$

$$UO_2^{2+} + 4\,H^+ + 2\,e^- \rightleftharpoons U^{4+} + 2\,H_2O; \qquad E^\circ = 0.33\ V$$

Section 15
Electrolysis

A chemical reaction which spontaneously goes from a high to a low energy state will release energy. In a half-cell reaction, the energy is given off as a flow of electrons.

If an electrochemical cell has a *negative* voltage, that is, the electrical potential to do work is negative, then we must put work *into* the system to make the cell operate.

Example: The value of $E°$ for $2 H_2O \rightarrow 2 H_2 + O_2$ is -1.229 V, which means that H_2O will not appreciably decompose into H_2 and O_2 under normal conditions. However, if we supply energy to H_2O, in the form of an electric current, the H_2O *will* be decomposed into H_2 and O_2.

> We can define ELECTROLYSIS as the process of supplying electrical energy to a non-spontaneous electrochemical cell.

The oxidation-reduction processes which occur in electrolysis are fundamentally similar to the processes in electrochemical cells. Hence, similar to electrochemical cells,

> In electrolysis we find that the REDUCTION half-cell having the highest reduction potential and the OXIDATION half-cell having the highest tendency to oxidize (*i.e.*, lowest reduction potential) will occur preferentially.

Example: A solution which was 1 kmol/m³ in Co^{2+}, Pb^{2+} and I^- was electrolyzed using a silver anode and an inert carbon cathode.

As before, we have oxidation at the anode and reduction at the cathode. The *only* important difference is the fact that energy is *supplied to the system.*

The reaction which is preferred is:

$$\begin{array}{llr}
Pb^{2+} + 2\,e^- \rightarrow Pb; & E^\circ = -0.126 \text{ V} \\
2\,I^- \rightarrow I_2 + 2\,e^-; & -E^\circ = -0.535 \text{ V} \\
\hline
Pb^{2+} + 2\,I^- \rightarrow Pb + I_2; & E^\circ_{cell} = -0.661 \text{ V}
\end{array}$$

Note that other reactions, such as:

$$\begin{array}{llr}
Co^{2+} + 2\,e^- \rightarrow Co; & E^\circ = -0.28 \text{ V} \\
2\,Ag \rightarrow 2\,Ag^+ + 2\,e^-; & -E^\circ = -0.80 \text{ V} \\
\hline
2\,Ag + Co^{2+} \rightarrow 2\,Ag^+ + Co; & E^\circ_{cell} = -1.08 \text{ V}
\end{array}$$

will require a *greater input of energy* in order to occur and hence will not be preferred (*i.e.,* the reaction requiring the minimum input of energy is preferred).

I. THE ANODE AND CATHODE PROCESSES OF ELECTROLYSIS

A. Electrolysis of Aqueous NiI_2 Using Inert Electrodes

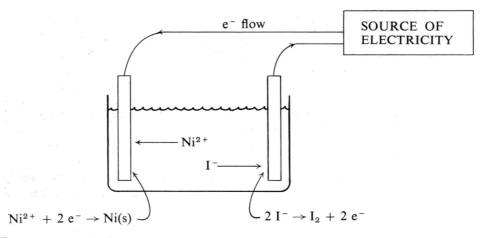

Inert or unreactive electrodes (such as platinum or carbon) are used to ensure that the electrode material cannot enter into the reaction.

The following reactions occur (notice the reversal of the half-cells):

$$\begin{array}{lllr}
\text{at the CATHODE:} & Ni^{2+} + 2\,e^- \rightarrow Ni; & E^\circ = -0.23 \text{ V} \\
\text{at the ANODE:} & 2\,I^- \rightarrow I_2 + 2\,e^-; & -E^\circ = -0.54 \text{ V} \\
\hline
& Ni^{2+} + 2\,I^- \rightarrow Ni + I_2; & E^\circ_{cell} = -0.77 \text{ V}
\end{array}$$

The energy required to overcome the negative $E°$ value is supplied by the external source of electricity. A voltage of *at least* $+0.77$ V is required to make the cell operate.

B. Electrolysis of Water Under Acidic, Neutral and Basic Conditions

Let us examine the following set of reduction half-cells. The labels "acidic", "neutral" and "basic" refer to the conditions used to oxidize or reduce acidic, neutral and basic water.

Half-Cell	$E°$
$Au^{3+} + 3\,e^- \rightleftharpoons Au$	1.42
$\frac{1}{2}\,O_2(g) + 2\,H^+ + 2\,e^- \rightleftharpoons H_2O$	1.229 (acidic)
$N_2O_4 + 2\,e^- \rightleftharpoons 2\,NO_2^-$	0.88
$\frac{1}{2}\,O_2(g) + 2\,H^+(10^{-7}\,kmol/m^3) + 2\,e^- \rightleftharpoons H_2O$	0.815 (neutral)
$I_2 + 2\,e^- \rightleftharpoons 2\,I^-$	0.535
$\frac{1}{2}\,O_2(g) + H_2O + 2\,e^- \rightleftharpoons 2\,OH^-$	0.401 (basic)
$AgCl + e^- \rightleftharpoons Ag + Cl^-$	0.222
$2\,H^+ + 2\,e^- \rightleftharpoons H_2(g)$	0.000 (acidic)
$Ni^{2+} + 2\,e^- \rightleftharpoons Ni$	-0.23
$2\,H^+(10^{-7}\,kmol/m^3) + 2\,e^- \rightleftharpoons H_2(g)$	-0.414 (neutral)
$Zn^{2+} + 2\,e^- \rightleftharpoons Zn$	-0.763
$2\,H_2O + 2\,e^- \rightleftharpoons H_2(g) + 2\,OH^-$	-0.828 (basic)
$Mn^{2+} + 2\,e^- \rightleftharpoons Mn$	-1.029

a) Electrolysis of 1 kmol/m³ H^+ (aq)

The preferred reaction will be:

$$2\,H^+ + 2\,e^- \rightarrow H_2(g); \qquad E° = -0.000\text{ V}$$
$$H_2O \rightarrow \tfrac{1}{2}\,O_2(g) + 2\,H^+ + 2\,e^-; \quad -E° = -1.229\text{ V}$$
$$\overline{H_2O \rightarrow H_2(g) + \tfrac{1}{2}\,O_2(g); \qquad E°_{cell} = -1.229\text{ V}}$$

b) Electrolysis of Neutral Water ($[H^+] = 10^{-7}$ kmol/m³)

The preferred reaction will be:
$$2\,H^+(10^{-7}\,kmol/m^3) + 2\,e^- \rightarrow H_2(g); \qquad E° = -0.414\text{ V}$$
$$H_2O \rightarrow \tfrac{1}{2}\,O_2(g) + 2\,H^+(10^{-7}\,kmol/m^3) + 2\,e^-; \quad -E° = -0.815\text{ V}$$
$$\overline{H_2O \rightarrow H_2(g) + \tfrac{1}{2}\,O_2(g); \qquad E°_{cell} = -1.229\text{ V}}$$

121

Note that the reaction and required voltage are the same for both neutral and acidic water (and basic, as we shall see later). By Le Chatelier's principle, lowering $[H^+]$ in both

$$\tfrac{1}{2} O_2(g) + 2\,H^+ + 2\,e^- \rightleftharpoons H_2O \qquad (1)$$

and

$$2\,H^+ + 2\,e^- \rightleftharpoons H_2(g) \qquad (2)$$

will lower the reduction potential. It can be shown that the potential of each half-cell is lowered by the same amount and hence the difference between the potentials of (1) and (2), *i.e.*, E°_{cell}, remains unaltered.

c) Electrolysis of 1 $kmol/m^3$ OH^-(aq)

The preferred reaction will be

$$\begin{array}{lll} 2\,H_2O + 2\,e^- \rightarrow H_2(g) + 2\,OH^-; & E^\circ = -0.828\ V \\ 2\,OH^- \rightarrow \tfrac{1}{2} O_2(g) + H_2O + 2\,e^-; & -E^\circ = -0.401\ V \\ \hline H_2O \rightarrow H_2(g) + \tfrac{1}{2} O_2(g); & E^\circ_{cell} = -1.229\ V \end{array}$$

d) Electrolysis of Aqueous Solutions

If we electrolyze a neutral 1 $kmol/m^3$ solution of NiI_2(aq), the Ni^{2+} has a higher reduction potential (-0.23 V) than the neutral water (-0.414 V) and hence Ni(s) is formed at the cathode. On the other hand, if we try to electrolyze ZnI_2, the neutral water has a higher reduction potential (-0.414 V) than the Zn^{2+} (-0.763 V) and hence H_2(g) is formed at the cathode, leaving the Zn^{2+} unaffected.

At the anode, I^- has a higher tendency to oxidize ($-E^\circ = -0.535$ V) than does neutral water ($-E^\circ = -0.815$ V) and hence I_2 is formed. If we try to electrolyze NO_2^-, rather than I^-, then the water has a higher tendency to oxidize ($-E^\circ = -0.815$ V) than does NO_2^- ($-E^\circ = -0.88$ V) and hence O_2(g) is formed at the anode, leaving the NO_2^- unaffected.

If we wish to reduce Zn^{2+}(aq), we should make the solution 1 $kmol/m^3$ in OH^-, so as to lower the reduction potential of the water to -0.828 V. Zn^{2+}, having $E^\circ = -0.763$ V, will then be able to form at the cathode.

Note that an aqueous solution of Mn^{2+} ($E^\circ = -1.029$ V) can *never* be reduced to Mn(s), since water will always be preferentially reduced to H_2(g). Similarly, Au(s) ($-E^\circ = -1.42$ V) can never be oxidized to Au^{3+}(aq) since water will always be preferentially oxidized to O_2(g).

IMPORTANT NOTE: In actual practice, it is almost always found that *more* than the calculated voltage must be applied to an electrolysis cell before water will be oxidized to $O_2(g)$ or reduced to $H_2(g)$. Hence, electrolysis of $Br^-(aq)$ and $Cl^-(aq)$ will produce Br_2 and Cl_2, respectively, at the anode, *contrary to our usual expectations.* (F^- will not, however, form F_2.)

C. Metal Plating

When we electrolyze a solution of $CuSO_4$ using an anode made of copper metal and a cathode made of *any conductor*, the following processes occur.
1. The anode metal oxidizes and goes into solution (because Cu has the greatest tendency to oxidize of any species present):

$$Cu(s) \rightarrow Cu^{2+}(aq) + 2\,e^-; \qquad -E^\circ = -0.34 \text{ V.}$$

2. The Cu^{2+} formed, and the Cu^{2+} already in solution, migrate toward the cathode.
3. At the cathode the incoming Cu^{2+} ions are reduced to Cu(s) (because the Cu^{2+} has the greatest tendency to reduce of any species present):

$$Cu^{2+}(aq) + 2\,e^- \rightarrow Cu(s); \qquad E^\circ = 0.34 \text{ V}$$

The copper metal produced therefore "plates out" over the cathode. The overall reaction is $Cu + Cu^{2+} \rightarrow Cu^{2+} + Cu$; $E^\circ = 0.00$ V. However, in order to overcome the -0.34 V potential for the oxidation of Cu(s) we must apply at least $+0.34$ V to the cell (*i.e.*, we must supply the activation energy for the oxidation of Cu).

We should note that the cathode could be any conductive substance, but in practice we normally only use the "metal plating" process to protect or disguise the underlying metal, or to purify the anode metal. For example, copper is purified commercially by using an anode made of impure copper, electrolyzing the solution, and collecting pure copper at the cathode. (See Problem 4.)

II. THE PRODUCTS OF ELECTROLYSIS

The following units are associated with electrical flow.

A COULOMB, symbol "C", is an *amount* of electrical charge.
An AMPERE, symbol "A", is the *rate* of flow of electrical charge.
A VOLT is the *tendency* of electrons to flow; that is, the electrical *pressure* exerted by electrons.

In conjunction with the above units, we can also state that:

One farad (F) is the amount of electrical charge possessed by 1 mol of electrons. Experimentally it is found that

$$1 \text{ F} = 96\ 500 \text{ C}$$

Hence: 1 mol of electrons has a charge of 96 500 C.

Also: $1 \text{ ampere} = 1\ \dfrac{\text{coulomb}}{\text{second}}$, or: $1 \text{ A} = 1 \text{ C/s}$

Example: What mass of Ni(s) can be produced by passing 8.00 A through a solution of $NiCl_2$ for 5000 s?

Method A

  1. Find the moles of e^- required to produce 1 mol of Ni(s). Since

$$Ni^{2+} + 2\,e^- \rightleftharpoons Ni(s)$$

then 2 mol of e^- produce 1 mol of Ni (this is a conversion factor)

  2. Find the quantity of electricity available.

$$\text{number of coulombs} = \text{amperes} \times \text{seconds}$$
$$= 8.00 \text{ C/s} \times 5000 \text{ s} = 4.00 \times 10^4 \text{ C}$$

  3. Find the moles of electrons available.

$$\text{moles of } e^- = 4.00 \times 10^4 \text{ C} \times \frac{1 \text{ mol } e^-}{96\ 500 \text{ C}}$$
$$= 0.415 \text{ mol } e^-$$

  4. Find moles of Ni produced.

$$\text{moles Ni} = 0.415 \text{ mol } e^- \times \frac{1 \text{ mol Ni}}{2 \text{ mol } e^-} = 0.208 \text{ mol}$$

(conversion factor from part 1 of this calculation)

  5. Find mass of Ni produced.

$$\text{mass of Ni} = 0.208 \text{ mol} \times \frac{58.7 \text{ g}}{1 \text{ mol}} = \underline{\underline{12.2 \text{ g}}}$$

Method B. We can also perform the above calculations using a series of conversion factors, as follows.

$$\text{mass Ni} = 5000 \text{ s} \times \frac{8.00 \text{ C}}{\text{s}} \times \frac{1 \text{ mol e}^-}{96\ 500 \text{ C}} \times \frac{1 \text{ mol Ni}}{2 \text{ mol e}^-} \times \frac{58.7 \text{ g}}{1 \text{ mol Ni}}$$

$$= \underline{\underline{12.2 \text{ g}}}$$

Example: How long a time is required to deposit 0.100 g of cobalt metal from a solution of $CoSO_4$ by passing a 3.50 A current through the solution?

Method A
1. The reaction to produce Co is: $Co^{2+} + 2 \text{ e}^- \rightarrow Co$
2. The quantity of Co required.

$$\text{moles of Co} = 0.100 \text{ g} \times \frac{1 \text{ mol}}{58.9 \text{ g}} = 0.001\ 70 \text{ mol}$$

3. The quantity of electrons required.

$$\text{moles of e}^- = 0.001\ 70 \text{ mol Co} \times \frac{2 \text{ mol e}^-}{1 \text{ mol Co}} = 0.003\ 40 \text{ mol}$$

4. The quantity of electrical flow required.

$$\text{number of coulombs} = 0.003\ 40 \text{ mol e}^- \times \frac{96\ 500 \text{ C}}{1 \text{ mol e}^-} = 328 \text{ C}$$

5. Calculating the time required.

since: $\qquad \text{amperes} = \dfrac{\text{coulombs}}{\text{seconds}}$

then: $\qquad \text{seconds} = \dfrac{\text{coulombs}}{\text{amperes}} = \dfrac{328 \text{ C}}{3.50 \text{ A}} = \underline{\underline{93.7 \text{ s}}}$

Method B. Using conversion factors:

$$\text{number of seconds} = 0.100 \text{ g Co} \times \frac{1 \text{ mol Co}}{58.9 \text{ g Co}} \times \frac{2 \text{ mol e}^-}{1 \text{ mol Co}} \times \frac{96\ 500 \text{ C}}{1 \text{ mol e}^-} \times \frac{1 \text{ s}}{3.50 \text{ C}}$$

$$= \underline{\underline{93.7 \text{ s}}}$$

$$\left(\begin{array}{l} \text{note that a current of 3.50 A (\textit{i.e.}, 3.50 C/s)} \\ \text{implies that 3.50 C of charge flows in 1 s.} \end{array} \right)$$

We can summarize the calculations and conversion factors in an electrolysis problem as follows.

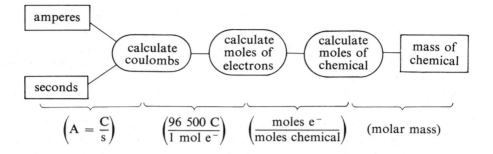

$$\left(A = \frac{C}{s}\right) \qquad \left(\frac{96\ 500\ C}{1\ mol\ e^-}\right) \qquad \left(\frac{moles\ e^-}{moles\ chemical}\right) \qquad (molar\ mass)$$

EXERCISES

A-1. If molten $CuCl_2$ is electrolyzed using inert electrodes, what substances will be produced at the anode and cathode?

A-2. An aqueous 1 kmol/m³ solution of $NiSO_4$ was electrolyzed using inert electrodes. What substance was produced at each of the electrodes. What is the minimum voltage which must be applied to the cell?

A-3. Predict the overall reactions which you would expect when the following are electrolyzed.
   a) 1 kmol/m³ NaI
   b) 1 kmol/m³ KCl
   c) 1 kmol/m³ CuF_2
   d) 1 kmol/m³ $Ni(OH)_2$
   e) 1 kmol/m³ K_2SO_4
   f) a solution which is 1 kmol/m³ in CoI_2 and HCl
   g) 1 kmol/m³ $Cu(NO_3)_2$
   h) 1 kmol/m³ NaOH, using Fe(s) electrodes
   i) 1 kmol/m³ HI, using Cu(s) electrodes
   j) 1 kmol/m³ $NiSO_4$, using Ni(s) electrodes

A-4. An aqueous solution of $CuSO_4$ was electrolyzed using copper electrodes. The copper anode contained a few percent of silver as an impurity. If 0.55 V is applied to the cell, will the copper in the anode oxidize? Will the silver oxidize? If the anode also contains a few percent of lead, will 0.55 V applied to the cell cause the lead to be oxidized? Which substances will undergo reduction at the cathode?

A-5. What voltage must be applied to a 1 kmol/m³ solution of HCl to cause any products to form at the electrodes? What products are formed at the anode and cathode?

A-6. An aqueous solution of Na_2SO_4 is electrolyzed. If litmus paper is dipped in the solution around the anode during the electrolysis, what colour will the litmus turn? What colour will the litmus turn when dipped in the solution around the cathode? If the electric current is turned off and the anode and cathode solutions are stirred together, what will be the pH of the resulting solution?

A-7. Why can aluminum metal not be produced by electrolysis of aqueous $AlCl_3$?

A-8. How many moles of $Cu(s)$ can be produced by passing a 2.50 A current through 1 $kmol/m^3$ $CuSO_4$ for 4000 s?

A-9. How many coulombs are required to produce 0.325 g of I_2 by electrolysis of an aqueous solution of KI?

B-10. A 12.5 A current was passed through a 1 $kmol/m^3$ solution of $Pb(NO_3)_2$ for 1 h using inert electrodes. How much will the mass of the cathode have increased after 1 h? What mass of product will be produced at the anode?

B-11. What quantity of electricity (in coulombs) is required to produce 1 kg of Br_2 by electrolyzing a KBr solution?

B-12. What mass of tin can be plated out of a Sn^{2+} solution if we pass 3.00 A for 6.00 h?

B-13. A certain amount of electricity deposits 45.0 g of Ag from a solution containing Ag^+ ions. What mass of copper will this amount of electricity deposit from a solution of $CuSO_4$?

B-14. An electrolysis cell contained X^+ ions. When 2.00 A were passed through the cell for 1.93×10^3 s, 5.32 g of elemental X were formed. What is the atomic mass of X? At which electrode did the element X appear?

B-15. When 6.95×10^4 C of electricity were passed through a solution of Pb^{2+} ions, a compound containing 74.6 g of lead is deposited at the anode. What is the charge on the lead in the compound that is deposited?

B-16. When a hot solution of KCl and KOH is electrolyzed, the oxidation reaction $Cl^- + 6\,OH^- \rightarrow ClO_3^- + 3\,H_2O + 6\,e^-$ occurs at the anode. How long must a current of 8.00 A be passed through the solution to produce 19.6 g of $KClO_3$?

B-17. What is the charge (in coulombs) on a single electron?

B-18. When $CuSO_4(aq)$ was electrolyzed using inert electrodes, 94.0 mL of $O_2(g)$, at STP, were liberated at the anode.
   a) How many grams of copper were deposited at the cathode?
   b) If a 2.50 A current was used in the electrolysis, what time was required to deposit the copper?

B-19. A 5.50 A current was passed through a solution of indium ions for 800 s. If 1.74 g of $In(s)$ was deposited at the cathode, what was the charge on the indium ions?

B-20. What current is required to produce 10.0 g of $Re(s)$ by passing electricity through a solution of Re^{3+} for 10.0 s?

B-21. What mass of $Zn(s)$ can be produced by passing 125 A through a solution of Zn^{2+} for 2.00 h?

B-22. How long must a current of 29.6 A be passed through a solution of HNO_3 to produce 48.7 g of $NO(g)$?

B-23. When 4.75×10^3 A were passed through a solution of ZO_4^- for 155 s, 140.0 g of elemental Z were formed. What is the atomic mass of Z? At which electrode did Z(s) appear?

B-24. A 5.57 A current was passed through $SbO^+(aq)$ for 4.38×10^3 s. If a yellow oxide containing 15.4 g of Sb was deposited at the anode, what was the formula of the yellow oxide?

B-25. A 2.95×10^4 A current was passed through a solution containing uranium ions for 0.100 s. If 4.13 g of UO_2^{2+} was formed at the anode, what was the charge on the uranium ions?

C-26. Electrolysis of NaBr(aq) with Ag electrodes forms $H_2(g)$ at the cathode and AgBr(s) at the anode. What is the molar mass of the bromine used if 338 mL of $H_2(g)$, at STP, and 5.67 g of AgBr is formed?

C-27. Electrolysis of $KXO_3(aq)$ with inert electrodes produces 0.583 g of X(s) at the cathode. The H_3O^+ produced at the anode can neutralize 229 mL of 0.250 $kmol/m^3$ NaOH. What is the molar mass of X?

C-28. The atomic mass of a metal Z is 50.9. A current passed through a liquid chloride of Z produced 412 mL of Cl_2, at STP, at the anode and 0.468 g of Z(s) at the cathode. What is the formula of the chloride of Z?

C-29. Gold has a density of 19.32 kg/L. If a solution of $AuCl_4^-$ was electrolyzed according to $AuCl_4^- + 3e^- \rightarrow Au + 4Cl^-$, using a 2.50 cm cube of Cu suspended by a wire as a cathode, what time was required to plate out a layer of gold over the copper to a thickness of 0.050 mm, using an 8.00 A current? (1 mL = 1 cm^3)

Section 16
Balancing Half-Cells

Example: Consider a half-cell involving the reaction

$$Sn^{2+} \rightleftharpoons Sn^{4+}$$

Although the mass is balanced, the charge is not, and hence we balance charges by adding electrons, e^-, that is, NEGATIVE CHARGES, to the side of the equation having the *greater* overall charge:

$$Sn^{2+} \rightleftharpoons Sn^{4+} + 2\,e^- \qquad \text{i.e., } +2 = +4 + (-2)$$

Note that we have to add a number of electrons equal to the difference between the overall charges on each side of the equation.

Example: Consider the following half-cell which occurs in ACIDIC solutions:

$$MnO_4^- \rightleftharpoons Mn^{2+}$$

To balance the O's we add H_2O to the right side (since the reaction occurs in aqueous solution):

$$MnO_4^- \rightleftharpoons Mn^{2+} + 4\,H_2O$$

To balance the H's we now add H^+ to the left side (since the reaction occurs in *acidic* solution):

$$8\,H^+ + MnO_4^- \rightleftharpoons Mn^{2+} + 4\,H_2O$$

Now that mass is balanced, we add electrons to balance the charge:

$$5\,e^- + 8\,H^+ + MnO_4^- \rightleftharpoons Mn^{2+} + 4\,H_2O \qquad (-5 + 8 - 1 = +2)$$

Example: Consider the following half-cell which occurs in BASIC solution:

$$Cu_2O \rightleftharpoons Cu(OH)_2$$

We proceed initially as if the solution were acidic:

STEP 1: $\qquad Cu_2O \rightleftharpoons 2\,Cu(OH)_2$ (balance Cu)

STEP 2: $3\,H_2O + Cu_2O \rightleftharpoons 2\,Cu(OH)_2$ (balance O)

STEP 3: $3\,H_2O + Cu_2O \rightleftharpoons 2\,Cu(OH)_2 + 2\,H^+$ (balance H)

STEP 4: $3\,H_2O + Cu_2O \rightleftharpoons 2\,Cu(OH)_2 + 2\,H^+ + 2\,e^-$ (balance charge)

Now we add on the equation $H^+ + OH^- \rightleftharpoons H_2O$ in the following way (note that the second equation is deliberately arranged so as to allow the $2\,H^+$ to cancel).

$$3\,H_2O + Cu_2O \rightleftharpoons 2\,Cu(OH)_2 + 2\,H^+ + 2\,e^- \qquad (1)$$

$$\underline{2\,H^+ + 2\,OH^- \rightleftharpoons 2\,H_2O} \qquad\qquad\qquad (2)$$

$$H_2O + Cu_2O + 2\,OH^- \rightleftharpoons 2\,Cu(OH)_2 + 2\,e^- \qquad (3)$$

> Note that equation (1) is written as if H^+ is produced (*i.e.*, the amount of H^+ in solution increases). Since the $[H^+]$ and $[OH^-]$ are related by the expression $K_w = [H^+][OH^-]$, then an increase in $[H^+]$ is accomplished by a decrease in $[OH^-]$. Some of the H^+ produced in (1) will therefore react with the OH^- in the solution, as shown in equation (2). Overall, in equation (3), we see that the reaction effectively uses up OH^-. Hence, equations (1) and (3) represent the *same process from two different viewpoints* (*i.e.*, increasing the amount of H^+ present, in (1), is equivalent to decreasing the amount of OH^- present, in (3)).

Example: If we are dealing with complete molecules, rather than just ions, we balance the equation using *whole* molecules (as far as possible).

Balance: $K_2Cr_2O_7 + H_2SO_4 \rightleftharpoons Cr_2(SO_4)_3 + K_2SO_4$

STEP 1: $K_2Cr_2O_7 + 4\,H_2SO_4 \rightleftharpoons Cr_2(SO_4)_3 + K_2SO_4$

(balance Cr, K and SO_4)

STEP 2: $K_2Cr_2O_7 + 4\,H_2SO_4 \rightleftharpoons Cr_2(SO_4)_3 + K_2SO_4 + 7\,H_2O$

(balance O)

STEP 3: $K_2Cr_2O_7 + 4\,H_2SO_4 + 6\,H^+ \rightleftharpoons Cr_2(SO_4)_3 + K_2SO_4 + 7\,H_2O$

(balance H)

STEP 4: $K_2Cr_2O_7 + 4\,H_2SO_4 + 6\,H^+ + 6\,e^- \rightleftharpoons Cr_2(SO_4)_3 + K_2SO_4 + 7\,H_2O$

(balance charge)

Notes

1. The presence of the H_2SO_4 means that this reaction occurs in ACID solution.

2. Since this reaction occurs in aqueous solution, the $K_2Cr_2O_7$, H_2SO_4, $Cr_2(SO_4)_3$ and K_2SO_4 will actually be ionized. However, in the next section (dealing with two half-cells combined to give a total cell) we will often treat the total reaction from a molecular viewpoint and hence we need to know how to deal with half-cells involving molecules as well as ions.

EXERCISES

Balance the following half-cells.

1. $Ce^{4+} \rightleftharpoons Ce^{2+}$
2. $I_2 \rightleftharpoons I^-$
3. $Mn^{2+} \rightleftharpoons MnO_2$ (acidic solution)
4. $O_2 \rightleftharpoons H_2O_2$ (acidic solution)
5. $S_2O_8^{2-} \rightleftharpoons HSO_4^-$ (acidic solution)
6. $H_3AsO_4 \rightleftharpoons HAsO_2$ (acidic solution)
7. $H_2SeO_3 \rightleftharpoons Se$ (acidic solution)
8. $N_2H_4 \rightleftharpoons N_2$ (basic solution)
9. $HO_2^- \rightleftharpoons O_2$ (basic solution)
10. $Cr_2O_7^{2-} \rightleftharpoons Cr^{3+}$ (acidic solution)
11. $HXeO_4^- \rightleftharpoons HXeO_6^{3-}$ (basic solution)
12. $HC_2H_3O_2 \rightleftharpoons C_2H_5OH$ (acidic solution)
13. $Cr(OH)_3 \rightleftharpoons CrO_4^{2-}$ (basic solution)
14. $CH_3CHO \rightleftharpoons CH_2CH_2$ (acidic solution)
15. $KNO_3 + H_2SO_4 \rightleftharpoons NO_2 + K_2SO_4$ (acidic solution)
16. $KClO_3 + NH_4HSO_4 \rightleftharpoons NH_4Cl + KHSO_4$ (acidic solution)
17. $FeHPO_3 \rightleftharpoons PO_4^{3-} + Fe(OH)_3$ (basic solution)
18. $Cu_2S \rightleftharpoons Cu^{2+} + H_2SO_3$ (acidic solution)
19. $FeS \rightleftharpoons Fe^{3+} + SO_4^{2-}$ (acidic solution)
20. $Hg_2PbS_2 \rightleftharpoons SO_4^{2-} + Pb(OH)_6^{2-} + Hg(OH)_2$ (basic solution)
21. $(NH_4)_2S \rightleftharpoons S$ (basic solution). [Hint: NH_4^+ is a Brönsted–Lowry acid.]

131

Section 17

Balancing Redox Equations Using Half-Cells

To balance a redox equation we break up the equation into an oxidation half-cell and a reduction half-cell.

Example: $H_2PO_2^- + CNO^- \rightarrow CN^- + HPO_3^-$ (acidic solution)
This equation breaks up into:

and

$$CNO^- \rightarrow CN^-$$
$$H_2PO_2^- \rightarrow HPO_3^-$$

We then balance each half-cell separately:

$$CNO^- + 2\,H^+ + 2\,e^- \rightarrow CN^- + H_2O$$
$$H_2PO_2^- + H_2O \rightarrow HPO_3^- + 3\,H^+ + 3\,e^-$$

Next we multiply the first half-cell by 3 and the second half-cell by 2, and add the two half-cells:

$$3\,CNO^- + 6\,H^+ + 6\,e^- \rightarrow 3\,CN^- + 3\,H_2O$$
$$\underline{2\,H_2PO_2^- + 2\,H_2O \rightarrow 2\,HPO_3^- + 6\,H^+ + 6\,e^-}$$
$$3\,CNO^- + 2\,H_2PO_2^- \rightarrow 3\,CN^- + 2\,HPO_3^- + H_2O$$

Note that we multiplied each half-cell such that the TOTAL NUMBER OF ELECTRONS *GIVEN OFF* IN ONE HALF-CELL EXACTLY EQUALS THE TOTAL NUMBER OF ELECTRONS *USED UP* IN THE OTHER HALF-CELL.

A final check should ALWAYS be made to ensure that the final equation is balanced for both mass and charge.

Example:

$$K_2Cr_2O_7 + KBr + H_2SO_4 \rightarrow K_2SO_4 + Cr_2(SO_4)_3 + Br_2 + H_2O$$

$$\left[\begin{array}{l} \text{It is reasonable to assume that Cr is involved in one half-cell and Br in another} \\ \text{half-cell. Note that } K^+ \text{ and } SO_4{}^{2-} \text{ are spectator ions, and that the presence of} \\ H_2SO_4 \text{ indicates acidic conditions.} \end{array} \right]$$

We select and balance the half-cell involving Cr:

$$K_2Cr_2O_7 + 4 H_2SO_4 + 6 H^+ + 6 e^- \rightarrow Cr_2(SO_4)_3 + K_2SO_4 + 7 H_2O$$

(after selecting the $K_2Cr_2O_7$ and $Cr_2(SO_4)_3$, the K_2SO_4 is required to balance K, the H_2SO_4 is required to balance SO_4 and the H_2O, H^+ and e^- complete the balance).
Next, we select and balance the half-cell involving Br:

STEP 1: $\qquad\qquad$ $2 KBr \rightarrow Br_2$ $\qquad\qquad$ (balance Br)
STEP 2: $\qquad\qquad$ $2 KBr \rightarrow Br_2 + K_2SO_4$ $\quad$ (balance K)
STEP 3: $2 KBr + H_2SO_4 \rightarrow Br_2 + K_2SO_4$ $\quad$ (balance SO_4)
STEP 4: $2 KBr + H_2SO_4 \rightarrow Br_2 + K_2SO_4 + 2 H^+ + 2 e^-$ $\quad$ (complete balance)

After multiplying the Br half-cell by 3 and adding it to the Cr half-cell we have the final answer:

$$K_2Cr_2O_7 + 7 H_2SO_4 + 6 KBr \rightarrow 3 Br_2 + 4 K_2SO_4 + Cr_2(SO_4)_3 + 7 H_2O$$

Example: Consider the reaction $P_4 \rightarrow H_2PO_2{}^- + PH_3$ (acidic)
Part of the P_4 is oxidized in one half-cell and part of the P_4 is reduced in a second half-cell. This oxidation and reduction of the same species is called DISPROPOR-TIONATION.

$$\begin{array}{l} 3 \times (P_4 + 8 H_2O \rightarrow 4 H_2PO_2{}^- + 8 H^+ + 4 e^-) \\ \underline{1 \times (P_4 + 12 H^+ + 12 e^- \rightarrow 4 PH_3)} \\ \quad 4 P_4 + 24 H_2O \rightarrow 12 H_2PO_2{}^- + 4 PH_3 + 12 H^+ \end{array}$$

or, dividing through by 4:

$$P_4 + 6 H_2O \rightarrow 3 H_2PO_2{}^- + PH_3 + 3 H^+$$

EXERCISES

Balance the following redox equations.

A-1. $U^{4+} + MnO_4{}^- \rightarrow Mn^{2+} + UO_2{}^{2+}$ $\quad$ (acidic)
A-2. $Zn + As_2O_3 \rightarrow AsH_3 + Zn^{2+}$ $\quad$ (acidic)
A-3. $Fe^{2+} + Cr_2O_7{}^{2-} \rightarrow Cr^{3+} + Fe^{3+}$ $\quad$ (acidic)
A-4. $Cl_2 + SO_2 \rightarrow Cl^- + SO_4{}^{2-}$ $\quad$ (acidic)

A-5. $Cu + NO_3^- \rightarrow Cu^{2+} + NO$ (acidic)

A-6. $S^{2-} + ClO_3^- \rightarrow Cl^- + S$ (basic)

A-7. $OCl^- \rightarrow Cl^- + ClO_3^-$ (basic)

A-8. $CN^- + IO_3^- \rightarrow I^- + CNO^-$ (basic)

A-9. $Sn^{2+} + H_2O_2 \rightarrow Sn^{4+}$ (basic)

A-10. $Mn^{2+} + HBiO_3 \rightarrow Bi^{3+} + MnO_4^-$ (acidic)

B-11. $HSO_3^- + IO_3^- \rightarrow I_2 + SO_4^{2-} + H^+ + H_2O$

B-12. $HNO_2 \rightarrow HNO_3 + NO + H_2O$

B-13. $Br_2 \rightarrow Br^- + BrO_3^-$ (basic)

B-14. $Sb_2S_3 + NO_3^- \rightarrow NO_2 + SO_4^{2-} + Sb_2O_5$ (acidic)

B-15. $As_2S_3 + NO_3^- \rightarrow NO + SO_4^{2-} + H_3AsO_4$ (acidic)

B-16. $H_2O_2 + Cr(OH)_4^- \rightarrow CrO_4^{2-}$ (basic)

B-17. $FeS + NO_3^- \rightarrow NO + SO_4^{2-} + Fe^{3+}$ (acidic)

B-18. $FeHPO_3 + Cr_2O_7^{2-} \rightarrow Cr^{3+} + H_3PO_4 + Fe^{3+}$ (acidic)

B-19. $SnS_2O_3 + MnO_4^- \rightarrow Mn^{2+} + SO_4^{2-} + Sn^{4+}$ (acidic)

B-20. $Hg_4Fe(CN)_6 + ClO_3^- \rightarrow Cl^- + NO + CO_2 + Fe^{3+} + Hg^{2+}$ (acidic)

B-21. $Fe_2Fe(CN)_6 + NO_3^- \rightarrow NO + CO_2 + Fe^{3+}$ (acidic)

B-22. $FeHPO_3 + OCl^- \rightarrow Cl^- + PO_4^{3-} + Fe(OH)_3$ (acidic)

B-23. $Cu_2SnS_2 + S_2O_8^{2-} \rightarrow SO_4^{2-} + Sn(OH)_6^{2-} + Cu(OH)_2$ (basic)

B-24. $CuS + HNO_3 \rightarrow Cu(NO_3)_2 + H_2O + NO_2 + SO_2$

B-25. $FeAsS + NO_3^- \rightarrow NO + SO_4^{2-} + H_3AsO_4 + Fe^{3+}$ (acidic)

B-26. $Sn(S_2O_3)_2^{2-} + FeS_2O_8^+ \rightarrow SO_4^{2-} + Sn^{4+} + Fe^{2+}$ (acidic)

B-27. $Ca_3(PO_4)_2 + SiO_2 + C \rightarrow P_4 + CaSiO_3 + CO$

B-28. $KMnO_4 + H_2S + H_2SO_4 \rightarrow K_2SO_4 + MnSO_4 + H_2O + S$

B-29. $C_2H_5OH + K_2Cr_2O_7 + H_2SO_4 \rightarrow$
$$CH_3COOH + Cr_2(SO_4)_3 + K_2SO_4 + H_2O$$

B-30. $K_4Fe(CN)_6 + KMnO_4 + H_2SO_4 \rightarrow$
$$KHSO_4 + Fe_2(SO_4)_3 + MnSO_4 + HNO_3 + CO_2 + H_2O$$

B-31. $NH_4SCN + MnO_4^- \rightarrow Mn^{2+} + N_2 + CO_2 + SO_4^{2-}$ (acidic)

B-32. $CrSCN^{2+} + BrO^- \rightarrow Br^- + NO_3^- + CO_3^{2-} + SO_4^{2-} + CrO_4^{2-}$ (acidic)

C-33. $Fe(CrO_2)_2 + Na_2O_2 \rightarrow Na_2CrO_4 + Fe_2O_3 + Na_2O$

C-34. $CuF_2 + NH_3 \rightarrow Cu_3N + NH_4F + N_2$

To gain extra practice in balancing redox equations by the method of half-cells, try the exercises at the end of Section 19.

Section 18

Oxidation Numbers

Oxidation numbers are fictitious numbers which represent the charge that an atom would possess if all the atoms making up a molecule were 100% ionic.

Example: SO_2 is actually covalent, but we *assume* that the molecule is ionic:

$$SO_2 = S^{4+} + 2\,O^{2-}$$

To calculate the oxidation numbers of the atoms in a molecule, we assume that:
Li, Na, K, Rb, Cs (1st column) are *always* $+1$
Be, Mg, Ca, Sr, Ba (2nd column) are *always* $+2$
F, Cl, Br, I (7th column) are *normally* -1 (many exceptions)
O is normally -2, except for peroxides (when it is -1)
H is normally $+1$, except for hydrides (when it is -1)
The oxidation number of any atom not in the above list must be either calculated or assumed.

The rule governing oxidation numbers is simply:

The sum of the positive charges plus negative charges must equal the total charge on the molecule.

Notes

1. Oxidation numbers may be fractions.

2. The oxidation number of an atom in its ELEMENTAL FORM is *zero* (*e.g.*, in S_8 the S atom has a zero charge).

3. The oxidation number of a monatomic ion is just the charge on the ion (*e.g.*, Sn^{2+} has $+2$ as an oxidation number).

Example:

$$+2 +x -8 = 0 \leftarrow \text{total charge } (+2 + x -8 = 0 \Rightarrow x = +6)$$
$$+1 \quad x -2 \leftarrow \text{oxidation numbers of individual atoms}$$
$$H_2 \quad S \quad O_4$$

Hence:
$$+1 +6 -2 \leftarrow \text{oxidation numbers of atoms}$$
$$H_2 \quad S \quad O_4$$

Example:

$$+4 +3x -14 = -1 \Rightarrow x = +3$$
$$+1 \quad x \quad -2$$
$$H_4 \quad B_3 \quad O_7^-$$

Hence, for $H_4B_3O_7^-$ we have:
$$+1 +3 -2$$
$$H_4 \quad B_3 \quad O_7^-$$

When we do not know the oxidation number of two different atoms in the molecule, we are *free* to *arbitrarily* choose an oxidation number for one of the atoms and then calculate the oxidation number of the other, based on this assumption.

Note: If you assume a value for an oxidation number, you MUST state the value you have assumed.

Example: C_2H_6S; we do not know the oxidation number of either C or S.
Since S^{2-} is often found (*e.g.*, sulphides), we shall assume a value of -2 for S. Then:

$$2x +6 -2 = 0 \Rightarrow x = -2$$
$$x +1 -2$$
$$C_2 \quad H_6 \quad S \qquad\qquad \text{Hence: } \begin{array}{ccc} -2 & +1 & -2 \\ C_2 & H_6 & S \end{array}$$

We could also have assumed (arbitrarily) that $S = +1$:

$$2x +6 +1 = 0 \Rightarrow x = -\tfrac{7}{2}$$
$$x +1 +1$$
$$C_2 \quad H_6 \quad S \qquad\qquad \text{Hence: } \begin{array}{ccc} -\tfrac{7}{2} & +1 & +1 \\ C_2 & H_6 & S \end{array}$$

EXERCISES

Determine all the oxidation number in the following.
A-1. SO_3, PF_3, PCl_5, Na_3P, S_2F_{10}, S_2O_7
A-2. NO_3^-, NO_2, N_2O_3, NO, N_2O, N_2, N_3^-, $N_2H_5^+$, NH_4^+

A-3. UO_3, U_3O_8, U_2O_5, K_2UO_4, MgU_2O_7

A-4. $MnSO_4$, MnO_2, $KMnO_4$, MnO_3^+, $MnCl_4^-$

A-5. H_2SO_3, $H_2S_2O_3$, $H_2S_2O_7$, $KHSO_4$, S_4, SO_2^{2-}

A-6. $SrSiO_3$, S_2OCl_4, $S_2O_3Cl_4$, H_2SO_5, SO_2ClF, NH_2OH

A-7. $C_2O_4^{2-}$, WO_4^{2-}, NO_2^-, ClO_4^-, HIO_6^{4-}, $P_2O_7^{4-}$, ClF_6^+

B-8. $Y(OH)_3$, $(NH_4)_2SO_3$, $Pb(CO_3)_2$, $Cd(NO_3)_2$, $Hg(IO_3)_2$

B-9. CH_4, CH_3Cl, CH_2Cl_2, C_2H_5OH, C_3H_6O

B-10. C_4H_6, CH_3OH, CH_3SH, CH_3NO_2, CH_3SO_3H

B-11. $C_4H_4O_4^{2-}$, $C_5H_{10}O$, $C_2H_3O_2^-$, C_3H_3Cl, $C_7H_5O_2^-$

B-12. $C_8H_{11}N_2O_3^-$, $C_6H_5SO_3^-$, $C_6H_3(OH)_2NO_2$

B-13. $Ge(C_3H_7)_4$, $B(OC_2H_5)_3$, $Sn(SCH_3)_4$, $C_{10}H_7HgCl$, $[(CH_3)_3Sn]_2O$

Section 19

Balancing Redox Equations Using Oxidation Numbers

In any redox equation, the oxidation numbers of one or more atoms will *increase*, while at the same time the oxidation numbers of one or more atoms will *decrease*. We can define:

> OXIDATION = an INCREASE in oxidation number
> REDUCTION = a DECREASE in oxidation number

Example: In the half-cell:

$$Sn^{4+} + 2\,e^- \rightleftharpoons Sn^{2+}$$

we say the Sn^{4+} has been *reduced* since the oxidation number *decreases* from $+4$ to $+2$ when the Sn^{4+} forms Sn^{2+}. Note that the Sn^{4+} ion has decreased its oxidation number by 2, and simultaneously the Sn^{4+} ion has gained 2 electrons.

Example: In the half-cell:

$$2\,Br^- \rightleftharpoons Br_2 + 2\,e^-$$

we say the Br^- has been *oxidized* since the oxidation number *increases* from -1 to 0 when the Br^- forms Br_2. Note that each Br^- ion has increased its oxidation number by 1, and simultaneously each Br^- ion has lost 1 electron.

From the above examples we can see that a gain or loss of electrons is directly related to a decrease or increase in oxidation number. Since the total number of electrons lost in an oxidation half-cell must equal the total number of electrons gained in a reduction half-cell then:

138

1. Any increase in oxidation numbers must be exactly balanced by a corresponding decrease in oxidation numbers.
2. In any redox equation the OVERALL change in oxidation numbers *must* be *zero*.

Example: Balance the following equation

$$U^{4+} + MnO_4^- \rightarrow Mn^{2+} + UO_2^{2+} \qquad \text{(acidic solution)}$$

We first assign oxidation numbers to all species involved in a change of oxidation number

$$\overset{}{U^{4+}} + \overset{+7}{MnO_4^-} \longrightarrow Mn^{2+} + \overset{+6}{UO_2^{2+}}$$

$$\Delta ON = -5$$
$$\Delta ON = +2$$

where ΔON means "change in oxidation number". Now, since the *total* ΔON must be *zero* then we take:

$$\left. \begin{array}{l} 2 \times (MnO_4^- \rightarrow Mn^{2+}; \ \Delta ON = -5) \\ 5 \times (U^{4+} \quad \rightarrow UO_2^{2+}; \ \Delta ON = +2) \end{array} \right\} \text{ total } \Delta ON = -10 + 10 = 0$$

Hence:
$$5\,U^{4+} + 2\,MnO_4^- \rightarrow 2\,Mn^{2+} + 5\,UO_2^{2+}.$$

We must now balance the O's by adding H_2O and *then* balance the H's by adding H^+ (recall that the reaction occurs in acidic solution):

$$5\,U^{4+} + 2\,MnO_4^- + 2\,H_2O \rightarrow 2\,Mn^{2+} + 5\,UO_2^{2+} + 4\,H^+$$

Now that the equation is balanced for atoms (*i.e.*, mass), we *MUST* CHECK THAT CHARGE IS BALANCED:

Left-hand side $= (5 \times +4) + (2 \times -1) = +18$
Right-hand side $= (2 \times +2) + (5 \times +2) + (4 \times +1) = +18$
$\therefore$ checks out.

Example:

$$Zn + As_2O_3 \rightarrow AsH_3 + Zn^{2+} \qquad \text{(basic solution)}$$

After establishing which atoms are being oxidized and reduced, we do a PRELIMINARY balance of the As atoms so that the number of As atoms involved in the reduction are the same on both sides of the equation. Then:

139

$$\overset{+3}{Zn} + \overset{}{As_2O_3} \longrightarrow 2\ \overset{-3}{AsH_3} + Zn^{2+}$$

$$\Delta ON = 2 \times -6 = -12$$

$$\Delta ON = +2$$

and to balance the changes in the oxidation numbers we take

$$\left.\begin{array}{l} 6 \times (Zn \rightarrow Zn^{2+}; \Delta ON = +2) \\ 1 \times (As_2O_3 \rightarrow 2\ AsH_3; \Delta ON = -12) \end{array}\right\} \text{total } \Delta ON = +12 + -12 = 0$$

Hence: $\qquad\qquad 6\ Zn + As_2O_3 \rightarrow 2\ AsH_3 + 6\ Zn^{2+}$

To complete the mass balance, we first assume that the reaction occurs in an *acidic* solution:

$$6\ Zn + As_2O_3 + 12\ H^+ \rightarrow 2\ AsH_3 + 6\ Zn^{2+} + 3\ H_2O$$

and then add in the equation $H_2O \rightarrow H^+ + OH^-$ so as to make the 12 H^+ cancel:

$$6\ Zn + As_2O_3 + 12\ H^+ \rightarrow 2\ AsH_3 + 6\ Zn^{2+} + 3\ H_2O$$
$$\underline{\qquad\qquad 12\ H_2O \rightarrow 12\ H^+ + 12\ OH^-\qquad\qquad}$$
$$6\ Zn + As_2O_3 + 9\ H_2O \rightarrow 2\ AsH_3 + 6\ Zn^{2+} + 12\ OH^-$$

Again, we check that the charges on the left- and right-hand sides are equal. In this case both sides are equal to zero.

Example:

$$\overset{+2\ -3}{CN^-} + \overset{+7}{MnO_4^-} \rightarrow Mn^{2+} + \overset{+5}{NO_3^-} + \overset{+4}{CO_3^{2-}} \qquad \text{(acidic solution)}$$

If we use the oxidation numbers assigned above, we assign a *GROUP CHANGE* in oxidation number:

$$\overset{+2\ -3}{C\ N^-} + \overset{+7}{MnO_4^-} \longrightarrow Mn^{2+} + \overset{+5}{NO_3^-} + \overset{+4}{CO_3^{2-}}$$

$$\Delta ON = -5$$

$$\left.\begin{array}{l} \Delta ON = +8 \\ \Delta ON = +2 \end{array}\right\} CN^- \text{ group } \Delta ON = +10$$

and to balance the changes in the oxidation numbers we take:

$$\left.\begin{array}{l} 2 \times (MnO_4^- \rightarrow Mn^{2+}; \Delta ON = -5) \\ 1 \times (CN^- \rightarrow NO_3^- + CO_3^{2-}; \Delta ON = +10) \end{array}\right\} \text{total } \Delta ON = -10 + 10 = 0$$

Hence: $\qquad\qquad CN^- + 2\ MnO_4^- \rightarrow 2\ Mn^{2+} + NO_3^- + CO_3^{2-}$

and after balancing for mass (and checking for charge) we have:

$$CN^- + 2\,MnO_4^- + 4\,H^+ \rightarrow 2\,Mn^{2+} + NO_3^- + CO_3^{2-} + 2\,H_2O$$

Example:

$$P_4 \rightarrow H_2PO_2^- + PH_3 \quad \text{(acidic solution)}$$

In a *disproportionation* reaction such as this (see Section 14) we think of P_4 acting in two different ways:

$$\overset{0}{P_4} + \overset{0}{P_4} \longrightarrow 4\,\overset{+1}{H_2PO_2^-} + 4\,\overset{-3}{PH_3}$$

$$\Delta ON = 4 \times +1 = +4$$
$$\Delta ON = 4 \times -3 = -12$$

Notice that we have done a *preliminary* balance for:

$$P_4 \rightarrow 4\,H_2PO_2^-$$

and

$$P_4 \rightarrow 4\,PH_3$$

and to balance the changes in the oxidation numbers we take:

$$\left.\begin{array}{l} 3 \times (P_4 \rightarrow 4\,H_2PO_2^- ; \Delta ON = +4) \\ 1 \times (P_4 \rightarrow 4\,PH_3 ; \Delta ON = -12) \end{array}\right\} \text{total } \Delta ON = +12 + -12 = 0$$

Hence:

$$3\,P_4 + P_4 \rightarrow 12\,H_2PO_2^- + 4\,PH_3$$

or (dividing by 4) we have:

$$P_4 \rightarrow 3\,H_2PO_2^- + PH_3$$

Finally we balance for mass and check for charge:

$$P_4 + 6\,H_2O \rightarrow 3\,H_2PO_2^- + PH_3 + 3\,H^+$$

EXERCISES

Balance the following using oxidation numbers.

A-1. $SeO_3^{2-} + I^- \rightarrow Se + I_2$ (acidic conditions)
A-2. $I_2 + HOCl \rightarrow IO_3^- + Cl^-$ (acidic)
A-3. $Zn + NO_3^- \rightarrow ZnO_2^{2-} + NH_3$ (basic)
A-4. $SO_3^{2-} + Cr_2O_7^{2-} \rightarrow SO_4^{2-} + Cr^{3+}$ (acidic)
A-5. $AuCl_4^- + C_2O_4^{2-} \rightarrow Au + Cl^- + CO_2$
A-6. $H_2PO_2^- + TeO_4^{2-} \rightarrow PO_4^{3-} + Te$ (acidic)
A-7. $CdS + NO_3^- \rightarrow Cd^{2+} + S + NO$ (acidic)

A-8. $As_4 + NaOCl + H_2O \rightarrow H_3AsO_4 + NaCl$

A-9. $PbS + NO_3^- \rightarrow Pb(NO_3)_2 + NO + S$ (acidic)

A-10. $CH_3NO_2 + Ti^{3+} \rightarrow CH_3NH_2 + Ti^{4+}$ (acidic)

A-11. $Cr_2O_7^{2-} + HCHO \rightarrow Cr^{3+} + HCOOH$ (acidic)

A-12. $Pt + NO_3^- + Cl^- \rightarrow PtCl_6 + NO$ (acidic)

A-13. $Tl_2SO_4 + K_3Fe(CN)_6 + KOH \rightarrow Tl_2O_3 + K_4Fe(CN)_6 + K_2SO_4 + H_2O$

B-14. $MnO_4^- + Sb_2O_3 \rightarrow Mn^{2+} + Sb_2O_5$ (acidic)

B-15. $Al_2O_3 + Co(NO_3)_2 \rightarrow CoAl_2O_4 + NO_2 + O_2$

B-16. $MnO_4^- + HN_3 + SO_4^{2-} \rightarrow MnSO_4 + N_2$ (acidic)

B-17. $H_2SeO_3 + SCN^- \rightarrow Se + CO_2 + NH_4^+ + HSO_4^-$ (acidic)

B-18. $VO_4^{3-} + I^- + IO_3^- + Cl^- \rightarrow VO^{2+} + ICl$ (basic)

B-19. $Sb_2O_4 + Na_2CO_3 + S \rightarrow Na_3SbS_4 + SO_2 + CO_2$

B-20. $Co(NO_3)_2 + KNO_2 + HC_2H_3O_2 \rightarrow$
$$K_3Co(NO_2)_6 + KNO_3 + KC_2H_3O_2 + NO + H_2O$$

B-21. $Cr_2(SO_4)_3 + Na_2CO_3 + KNO_3 \rightarrow Na_2CrO_4 + KNO_2 + Na_2SO_4 + CO_2$

B-22. $(NH_4)_2PtCl_6 + N_2H_4 \cdot 2HCl + NH_3 \rightarrow NH_4Cl + N_2 + Pt$

B-23. $MnSO_4 + Ag_2O_2 + NO_3^- \rightarrow MnO_4^- + AgNO_3 + SO_4^{2-}$ (acidic)

B-24. $IO_3^- + CuSCN + Cl^- \rightarrow ICl + Cu^{2+} + HSO_4^- + HCN$ (acidic)

C-25. $FeS_2 + Na_2O_2 \rightarrow Fe_2O_3 + Na_2SO_4 + Na_2O$

To gain extra practice in balancing redox equations by the method of oxidation numbers, try the exercises at the end of Section 17.

Section 20
Electron Configurations

Introduction

The following ELECTRON ENERGY LEVELS within an atom have been determined as the result of experiments. Each dash, "—", represents the energy associated with a region of space called an ORBITAL. Electrons within an atom will occupy the various orbitals available and will possess the amount of energy associated with their orbital. An orbital may or may not actually be occupied by an electron; an unoccupied orbital can be thought of as an energy requirement which must be met before an electron can occupy a region of space within the atom.

The numbers, or "n-values", in Figure 20-1 (*e.g.*, 1s, 2s, 3s) are used to distinguish between the major energy groupings and sizes of orbitals within an atom.

The symbols *s*, *p*, *d* and *f* represent the sub-groupings of orbitals within a given major grouping.

> We define a SHELL to be the set of all the oribitals having the same *n*-value.

Example:

1st shell consists of 1*s* orbital
2nd shell consists of 2*s*, 2*p* orbitals
3rd shell consists of 3*s*, 3*p*, 3*d* orbitals
4th shell consists of 4*s*, 4*p*, 4*d*, 4*f* orbitals

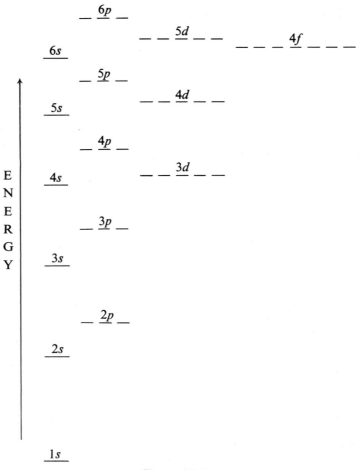

Figure 20-1

The symbols *s*, *p*, *d* and *f*, as mentioned previously, represent the different types of orbitals which make up a shell. A given shell can contain *at most*

        1 *s*-orbital,
        3 *p*-orbitals,
        5 *d*-orbitals,
and   7 *f*-orbitals   (see Figure 20-1).

> Within a shell, the set of orbitals of a given type is called a SUBSHELL.

Example: The 4th shell has 4 subshells, namely:

<blockquote>
the 4*s* subshell (1 orbital in the set),
the 4*p* subshell (3 orbitals in the set),
the 4*d* subshell (5 orbitals in the set),
</blockquote>

and   the 4*f* subshell (7 orbitals in the set).

Notes

1. Experiments show that the energy levels associated with the various subshells within a shell are shifted to higher energies as each additional type of subshell becomes possible:

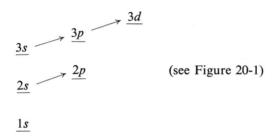

(see Figure 20-1)

2. The set of three orbitals of *equal energy* making up the *p* subshell can be further broken down into p_x, p_y and p_z orbitals. Although the separate orbitals within the *d* and *f* subshells can also be individually labelled, we will not require such labelling.

WRITING ELECTRON CONFIGURATIONS OF ATOMS

Hydrogen has *one* 1*s* electron, and we say that H has the ELECTRON CONFIGURATION: H($1s^1$). If we now consider He, with two electrons, we have:

$$He(1s^2) \quad \text{pronounced "one } s \text{ two", } not \text{ "one } s \text{ squared".}$$

> Experiments indicate that each individual orbital can hold a maximum of *two* electrons.

After 2 electrons, we have completely filled the 1st shell and we say that we have a FULL SHELL. When all the orbitals in the 2nd shell are eventually filled, we will again have a FULL SHELL.

When adding electrons to the orbitals of Figure 20-1, we fill up the orbitals in order from lowest energy to highest energy.

Example: As more electrons become available for filling orbitals, we fill the $1s$ orbital first and then proceed to fill the $2s$, $2p$, $3s$, $3p$, $4s$, $3d$, $4p$, $5s$, $4d$, $5p$, etc. orbitals.

If we now add electrons one at a time we find:

H($1s^1$)
He($1s^2$)
Li($1s^2 2s^1$)
Be($1s^2 2s^2$)
B($1s^2 2s^2 2p_x^1$),   or   B($1s^2 2s^2 2p^1$), in short form
C($1s^2 2s^2 2p_x^1 2p_y^1$),   or   C($1s^2 2s^2 2p^2$)
N($1s^2 2s^2 2p_x^1 2p_y^1 2p_z^1$),   or   N($1s^2 2s^2 2p^3$)
O($1s^2 2s^2 2p_x^2 2p_y^1 2p_z^1$),   or   O($1s^2 2s^2 2p^4$)
F($1s^2 2s^2 2p_x^2 2p_y^2 2p_z^1$),   or   F($1s^2 2s^2 2p^5$)
Ne($1s^2 2s^2 2p_x^2 2p_y^2 2p_z^2$),   or   Ne($1s^2 2s^2 2p^6$)

Notes

1. When filling up the p orbitals (and the d and f orbitals) we do not pair up the electrons until we are forced to do so by a lack of more vacant p orbitals. The total energy is lower for two unpaired electrons in two separate, equal-energy orbitals within the same subshell than for two electrons paired up in the same orbital. Having to pair up electrons requires extra amounts of energy and hence electron-pairing is avoided until it becomes necessary. "Pairing up" becomes necessary if we have to put electrons in orbitals with *higher* energy in order to avoid pairing.

2. Experimentally it is found that He and Ne are totally INERT, that is, form no compounds. The He atom has two electrons, which *completely fill* the 1st shell. The Ne atom has ten electrons, which permit Ne to *completely fill* the 2nd shell:

$$\underbrace{\text{Ne}(1s^2}_{\substack{\text{1st} \\ \text{shell} \\ 2\,e^-}} \quad \underbrace{2s^2 2p^6)}_{\substack{\text{2nd} \\ \text{shell} \\ 8\,e^-}} \quad = 10\,e^-$$

Hence we can conclude that:

> A completely filled shell of electrons is extremely stable (*i.e.*, unreactive).

3. Since each individual orbital can hold *two* electrons, then:

        an s subshell (1 orbital in set) can hold 2 e^-,
        a p subshell (3 orbitals in set) can hold 6 e^-,
        a d subshell (5 orbitals in set) can hold 10 e^-,
and   an f subshell (7 orbitals in set) can hold 14 e^-.

4. Each shell can contain more electrons than a preceding shell and thus is larger than preceding shells. As a result, a 2s (or 2p) orbital is closer to the nucleus than a 3s (or 3p or 3d) orbital (*i.e.*, the 2nd shell is smaller than the 3rd shell and hence is "buried" under the 3rd shell).

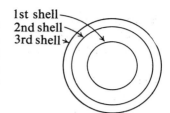

Based on Figure 20-1 and the way we built up the atoms from H to Ne, we can look at the periodic table in the following way.

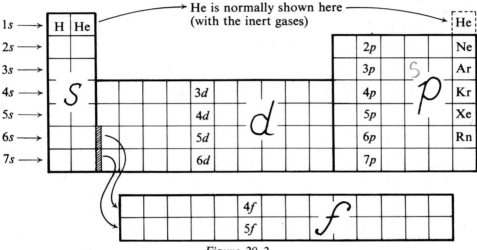

Figure 20-2

Note that the s-orbital block of elements in Figure 20-2 is 2 elements wide since an s subshell can hold 2 electrons, and the p-orbital block is 6 elements wide since a p subshell can hold 6 electrons. Similarly, the d subshell can hold 10 electrons and the d-orbital block is 10 elements wide, and the f subshell can hold 14 electrons and the f-orbital block is 14 elements wide.

Using the periodic table, and the manner in which it gives information on the energy level ordering of orbitals, we can write the electron configuration of most atoms.

Example: $S(1s^2 2s^2 2p^6 3s^2 3p^4)$. We can trace out the orbitals occupied in an atom simply by looking at the periodic table. In the first row we have only the 1s orbital being used. Hence, $1s^2$. In the second row we pass through the 2s and 2p orbitals. Hence, $1s^2 2s^2 2p^6$. Finally, in the third row we pass through the 3s orbital and the first 4 electrons in the 3p orbitals. Hence, overall we have $S(1s^2 2s^2 2p^6 3s^2 3p^4)$.

147

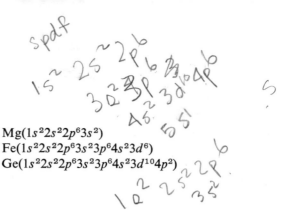

Further Examples:

$$Mg(1s^22s^22p^63s^2)$$
$$Fe(1s^22s^22p^63s^23p^64s^23d^6)$$
$$Ge(1s^22s^22p^63s^23p^64s^23d^{10}4p^2)$$

CORE NOTATION

The set of electrons belonging to a given atom can be divided into two subsets: the CORE electrons and the OUTER electrons. We can define the *core* to be the set of electrons having the configuration of the nearest inert gas with an atomic number *less* than that of the atom we are considering. The *outer* electrons consist of all the electrons OUTSIDE the core electrons. Since core electrons normally do not take part in chemical reactions, we can normally ignore such electrons when writing the electron configuration of an atom.

Example: We can re-write

$$Rb(1s^22s^22p^63s^23p^64s^23d^{10}4p^65s^1)$$

as $\qquad\qquad\qquad Rb([Kr]\,5s^1)$

The symbol [Kr] means "the set of core electrons having the same configuration as the atom Kr". This short way of writing the electron configuration of an atom is called CORE NOTATION.

Further examples of core notation:

$$Mg([Ne]\,3s^2)$$
$$Mn([Ar]\,4s^23d^5)$$
$$As([Ar]\,4s^23d^{10}4p^3)$$
$$Ar([Ne]\,3s^33p^6)$$

Note that we "back up" to the previous inert gas configuration. Ar([Ar]) is NOT acceptable.

ELECTRON CONFIGURATIONS OF IONS

When writing the electron configurations of NEGATIVE ions we merely add electrons to the last unfilled subshell, or start the next subshell if the previous one is filled.

Example:

$$O([He]\ 2s^2 2p^4) + 2\ e^- \rightarrow O^{2-}([He]\ 2s^2 2p^6)$$

When writing the electron configurations of POSITIVE ions we must consider both the sizes of the orbitals involved and the relative energies of the electrons in the orbitals in order to decide which electrons are removed.

> Electrons in the outermost shell will be removed first.

Example:

$$Ni([Ar]\ 4s^2 3d^8) \rightarrow 2\ e^- + Ni^{2+}([Ar]\ 3d^8)$$

Electrons in the 4th shell are farther from the nucleus than electrons in the 3rd shell. Being farther from the nucleus, the electrons are less tightly held and more easily removed. Hence, $4s$ is removed before $3d$.

> Within a given shell, electrons are moved from the subshell having the highest energy first.

Example:

$$S([Ne]\ 3s^2 3p^4) \rightarrow e^- + S^+([Ne]\ 3s^2 3p^3)$$

The $3p$ electrons have a higher energy than the $3s$ electrons and hence the $3p$ electrons *require the smallest additional amount of energy* to remove them from the atom completely. Hence $3p$ is removed before $3s$.

Further Examples:

$$V([Ar]\ 4s^2 3d^3) \rightarrow 3\ e^- + V^{3+}([Ar]\ 3d^2)$$
$$Sn([Kr]\ 5s^2 4d^{10} 5p^2) \rightarrow 2\ e^- + Sn^{2+}([Kr]\ 5s^2 4d^{10})$$
$$Sn([Kr]\ 5s^2 4d^{10} 5p^2) \rightarrow 4\ e^- + Sn^{4+}([Kr]\ 4d^{10})$$

FIRST EXCITED STATES

The GROUND STATE of an atom or ion is the electron configuration occurring when all the electrons occupy the lowest possible energy levels.

An EXCITED STATE of an atom or ion is the electron configuration occurring when one or more electrons are in a higher energy level than they would normally occupy in the ground state.

Example:

$2p$ — — —	$2p$ + — —	$2p$ + — —	$2p$ + + —
$2s$ +	$2s$ +	$2s$ +	$2s$ —
$1s$ + (electrons)	$1s$ +	$1s$ +	$1s$ +
ground state	(a)	(b)	(c)

excited states

The **FIRST EXCITED STATE** of an atom or ion is the excited state which can be formed by the least input of energy. [For example, excited state (a), above, is the *first* excited state of Be($1s^22s^2$).] In most cases, an electron from the highest-energy filled subshell is "promoted" to an orbital in the incompletely filled subshell having the lowest energy.

Example:

ground state	first excited state
Mg([Ne] $3s^2$)	Mg([Ne] $3s^13p^1$)

$$\begin{bmatrix} 3p \text{ — — —} \\ \\ 3s \text{ +} \end{bmatrix} \qquad \begin{bmatrix} 3p \text{ + — —} \\ \\ 3s \text{ +} \end{bmatrix}$$

Cl([Ne] $3s^23p^5$)	Cl([Ne] $3s^13p^6$)

$$\begin{bmatrix} 3p \text{ + + +} \\ \\ 3s \text{ +} \end{bmatrix} \qquad \begin{bmatrix} 3p \text{ + + +} \\ \\ 3s \text{ +} \end{bmatrix}$$

K([Ar] $4s^1$)	K([Ar] $3d^1$)

$$\begin{bmatrix} 4p \text{ — — —} \\ 3d \text{ — — — — —} \\ 4s \text{ +} \end{bmatrix} \qquad \begin{bmatrix} 4p \text{ — — —} \\ 3d \text{ + — — — —} \\ 4s \text{ —} \end{bmatrix}$$

150

Ni([Ar] $4s^23d^8$)

$$\begin{bmatrix} 4p\ \text{—}\ \text{—}\ \text{—} \\ 3d\ \text{⥮}\ \text{⥮}\ \text{⥮}\ \text{+}\ \text{+} \\ 4s\ \text{⥮} \end{bmatrix}$$

Ni([Ar] $4s^13d^9$)

$$\begin{bmatrix} 4p\ \text{—}\ \text{—}\ \text{—} \\ 3d\ \text{⥮}\ \text{⥮}\ \text{⥮}\ \text{⥮}\ \text{+} \\ 4s\ \text{+} \end{bmatrix}$$

Zn([Ar] $4s^23d^{10}$)

$$\begin{bmatrix} 4p\ \text{—}\ \text{—}\ \text{—} \\ 3d\ \text{⥮}\ \text{⥮}\ \text{⥮}\ \text{⥮}\ \text{⥮} \\ 4s\ \text{⥮} \end{bmatrix}$$

Zn([Ar] $4s^13d^{10}4p^1$)

$$\begin{bmatrix} 4p\ \text{+}\ \text{—}\ \text{—} \\ 3d\ \text{⥮}\ \text{⥮}\ \text{⥮}\ \text{⥮}\ \text{⥮} \\ 4s\ \text{+} \end{bmatrix}$$

$$\begin{bmatrix} \text{Note that it is easier to take an electron} \\ \text{from a } 4s \text{ orbital than from a } 3d \text{ orbital} \\ \text{(recall ``Electron Configurations of Ions'').} \end{bmatrix}$$

ELECTRON CONFIGURATION EXCEPTIONS

There are two exceptions to the expected configurations for the elements up to Kr. We expect:

Cr([Ar] $4s^23d^4$)   ‵one electron short of a half-filled subshell and

Cu([Ar] $4s^23d^9$)   ‵one electron short of a filled subshell

but experimentally we find:

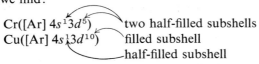

Cr([Ar] $4s^13d^5$)   ‵two half-filled subshells
Cu([Ar] $4s^13d^{10}$)   filled subshell
    half-filled subshell

Based on the behaviour of Cr, Cu and a few other atoms and ions we say that

---

A filled or exactly half-filled subshell is especially stable and is favoured by a lowered energy.

Hence we propose the following:

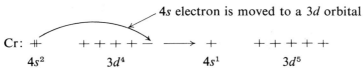

4s electron is moved to a 3d orbital

Cr: ⥮   + + + + + ⟶ +   + + + + +
    $4s^2$ $3d^4$ $4s^1$ $3d^5$

The energy required to move a $4s$ electron to a $3d$ orbital is more than made up by the lowering of energy which occurs when the two half-filled subshells are created.

The order of preference, from an energy point of view, for the filling or orbitals is:

order	greatest	filled shell
of	↓	filled (or empty) subshell
preference	least	half-filled subshell
		none of the above

PREDICTING THE NUMBER OF VALENCE ELECTRONS

VALENCE ELECTRONS are electrons which can take part in chemical reactions.

Example:

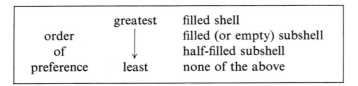

Al([Ne] $3s^2 3p^1$) has 3 valence electrons (*i.e.*, $3s^2 3p^1$)

core e⁻   these electrons can be used in chemical
(inert)   reactions (*e.g.*, form Al^{3+})

Electrons in *filled d* and *f* subshells are *NOT* counted as valence electrons: they are too unreactive to take part in reactions.

Example:

Ga([Ar] $4s^2 3d^{10} 4p^1$) has 3 valence electrons

$\left[\begin{array}{l} \textit{(i.e., } 4s^2 4p^1 \textit{) The filled } 3d \text{ subshell completes the underlying 3rd shell } (3s^2 3p^6 3d^{10}) \\ \text{and a filled shell is very unreactive.} \end{array}\right]$

Pb([Xe] $6s^2 4f^{14} 5d^{10} 6p^2$) has 4 valence electrons

$\left[\begin{array}{l} \textit{(i.e., } 6s^2 6p^2 \textit{) The filled } 5d \text{ subshell is buried inside the atom, although the 5th} \\ \text{shell is not yet complete, and the } 4f \text{ subshell is deeply buried as well as com-} \\ \text{pleting the 4th shell } (4s^2 4p^6 4d^{10} 4f^{14}). \text{ Hence, in this case both the } 5d \text{ and } 4f \\ \text{electrons will not take part in chemical reactions.} \end{array}\right]$

Xe([Kr] $5s^2 4d^{10} 5p^6$) has zero valence electrons since it has an inert gas configuration.

IONIZATION ENERGIES

We define IONIZATION ENERGY to be the energy required to remove the most loosely bound electron from a *gaseous* atom.

In other words, the ionization energy (abbreviated IE) is the energy required to form a $+1$ ion.

Example:

$$Mg([Ne]\,3s^2) + 737.6\text{ kJ/mol} \rightarrow Mg^+([Ne]\,3s^1) + e^-$$
$$Cl([Ne]\,3s^23p^5) + 1255\text{ kJ/mol} \rightarrow Cl^+([Ne]\,3s^23p^4) + e^-$$
$$Ni([Ar]\,4s^23d^8) + 736.5\text{ kJ/mol} \rightarrow Ni^+([Ar]\,4s^13d^8) + e^-$$

In a similar fashion, after one electron has been removed, we define the SECOND IONIZATION ENERGY to be the energy required to form a $+2$ ion, that is to remove a second electron.

Successive ionizations of the same atom become more difficult because there is more "un-neutralized" charge on the nucleus to hold on to the remaining electrons.

Example:

$Al^+ \longleftarrow e^-$

each electron is attracted by one excess positive charge

$Al^+ \longleftarrow e^-$

each electron is attracted by two excess positive charges

$Al^+ \longleftarrow e^-$

each electron is attracted by three excess positive charges

Let us now examine the successive ionizations of silicon.

$$Si([Ne]\,3s^23p^2) + 786\text{ kJ} \rightarrow Si^+([Ne]\,3s^23p^1) + e^-$$
$$Si^+([Ne]\,3s^23p^1) + 1577\text{ kJ} \rightarrow Si^{2+}([Ne]\,3s^2) + e^-$$
$$Si^{2+}([Ne]\,3s^2) + 3231\text{ kJ} \rightarrow Si^{3+}([Ne]\,3s^1) + e^-$$
$$Si^{3+}([Ne]\,3s^1) + 4354\text{ kJ} \rightarrow Si^{4+}([Ne]) + e^-$$
$$Si^{4+}([Ne]) + 16\,087\text{ kJ} \rightarrow Si^{5+}([He]\,2s^22p^5) + e^-$$

The 1st, 2nd, 3rd and 4th IE are slowly increasing, as would be expected from the increasing excess positive charge on the nucleus, which attracts the remaining electrons more strongly. On the other hand, the 5th IE is very large since the 5th electron must be removed from an inert Ne core.

In general, a large "jump" in the successive ionization energies is a signal which indicates that the last valence electron is gone and that the jump is due to the removal of an electron from the core.

153

EXERCISES

1. Predict the electron configurations of the following. Do *NOT* use core notation.
   a) P   b) Ti   c) Co   d) Br
   e) Sr   f) Tc   g) As   h) Cd
   i) Ca   j) Kr   k) Cs   l) Ar
   m) Ga   n) Y   o) Mo (care!)   p) Au (care!)

2. Re-write the electron configurations in question 1, using core notation.

3. Predict the electron configuration of the following ions, using core notation.
   a) H^- b) Sr^{2+} c) Br^- d) N^{3+}
   e) Ti^{2+} f) N^{2-} g) Mn^{2+} h) Cu^+
   i) Au^{3+} j) Ge^{2+} k) Ru^{3+} l) Sb^{3+}

4. Predict the first excited state configuration of the atoms in question 1, using core notation.

5. How many valence electrons do the following contain?
   a) O   b) Cl^- c) Ag^+ d) Nb^{3+}
   e) Zn^{2+} f) Ge^{4+} g) I^{5+} h) Xe^{2+}
   i) Tc^{4+} j) Sb^{3+}

6. Predict the number of valence electrons in the following. (All energies are in kilojoules per mole.)
   a) Element V: 1st IE = 800,   2nd IE = 2427,   3rd IE = 3659,
                    4th IE = 25 019,   5th IE = 32 818.
   b) Element W: 1st IE = 1012,   2nd IE = 1903,   3rd IE = 2910,
                    4th IE = 4955,   5th IE = 6272,   6th IE = 21 267,
                    7th IE = 25 406.
   c) Element X: 1st IE = 520,   2nd IE = 7296,   3rd IE = 11 812.
   d) Element Y: 1st IE = 738,   2nd IE = 1450,   3rd IE = 7732,
                    4th IE = 10 545,   5th IE = 13 627.
   e) Element Z: 1st IE = 1681,   2nd IE = 3375,   3rd IE = 6045,
                    4th IE = 8408,   5th IE = 11 020,   6th IE = 15 160,
                    7th IE = 17 863,   8th IE = 92 010.

7. Predict the ions which are likely to be formed by the following atoms. (All energies are in kilojoules per mole.)
   a) A: 1st IE = 496,   2nd IE = 4563,   3rd IE = 6920,
           4th IE = 9541.
   b) B: 1st IE = 758,   2nd IE = 1645,   3rd IE = 3231,
           4th IE = 8018.
   c) C: 1st IE = 715,   2nd IE = 1450,   3rd IE = 3081,
           4th IE = 4082,   5th IE = 6638.
   d) D: 1st IE = 664,   2nd IE = 1382,   3rd IE = 2416,
           4th IE = 3695,   5th IE $\simeq$ 4800,   6th IE $\simeq$ 9940,
           7th IE $\simeq$ 21 100.

e) E: 1st IE = 650,   2nd IE = 1414,   3rd IE = 2828,
      4th IE ≃ 4600,   5th IE ≃ 6300,   6th IE ≃ 12 400,
      7th IE ≃ 14 600,   8th IE ≃ 16 400.

f) F: IE = 577,   2nd IE = 1816,   3rd IE = 2744,
      4th IE = 11 575,   5th IE = 14 837,   6th IE = 18 373.

g) G: 1st IE = 589,   2nd IE = 1970,   3rd IE = 2875,
      4th IE = 4892.

Section 21

Lewis Structures and Shapes of Molecules

A. LEWIS STRUCTURES

The formation of a chemical bond involves the sharing of two or more electrons between bonded atoms. A bond involving the EQUAL SHARING of the electrons in the bond is called a COVALENT BOND.

A general result of bond formation is:

> *THE OCTET RULE.* If at all possible, an atom will bond with enough atoms of the same or different type to enable ALL the atoms involved to reach an inert gas configuration having EIGHT valence electrons.

There are many exceptions to this rule, so that it should only be regarded as a "rule of thumb".

Writing Lewis Structures

The bonding in a molecule can be represented by a kind of chemical shorthand called the LEWIS STRUCTURE or ELECTRON DOT STRUCTURE, in which the VALENCE electrons are shown as dots (or x's) surrounding the symbol for the atom. For example, the bonding in HF can be written as follows. (We will represent the H electron by an "x" to help us see how this electron takes part in bonding.)

$$H^\times \ + \ .\overset{..}{\underset{..}{F}}: \ \longrightarrow \ H\overset{..}{\underset{..}{\overset{\times}{F}}}:$$ the electrons *between* the atoms are the bonding electrons and are shared by each atom

$$1s^1 \qquad 2s^2 2p^5$$

Note that we show the dots for F in *pairs*, to correspond to pairs of electrons filling the valence orbitals. No attempt is made to differentiate between *s* and *p* electrons.

We shall now summarize a procedure which can be used to write the Lewis structure for a molecule. We shall assume that we know which atoms are bonded to each other. For the purposes of the following discussion we shall define:

CENTRAL ATOM: The central atom of a molecule is the atom to which all other atoms or groups are considered to be attached.

Example: (the underlined atoms are "central" atoms)

The "central" atom is actually just the atom on which we choose to focus our attention. There may be more than one "central" atom present.

Example:

$$H-O-O-H \equiv \begin{cases} H-O-OH \\ \text{or } HO-O-H \end{cases} \begin{pmatrix} \text{both oxygen atoms can} \\ \text{be considered "central"} \end{pmatrix}$$

ATTACHED ATOM, ATTACHED GROUP: These terms refer to any atom or group of atoms attached to a central atom.

Example:

A. Count up the number of valence electrons on each atom and stockpile the electrons at some out-of-the-way side of the symbol for the atom.

Example:

$$\overset{..}{H} \overset{\overset{..}{..}}{\underset{..}{O}} \overset{..}{H}, \quad \overset{\overset{..}{..}}{\underset{..}{O}} \overset{..}{\underset{..}{C}} \overset{\overset{..}{..}}{\underset{..}{O}}$$

157

> B. Assign to each attached atom's bond a sufficient number of electrons from the neighbouring central atom to complete the electron requirements of the attached atom.

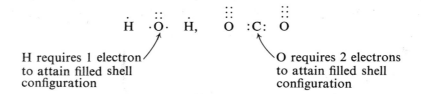

H requires 1 electron to attain filled shell configuration

O requires 2 electrons to attain filled shell configuration

Note: If the molecule possesses an overall negative charge, the extra electrons can be used at this time (if required) to help satisfy the electron requirements of the attached atoms.

Example: BF_4^-. B has only 3 valence electrons available, but each F requires 1 electron. Hence we require the extra electron resulting from the negative charge.

$$\cdot \colon\colon\colon F \quad \cdot \dot{B} \cdot \quad F \colon\colon\colon \cdot$$

extra electron

> C. Complete the electron requirements of the central atom(s) by
>   a) borrowing electrons from the attached atoms, or
>   b) borrowing electrons from other central atoms, or
>   c) simply gaining or losing a number of electrons consistent with the charge on the molecule.

Example:

a) $H \cdot \quad \cdot \dot{O} \cdot \quad \cdot H$ (O fills its octet by obtaining electrons from H's)

b) $\colon\ddot{C}l \cdot \quad \cdot \dot{S} \cdot \quad \cdot \dot{S} \cdot \quad \cdot \ddot{C}l \colon$ (each S fills its octet by obtaining electrons from Cl and other S)

c) $\left[\times \dot{S} \cdot \quad \cdot \ddot{C}l \colon \right]^-$ (S fills its octet by obtaining electrons from Cl and the extra negative charge)

158

Notes

1. All bonds MUST end up with an EVEN number of electrons. Normally, both atoms involved in a bond will donate an equal number of electrons to the bond.

2. Occasionally an atom finds itself in a situation where it has two or more unpaired electrons in its valence shell and encounters another atom with two or more unpaired electrons. In this case, more than one bond is formed between the atoms.

Example:

$$\begin{matrix} H & H \\ \ddot{C}: & :\ddot{C} \\ H & H \end{matrix} \qquad \text{(double bond between carbon atoms)}$$

and $\qquad H:C\vdots \;\; \vdots C:H \qquad$ (triple bond between carbons)

3. If both the electrons in a single bond have been donated by the same atom, we say the electrons are in a DATIVE COVALENT BOND.

Example:

$$SO_2 \text{ is } \ddot{O}: \;\; :S\raisebox{-2pt}{$\cdot$}\; \ddot{O}: \qquad \text{(both electrons donated by S)}$$

Dative covalent bonds to an attached atom normally only occur when the attached atom requires 2 electrons to fill its octet (*e.g.*, O, S).

Example Lewis structures:

1. NH_3 $\qquad$ H N H $\rightarrow$ H $\cdot\ddot{N}\cdot$ H $\rightarrow$ H$\cdot$ $\cdot\ddot{N}\cdot$ $\cdot$H $\qquad$ or $\qquad$ $\boxed{\begin{matrix} H:\ddot{N}:H \\ \ddot{H} \end{matrix}}$

2. N_2 $\qquad$ N N $\rightarrow$ N$\vdots$ $\vdots$N $\qquad$ or $\qquad$ $\boxed{:N\vdots\vdots N:}$

3. SO_3^{2-} $\qquad$ O S O $\rightarrow$ $\ddot{O}$:S: $\ddot{O}$ $\rightarrow$ $\left[:\ddot{O}\; \overset{\times\times}{:S:}\; \ddot{O}:\right]^{2-}$ $\quad$ $\left(\begin{matrix}\text{note that S}\\ \text{forms three}\\ \text{dative bonds}\end{matrix}\right)$
$\qquad\qquad\qquad$ O$\vdots\vdots$ $\qquad$ O$\vdots\vdots$ $\qquad\qquad$ $:\ddot{O}:$

159

4. NOCl $\overset{\cdot\cdot}{\underset{\cdot\cdot}{N}}$ $\overset{\cdot\cdot}{\underset{\cdot\cdot}{O}}$ $\overset{\cdot\cdot}{\underset{\cdot\cdot}{Cl}}$ → N $:\overset{\cdot\cdot}{\underset{\cdot\cdot}{O}}\cdot$ Cl → $\overset{\cdot\cdot}{N}\cdot$ $:\overset{\cdot\cdot}{O}\cdot$ $\cdot\overset{\cdot\cdot}{\underset{\cdot\cdot}{Cl}}:$ or $\boxed{\overset{\cdot\cdot}{\underset{\cdot\cdot}{N}}::\overset{\cdot\cdot}{O}:\overset{\cdot\cdot}{\underset{\cdot\cdot}{Cl}}:}$

note unequal sharing

Stick Diagrams

A short-hand diagram used as an alternate method of representing molecular bonding is called a STICK DIAGRAM. The stick diagram gives the same information as a Lewis structure, except that a straight line is used to represent each *pair of electrons in a bond*.

Example:

	Lewis structure	Stick diagram

1.	H : $\overset{\cdot\cdot}{N}$: H
	H
		H—$\overset{\cdot\cdot}{N}$—H
		    |
		    H

2.	: N ⦂ ⦂ N :	: N≡N :
3.	$\left[\begin{array}{c} :\overset{\cdot\cdot}{O}:\overset{\cdot\cdot}{S}:\overset{\cdot\cdot}{O}: \\ :\overset{\cdot\cdot}{O}: \end{array}\right]^{2-}$	$\left[\begin{array}{c} :\overset{\cdot\cdot}{O}{\leftarrow}S{\rightarrow}\overset{\cdot\cdot}{O}: \\ :\overset{\cdot\cdot}{O}: \end{array}\right]^{2-}$

indicates a dative covalent bond

Free Radicals

The Lewis structure of SCl is

$$\cdot\overset{\cdot\cdot}{S}:\overset{\cdot\cdot}{\underset{\cdot\cdot}{Cl}}:$$

As we see, the sulphur atom has an *unpaired* electron and hence is unable to complete its octet. The name FREE RADICAL is given to a MOLECULE having an unpaired electron.

Although a free radical is STABLE (*i.e.*, will not fall apart) it will be very RE-ACTIVE. The unpaired electron will normally make itself available to other molecules having an unpaired electron available for bonding.

Example:

$$:\overset{\cdot\cdot}{\underset{\cdot\cdot}{Cl}}:\overset{\cdot\cdot}{S}\cdot \; + \; \cdot\overset{\cdot\cdot}{S}:\overset{\cdot\cdot}{\underset{\cdot\cdot}{Cl}}: \rightarrow :\overset{\cdot\cdot}{\underset{\cdot\cdot}{Cl}}:\overset{\cdot\cdot}{S}:\overset{\cdot\cdot}{S}:\overset{\cdot\cdot}{\underset{\cdot\cdot}{Cl}}:$$

Because of their high reactivity, free radicals may even attack molecules which do not have unpaired electrons.

> *Quick check for free radicals:* If you suspect a molecule may be a free radical, simply add up all the valence electrons involved.
>
> $$ODD \text{ number of valence electrons} = \text{free radical}$$
> $$EVEN \text{ number of valence electrons} = not \text{ a free radical}$$
>
> **Example:** CH_3 has $4 + 3 = 7$ valence electrons, $\therefore$ free radical
> CH_3^- has $4 + 3 + 1 = 8$ valence electrons, $\therefore$ not free radical

Valence States

If an element can form only one bond (*e.g.*, H), we say it is MONOVALENT; if two bonds can be formed (*e.g.*, O) it is DIVALENT; if three bonds can be formed (*e.g.*, N) it is TRIVALENT; if four bonds can be formed (*e.g.*, C, see later) it is TETRAVALENT.

At first glance we might expect carbon to be divalent. $C(1s^2 2s^2 2p_x^1 2p_y^1)$ would be expected to form two bonds so as to fill the $2p_x$ and $2p_y$ orbitals. The $2p_z$ would remain empty since it can contribute no electrons to a bond. However, carbon is rather unusual in the sense that its *first excited state is stabilized by a lowering of the energy of the excited state configuration.* This excited state has a very stable half-filled $2p$ subshell. The term VALENCE STATE is used to describe the state in which an atom must be in order to react and form a bond. As a result, carbon in its valence state is: $C(1s^2 2s^1 2p_x^1 2p_y^1 2p_z^1)$ and hence is tetravalent.

Example:

$$
\begin{array}{c}
H \\
\ddot{} \\
H : \overset{\cdot\cdot}{\underset{\cdot\cdot}{C}} : H \\
\ddot{} \\
H
\end{array}
$$

Whenever an atom reacts, it is the valence state which determines the number of bonds formed. In most cases, such as those studied previously, the *valence state* and the *ground state* are identical. However, carbon and a few other atoms have valence states which are actually excited states.

Electron Deficient Molecules

As was the case with carbon, B and Be both have excited valence states available to them, although the excited state is not easily formed. Hence, we expect B to be TRIVALENT and Be to be DIVALENT.

$$B(1s^22s^22p_x{}^1) \xrightarrow{\text{excite}} B(1s^22s^12p_x{}^12p_y{}^1)$$

$$Be(1s^22s^2) \xrightarrow{\text{excite}} Be(1s^22s^12p_x{}^1)$$

Example:

$$\text{H} : \text{B} : \text{H} \qquad \text{H} : \text{Be} : \text{H}$$
$$\text{H}$$

Note that neither B nor Be will attain a closed shell configuration. Since they have less than an octet of electrons after forming bonds, B and Be are said to form ELECTRON DEFICIENT MOLECULES.

We previously mentioned that an element may take part in a *dative covalent* bond by donating (or receiving) both of the electrons involved in the bond. BH_3 readily reacts to form compounds involving dative bonds by accepting from a donor molecule a pair of electrons which can be put into the *vacant* $2p_z$ orbital of the B atom.

Example:

$$
\begin{array}{ccccccc}
\text{H} & \text{H} & & \text{H} \ \text{H} & & \text{H} \ \ \text{H} \\
\text{H} : \text{N} : & + & \text{B} : \text{H} & \rightarrow & \text{H} : \text{N} : \text{B} : \text{H} & \text{or} & \text{H}{-}\text{N}{\rightarrow}\text{B}{-}\text{H} \\
\text{H} & \text{H} & & \text{H} \ \text{H} & & \text{H} \ \ \text{H}
\end{array}
$$

We call NH_3 (which is "electron-rich", *i.e.*, has left-over electrons not required in bonds) an "electron donor", and we call BH_3 (which is "electron-poor", *i.e.*, is electron deficient) an "electron acceptor".

B. SHAPES OF MOLECULES

The VALENCE BOND THEORY assumes that a covalent bond is formed when an orbital on one atom overlaps with an orbital on another atom, such that all the electrons in the overlapping "atomic" orbitals can be shared by both atoms. The valence bond theory also assumes that the more the orbitals overlap the more the electrons can be shared and hence the stronger the bond. As a result of this increased sharing of electrons, the atoms will tend to become positioned in such a way as to allow the maximum possible orbital overlap.

We will use a simplified version of the valence bond theory called the VALENCE-SHELL ELECTRON-PAIR REPULSION THEORY (VSEPR Theory).

We shall require the following additional definitions.

1. *Bonding Orbitals, Bonding Pair:* These terms refer to orbitals which are directly involved in forming bonds, and to the pairs of electrons which occupy such orbitals. The origin of the electrons in a bond orbital is unimportant. Each of the electrons forming an electron pair in a bond may come from either of the atoms involved in the bond.

2. *Lone Pair Orbital, Lone Pair Electrons:* These terms refer to a valence orbital which contains electrons NOT directly involved in a bond.

Example:

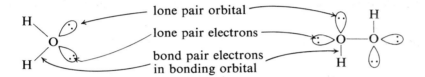

The VSEPR theory is based on the following assumption, which is strongly supported by experimental evidence.

The OCCUPIED valence orbitals in a *molecule* are somewhat different from the orbitals in an *atom*, and consist of "lobes" extending out from the atom in ONE direction. The position of these lobes, relative to each other, can be shifted about easily so as to minimize the electrical repulsions existing between the electrons in the orbital lobes.

Consider the following examples.

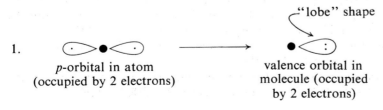

1.

p-orbital in atom
(occupied by 2 electrons)

valence orbital in
molecule (occupied
by 2 electrons)

163

2.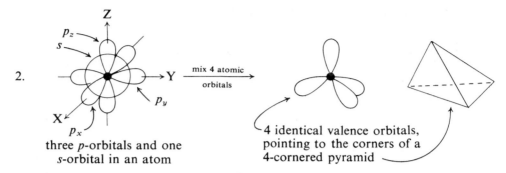

three *p*-orbitals and one
s-orbital in an atom

4 identical valence orbitals,
pointing to the corners of a
4-cornered pyramid

Because electrons repel each other, the occupied valence orbitals in an atom will tend to stay as far away from each other as possible. Lone pair electrons are confined to a small region of space around a single atom, whereas bonding electrons have the option of moving away from the central atom, via the bonding orbital, onto the adjacent atom. Hence, bonding electrons will suffer less repulsion from other central-atom electrons because the bonding electrons can retreat farther from the central atom. As a result of differing amounts of repulsion for bond pair and lone pair electrons, the following rules apply:

$$\begin{pmatrix} \text{repulsion} \\ \text{between 2} \\ \text{LONE PAIRS} \end{pmatrix} > \begin{pmatrix} \text{repulsion between} \\ \text{a LONE PAIR and} \\ \text{a BOND PAIR} \end{pmatrix} > \begin{pmatrix} \text{repulsion} \\ \text{between 2} \\ \text{BOND PAIRS} \end{pmatrix}$$

The VSEPR theory has a fairly general application, but is best suited to species in which the central atom is a REPRESENTATIVE element (*i.e.*, one of the block of elements with a partially filled *p*-orbital) or a transition element which has either 0, 5 or 10 electrons in its *d*-shell *which are not involved in bonding.*

One initially puzzling feature of the VSEPR theory is the fact that the central atom may bond to 5 or 6 (or even more) attached groups. This implies that 10 or 12 (or more) electrons can exist in the valence shell, even though we expect only a maximum of 8 electrons (the OCTET RULE). The puzzle is immediately explained once we realize that one or more of the lowest lying *d*-orbitals can become involved in bonding.

Example: SF_6 has 12 valence electrons surrounding the S atom. The S fills its $3s$ and $3p$ subshells with 8 electrons (as expected) and then puts the remaining 4 electrons in the previously empty $3d$ subshell (*i.e.*, S attains the configuration $3s^2 3p^6 3d^4$). We say that the sulphur atom has *expanded its octet.*

We shall now summarize a procedure by which one can find the shape of a molecule. We shall include in the summary the rules for finding the electron dot formula of a molecule, as previously given, with some additions.

164

TABLE I. SHAPES OF MOLECULES AND IONS. THE CENTRAL ATOMS ARE "REPRESENTATIVE" OR d^0, d^5 AND d^{10} TRANSITION ELEMENTS

Total number of electron orbitals	Arrangement of orbitals	Number of bonding orbitals	Number of lone pair orbitals	Shape of species
2	Linear	2	0	Linear
3	Triangular plane	3	0	Triangular planar
		2	1	V-shape
4	Tetrahedron	4	0	Tetrahedron
		3	1	Trigonal pyramid
		2	2	V-shape
5	Trigonal bipyramid	5	0	Trigonal bipyramid
		4	1	Irregular tetrahedron*
		3	2	T-shape*
		2	3	Linear*
6	Octahedron	6	0	Octahedron
		5	1	Square pyramid
		4	2	Square planar*

* Shape due to stronger repulsion of lone pair electrons.

All the shapes in Tables I and II are based on one simple principle: arranging the total number of electron orbitals in space so that the maximum distance (*i.e.*, maximum angle) exists between the orbitals.

A. Count up the number of valence electrons on the central atom.

Notes

1. Ignore any full d subshells. Full d subshells do not participate in bonding (*e.g.*, $Zn(4s^2 3d^{10})$ is assumed to have only two s-electrons in its valence shell).

2. If the species has an overall charge, add the extra electrons directly onto the number of valence electrons already on the central atom.

TABLE II. Shapes of Species

Total number of electron orbitals	= Central atom ──── = Bonding orbital = Attached atom - - - = Lone pair orbital
2	Linear
3	Triangular planar V-shaped
4	Tetrahedron Trigonal pyramid V-shaped
5	Trigonal bipyramid Irregular tetrahedron T-shape Linear
6	Octahedron Square pyramid Square planar

3. If d orbitals are involved, then:
   a) count ALL the d-electrons if there are 1, 2, 3, 4 or 5 d-electrons (*not including extra electrons due to a charge on the species*).
   b) if more than 5 d-electrons are present, count only those electrons over and above the d^5 configuration (*i.e.*, $d^6 = 1$ valence e$^-$, $d^7 = 2$, $d^8 = 3$, $d^9 = 4$).

Example: V has a total of 5 valence electrons (*i.e.*, $4s^2 3d^3$), and Fe has a total of 3 valence electrons (*i.e.*, $4s^2 3d^1$).

B. Assign to the attached groups a sufficient number of valence electrons from the central atom, so as to meet the electron requirements of the attached groups.

Notes

1. Attached groups such as NH_3, H_2O and CO require NO extra electrons, and hence form dative covalent bonds only *to* the central atom.

2. If the central atom does not have a full octet, one or more of the attached groups will have to donate electrons to the central atom (if possible), forming one or more double or triple bonds.

3. For the purposes of predicting shapes of molecules, experimental evidence indicates that double and triple bonds can be considered to form a SINGLE ORBITAL (*i.e.*, they act as if they were "extra thick" single bonds).

C. Assign to lone pair orbitals those valence electrons which are not required for bonding.

D. Determine the number of:
   a) bond orbitals, and
   b) lone pair orbitals
and hence find the total number of orbitals involved.

Notes

1. The number of bonding orbitals will *always equal the number of attached groups*.

2. The number of lone pair orbitals will equal one-half the number of lone pair electrons (providing the molecule is not a free radical).

3. If the molecule is a free radical, a separate lone pair orbital will be required to hold the unpaired electron.

Example: ClF_3: Cl has 7 valence electrons and each F requires *one* of Cl's electrons. The remaining 4 electrons on Cl form 2 lone pairs.

Hence, ClF_3 will have 3 bond orbitals (since it has 3 attached groups), and 2 lone pair orbitals, for a total of 5 electron orbitals.

ClF_3^+: (will be similar to ClF_3) Cl has $7 - 1 = 6$ valence electrons. Bonds to the 3 F's require 3 electrons and the remaining 3 electrons on Cl are assigned to lone pairs.

E. Assign a shape to the molecule, based on Tables I and II, the *total* number of electron orbitals and the number of lone pair orbitals.

Example: If a molecule has four electron orbitals, one of which is a lone pair orbital, then the shape of the molecule will be a trigonal pyramid (based on a tetrahedral arrangement of orbitals).

You are required to memorize the tables of molecular shapes. This task is not difficult and will be aided by the practice gained on the accompanying exercises.

Let us now consider a few examples to see how one arrives at the shape of a molecule.

Example: XeF_4. Xenon has a full valence shell, but nevertheless form some compounds. When Xe takes part in bonding, it has 8 valence electrons available ($5s^2 5p^6$); the $4d^{10}$ electrons do not get involved. Since each of the four F atoms needs one electron we have 4 bonding orbitals, and $8 - 4 = 4$ valence electrons in 2 lone pair

168

orbitals (2 electrons per orbital). ∴ total orbitals = 4 (bonds to F) + 2 (lone pair orbitals) = 6, and 6 orbitals means that XeF_4 is based on an octahedral arrangement of orbitals. Since the 2 lone pair orbitals cannot be "seen", the shape of XeF_4 can be described as a SQUARE PLANE (*i.e.*, 6 orbitals, 2 of which are lone pair orbitals, gives rise to a *square planar* shape).

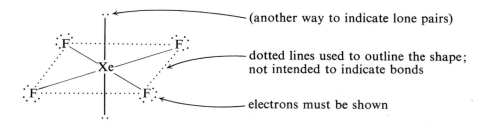

(another way to indicate lone pairs)

dotted lines used to outline the shape; not intended to indicate bonds

electrons must be shown

Note: Since Xe now has 12 electrons in its valence shell (it puts the extra 4 electrons in its previously unoccupied 5*d* subshell) we say that Xe HAS EXPANDED ITS OCTET.

The above process can be "boiled down" as follows:

number of valence e⁻	= 8	
number of bond e⁻	= 4	
number of lone pair e⁻	= 4	
number of bond orbitals	= 4	(= number of attached groups)
*number of lone pair orbitals	= 2	(= half of lone pair e⁻)
* total orbitals	= 6	

(these are the important results)

Example: SO_2.

number of valence e⁻	= 6	
number of bond e⁻	= 4	(each oxygen needs 2 e⁻)
number of lone pair e⁻	= 2	
number of bond orbitals	= 2	(= number of attached groups)
number of lone pair orbitals	= 1	
total orbitals	= 3	

Now, S needs 2 more electrons to complete its octet and hence *one* attached O donates 2 electrons to S, so as to form one double bond. The other bond to O must be a dative bond. Since 3 orbitals are involved, a triangular planar arrangement of orbitals must

169

occur. However, since the lone pair orbitals cannot be "seen", SO_2 must be described as V-SHAPED.

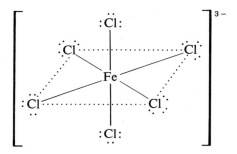

Example: $FeCl_6{}^{3-}$. Fe appears at first to have 11 valence electrons ($4s^2 3d^6$ + 3 extra e^- due to -3 charge) but we must remember that a d^6 configuration only contributes 1 valence electron. Hence:

$$
\begin{array}{rl}
\text{number of valence } e^- & = 6 \\
\text{number of bond } e^- & = 6 \\
\text{number of lone pair } e^- & = 0 \\
\hline
\text{number of bond orbitals} & = 6 \\
\text{number of lone pair orbitals} & = 0 \\
\text{total orbitals} & = 6
\end{array}
$$

The presence of 6 orbitals and no lone pairs means that the shape of $FeCl_6{}^{3-}$ can be described as an OCTAHEDRON.

$$
\left[
\begin{array}{c}
:\ddot{C}l: \\
:\ddot{C}l \cdots \cdots \cdots \ddot{C}l \\
Fe \\
:\ddot{C}l \cdots \cdots \cdots \ddot{C}l: \\
:\ddot{C}l:
\end{array}
\right]^{3-}
$$

Example: $Cu(NH_3)_4{}^+$. Cu has a $3d^{10}4s^1$ configuration, but Cu^+ has a $3d^{10}$ configuration and hence has NO valence electrons. Thus, to engage in bonding Cu^+ must *receive* electrons from its attached groups (*i.e.*, be on the receiving end of a dative bond). Since NH_3 can be drawn as:

then NH_3 has 2 electrons in a lone pair orbital which are not actively being used in bonding and hence NH_3 can act as an electron pair donor. Since Cu^+ thus forms 4 bonding orbitals and no lone pairs (note that Cu^+ has now filled its octet) $Cu(NH_3)_4{}^+$ can be described as a TETRAHEDRON.

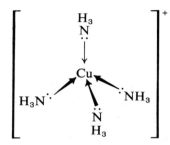

C. THE RELATIONSHIP BETWEEN THE SHAPE OF A MOLECULE AND ITS MOLECULAR DIPOLE

The tendency of an atom to attract electrons to itself is called the ELECTRO-NEGATIVITY of the atom (*i.e.*, is the tendency to attract a *negative electric* charge).

Example: F has a greater tendency to attract electrons than does H and hence:

$$\overset{\delta+}{H}—\overset{\delta-}{F} \quad \left(\begin{array}{l}\delta^- \text{ represents a partial negative charge,}\\ \delta^+ \text{ represents a partial positive charge.}\end{array}\right)$$

The electronegativities of the atoms in the periodic table show the following general trend:

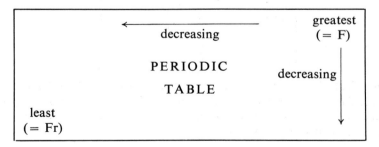

We say that a molecule has a "molecular dipole" if one side of the molecule is a " + " electric pole and the other side is a " − " pole (*i.e.*, a *di*pole).

Example: HF has a dipolar bond such that H is positive and F is negative:

$$\underset{\delta+ \quad \delta-}{H—F}$$

The HF molecule is therefore a molecular dipole.

171

A bond will be non-polar if both the atoms involved in the bond have the same electronegativity. Any bond involving two atoms with dissimilar electronegativities will be dipolar; the greater the difference in the electronegativities of the atoms, the greater the dipolar nature of the bond.

Example: In H_2O each O—H bond forms a dipole; O, being on the electronegative side (right-hand side) of the periodic table, forms the negative pole; H, being on the electropositive side (left-hand side) of the periodic table, forms the positive pole. Overall, for H_2O we have:

$$
\overset{\delta+}{H}\diagdown \atop \overset{\delta+}{H}\diagup \overset{\delta-}{O} \quad , \quad \text{or} \quad \overset{H}{}\diagdown \atop \overset{H}{}\diagup \overset{\delta+}{} O^{\delta-}
$$

and hence H_2O is a molecular dipole.

Example: BeF_2 is a linear molecule. The F end of a Be—F bond is negative and the Be end is positive.

$$\overset{\delta-}{F}\!-\!\overset{\delta+}{Be}\!-\!\overset{\delta-}{F}$$

Now, neither *end* of the molecule is different from the other and hence BeF_2 is NOT a molecular dipole.

Example: BF_3 is a triangular planar molecule. Since B and F have different electro-negativities, then each B—F bond will be polar. On the other hand, the BF_3 molecule does not exhibit any OVERALL polar behaviour (*i.e.*, is not dipolar). This non-dipolar character occurs because the polar contributions of the individual B—F bonds will cancel each other. To see this more clearly, imagine the dipoles of the three B—F bonds were forces pulling out from the central B atom: As can be seen intuitively, the forces will cancel each other exactly.

$$
\begin{matrix} F \\ \\ F \end{matrix} \!\!\diagup B \longrightarrow F
$$

Note: BF_2Cl would also be a triangular planar molecule: Since F and Cl do not have the same electronegativity, the B—F and B—Cl bonds do not have the same amount of dipolar character. Hence the "forces" will not cancel each other, and BF_2Cl *will* be a dipolar molecule.

$$
\begin{matrix} F \\ \\ F \end{matrix} \!\!\diagup B \!-\! Cl
$$

If all the attached groups are the same (which is the case much of the time) then the following molecular shapes NEVER give rise to a molecular dipole (*i.e.*, the molecular dipole equals ZERO):

linear	trigonal bipyramidal
triangular planar	octahedral
tetrahedral	square planar

Note that all of the above arrangements are HIGHLY SYMMETRICAL. The other, non-symmetrical arrangements ALWAYS form molecular dipoles.

EXERCISES

1. Draw Lewis structures for the following. In some cases the basic connections between atoms are shown.

   a) H_2S

   b) PCl_3

   c) S_2^{2-}

   d) OH^-

   e) BeI_2

   f) ClO

   g) NH_2^-

   h) H_3O^+

   i) HCN

   j) CH_3OH

   k) $C_2O_4^{2-}$

   l) $GeCl_3$

   m) CH_3CHO $(CH_3{-}\overset{\overset{\displaystyle O}{|}}{C}{-}H)$

   n) $HOCl$

   o) $HCCBr$

   p) $HCOOH$ $(H{-}\overset{\overset{\displaystyle O}{|}}{C}{-}O{-}H)$

   q) BF_3

   r) $HCCCH$

   s) $NCl_3 \cdot BCl_3$

   t) $AlCl_3$

   u) SiO_3^{2-}

   v) N_3^-

   w) SO_4^{2-}

   x) N_2F_2 $(F{-}N{-}N{-}F)$

   y) NO_2

   z) SO_3

   aa) N_2O_4

   bb) CO_3^{2-}

   cc) PO_4^{3-}

   dd) N_2O_3

2. Which of the above molecules are free radicals?
3. Write the electron dot structures and predict the shapes of the following.

   a) SeF_4

   b) SiF_6^{2-}

   c) BF_4^-

   d) $SbCl_5$

   e) SCl_2

   f) NCl_3

173

g) $AgBr_2^-$ h) KrF_4 i) IO_4^-
j) O_3 k) IF_5 l) AsF_5
m) I_3^- n) SF_6 o) IBr_3
p) PCl_3 q) ICl_4^- r) $SnCl_4$
s) ICl_5 t) ClO_2^- u) ClO_3^-
v) $PbCl_6^{2-}$ w) ClO_2 x) IO_3^-
y) VCl_3 z) CrO_3Cl^- aa) XeO_2F_2
bb) CrO_4^{2-} cc) FOO (F—O—O)   dd) $ZrOF_2$
ee) TiO_3^{2-} ff) $SnBr_2$

4. Which of the above would be free radicals?
5. Which of the above would be dipolar molecules?
6. Which member of each of the following pairs has the most dipolar bond?
   a) NCl_3, $BiCl_3$ b) $AlCl_3$, AlF_3 c) BaO, MgO
   d) MgTe, SrO   e) FrF, BaS
7. Write the electron dot structures for the following and indicate the shape of the molecule around each of the underlined atoms.

   a)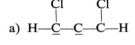

   b) H—C—N—O (with O double-bonded above C)

   c) $^-$O—C—NH_3^+ (with O double-bonded above C)

   d) ClSCN

   e)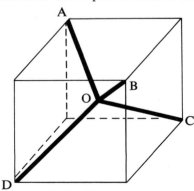

   f) H—C—C—N—N—CH_3

8. *EXTRA* (for mathematicians)
   A tetrahedron can be placed inside a cube as follows:

   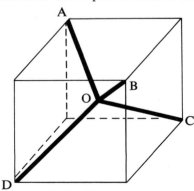

   A, B, C, D are the corners of the tetrahedron and O is the "central atom".

   Prove that: $\angle D—O—C = 109.47°$
   (Note that $\angle D—O—C = \angle A—O—B = \angle D—O—B = \angle B—O—C$, etc.)

Appendices

Appendix 1

PERIODIC TABLE

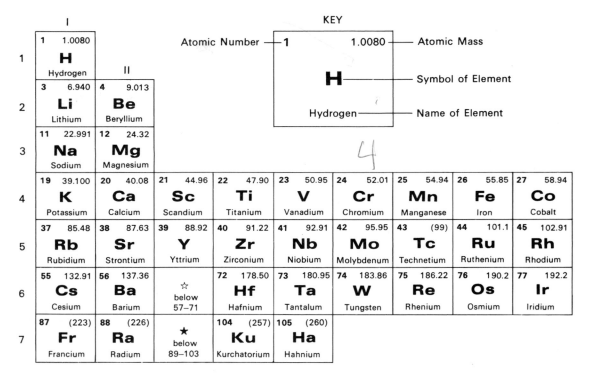

☆ LANTHANIDE SERIES

57 133.92 **La** Lanthanum	58 140.13 **Ce** Cerium	59 140.92 **Pr** Praseodymium	60 144.27 **Nd** Neodymium	61 (145) **Pm** Promethium	62 150.35 **Sm** Samarium	63 152.0 **Eu** Europium

★ ACTINIDE SERIES

89 (227) **Ac** Actinium	90 232.05 **Th** Thorium	91 (231) **Pa** Protactinium	92 238.07 **U** Uranium	93 (237) **Np** Neptunium	94 (242) **Pu** Plutonium	95 (243) **Am** Americium

					VIII
					2 4.003 **He** Helium

III	IV	V	VI	VII	
5 10.82 **B** Boron	**6** 12.011 **C** Carbon	**7** 14.008 **N** Nitrogen	**8** 16.0000 **O** Oxygen	**9** 19.00 **F** Fluorine	**10** 20.183 **Ne** Neon
13 26.98 **Al** Aluminum	**14** 28.09 **Si** Silicon	**15** 30.975 **P** Phosphorus	**16** 32.066 **S** Sulfur	**17** 35.457 **Cl** Chlorine	**18** 39.944 **Ar** Argon

			III	IV	V	VI	VII	
28 58.71 **Ni** Nickel	**29** 63.54 **Cu** Copper	**30** 65.38 **Zn** Zinc	**31** 69.72 **Ga** Gallium	**32** 72.60 **Ge** Germanium	**33** 74.91 **As** Arsenic	**34** 78.96 **Se** Selenium	**35** 79.916 **Br** Bromine	**36** 83.80 **Kr** Krypton
46 106.4 **Pd** Palladium	**47** 107.880 **Ag** Silver	**48** 112.41 **Cd** Cadmium	**49** 114.82 **In** Indium	**50** 118.70 **Sn** Tin	**51** 121.76 **Sb** Antimony	**52** 127.61 **Te** Tellurium	**53** 126.91 **I** Iodine	**54** 131.30 **Xe** Xenon
78 195.09 **Pt** Platinum	**79** 197.0 **Au** Gold	**80** 200.61 **Hg** Mercury	**81** 204.39 **Tl** Thallium	**82** 207.21 **Pb** Lead	**83** 209.00 **Bi** Bismuth	**84** (210) **Po** Polonium	**85** (210) **At** Astatine	**86** (222) **Rn** Radon

64 157.26 **Gd** Gadolinium	**65** 158.93 **Tb** Terbium	**66** 162.51 **Dy** Dysprosium	**67** 164.94 **Ho** Holmium	**68** 167.27 **Er** Erbium	**69** 168.94 **Tm** Thulium	**70** 173.04 **Yb** Ytterbium	**71** 174.99 **Lu** Lutetium
96 (248) **Cm** Curium	**97** (247) **Bk** Berkelium	**98** (249) **Cf** Californium	**99** (254) **Es** Einsteinium	**100** (253) **Fm** Fermium	**101** (256) **Md** Mendelevium	**102** (253) **No** Nobelium	**103** (259) **Lw** Lawrencium

Appendix 2

TABLE OF ATOMIC MASS
(Based on Carbon-12, the Most Common Isotope of Carbon)

Element	Symbol	Atomic number	Atomic mass	Element	Symbol	Atomic number	Atomic mass
Actinium	Ac	89	(227)	Mendelevium	Md	101	(256)
Aluminum	Al	13	26.9815	Mercury	Hg	80	200.59
Americium	Am	95	(243)	Molybdenum	Mo	42	95.94
Antimony	Sb	51	121.75	Neodymium	Nd	60	144.24
Argon	Ar	18	39.948	Neon	Ne	10	20.179
Arsenic	As	33	74.9216	Neptunium	Np	93	237.0482
Astatine	At	85	(210)	Nickel	Ni	28	58.71
Barium	Ba	56	137.34	Niobium	Nb	41	92.9064
Berkelium	Bk	97	(249)	Nitrogen	N	7	14.0067
Beryllium	Be	4	9.012 18	Nobelium	No	102	(254)
Bismuth	Bi	83	208.9806	Osmium	Os	76	190.2
Boron	B	5	10.81	Oxygen	O	8	15.9994
Bromine	Br	35	79.904	Palladium	Pd	46	106.4
Cadmium	Cd	48	112.40	Phosphorus	P	15	30.9738
Calcium	Ca	20	40.08	Platinum	Pt	78	195.09
Californium	Cf	98	(251)	Plutonium	Pu	94	(242)
Carbon	C	6	12.011	Polonium	Po	84	(210)
Cerium	Ce	58	140.12	Potassium	K	19	39.102
Cesium	Cs	55	132.9055	Praseodymium	Pr	59	140.9077
Chlorine	Cl	17	35.453	Promethium	Pm	61	(145)
Chromium	Cr	24	51.996	Protactinium	Pa	91	231.0359
Cobalt	Co	27	58.9332	Radium	Ra	88	226.0254
Copper	Cu	29	63.546	Radon	Rn	86	(222)
Curium	Cm	96	(247)	Rhenium	Re	75	186.2
Dysprosium	Dy	66	162.50	Rhodium	Rh	45	102.9055
Einsteinium	Es	99	(254)	Rubidium	Rb	37	85.4678
Erbium	Er	68	167.26	Ruthenium	Ru	44	101.07
Europium	Eu	63	151.96	Samarium	Sm	62	150.4
Fermium	Fm	100	(253)	Scandium	Sc	21	44.9559
Fluorine	F	9	18.9984	Selenium	Se	34	78.96
Francium	Fr	87	(223)	Silicon	Si	14	28.086
Gadolinium	Gd	64	157.25	Silver	Ag	47	107.868
Gallium	Ga	31	69.72	Sodium	Na	11	22.9898
Germanium	Ge	32	72.59	Strontium	Sr	38	87.62
Gold	Au	79	196.9665	Sulfur	S	16	32.06
Hafnium	Hf	72	178.49	Tantalum	Ta	73	180.9479
Hahnium	Ha	105	(260)	Technetium	Tc	43	98.9062
Helium	He	2	4.002 60	Tellurium	Te	52	127.60
Holmium	Ho	67	164.9303	Terbium	Tb	65	158.9254
Hydrogen	H	1	1.0080	Thallium	Tl	81	204.37
Indium	In	49	114.82	Thorium	Th	90	232.0381
Iodine	I	53	126.9045	Thulium	Tm	69	168.9342
Iridium	Ir	77	192.22	Tin	Sn	50	118.69
Iron	Fe	26	55.847	Titanium	Ti	22	47.90
Krypton	Kr	36	83.80	Tungsten	W	74	183.85
Kurchatovium	Ku	104	(257)	Uranium	U	92	238.029
Lanthanum	La	57	138.9055	Vanadium	V	23	50.9414
Lawrencium	Lr	103	(257)	Xenon	Xe	54	131.30
Lead	Pb	82	207.2	Ytterbium	Yb	70	173.04
Lithium	Li	3	6.941	Yttrium	Y	39	88.9059
Lutetium	Lu	71	174.97	Zinc	Zn	30	65.37
Magnesium	Mg	12	24.305	Zirconium	Zr	40	91.22
Manganese	Mn	25	54.9380				

Appendix 3

TABLE OF RELATIVE STRENGTHS OF ACIDS

In Aqueous Solution at Room Temperature

All ions are aquated

$$HB \rightleftarrows H^+(aq) + B^-(aq) \qquad K_A = \frac{[H^+][B^-]}{[HB]}$$

Acid	Reaction	K_A
perchloric acid	$HClO_4 \rightarrow H^+ + ClO_4^-$	very large
hydriodic acid	$HI \rightarrow H^+ + I^-$	very large
hydrobromic acid	$HBr \rightarrow H^+ + Br^-$	very large
hydrochloric acid	$HCl \rightarrow H^+ + Cl^-$	very large
nitric acid	$HNO_3 \rightarrow H^+ + NO_3^-$	very large
sulfuric acid	$H_2SO_4 \rightarrow H^+ + HSO_4^-$	large
oxalic acid	$HOOCCOOH \rightarrow H^+ + HOOCCOO^-$	5.4×10^{-2}
sulfurous acid ($SO_2 + H_2O$)	$H_2SO_3 \rightarrow H^+ + HSO_3^-$	1.7×10^{-2}
hydrogen sulfate ion	$HSO_4^- \rightarrow H^+ + SO_4^{-2}$	1.3×10^{-2}
phosphoric acid	$H_3PO_4 \rightarrow H^+ + H_2PO_4^-$	7.1×10^{-3}
ferric ion	$Fe(H_2O)_6^{+3} \rightarrow H^+ + Fe(H_2O)_5(OH)^{+2}$	6.0×10^{-3}
hydrogen telluride	$H_2Te \rightarrow H^+ + HTe^-$	2.3×10^{-3}
hydrofluoric acid	$HF \rightarrow H^+ + F^-$	6.7×10^{-4}
nitrous acid	$HNO_2 \rightarrow H^+ + NO_2^-$	5.1×10^{-4}
hydrogen selenide	$H_2Se \rightarrow H^+ + HSe^-$	1.7×10^{-4}
chromic ion	$Cr(H_2O)_6^{+3} \rightarrow H^+ + Cr(H_2O)_5(OH)^{+2}$	1.5×10^{-4}
benzoic acid	$C_6H_5COOH \rightarrow H^+ + C_6H_5COO^-$	6.6×10^{-5}
hydrogen oxalate ion	$HOOCCOO^- \rightarrow H^+ + OOCCOO^{-2}$	5.4×10^{-5}
acetic acid	$CH_3COOH \rightarrow H^+ + CH_3COO^-$	1.8×10^{-5}
aluminum ion	$Al(H_2O)_6^{+3} \rightarrow H^+ + Al(H_2O)_5(OH)^{+2}$	1.4×10^{-5}
carbonic acid ($CO_2 + H_2O$)	$H_2CO_3 \rightarrow H^+ + HCO_3^-$	4.4×10^{-7}
hydrogen sulfide	$H_2S \rightarrow H^+ + HS^-$	1.0×10^{-7}
dihydrogen phosphate ion	$H_2PO_4^- \rightarrow H^+ + HPO_4^{-2}$	6.3×10^{-8}
hydrogen sulfite ion	$HSO_3^- \rightarrow H^+ + SO_3^{-2}$	6.2×10^{-8}
ammonium ion	$HN_4^+ \rightarrow H^+ + NH_3$	5.7×10^{-10}
hydrogen carbonate ion	$HCO_3^- \rightarrow H^+ + CO_3^{-2}$	4.7×10^{-11}
hydrogen telluride ion	$HTe^- \rightarrow H^+ + Te^{-2}$	1.0×10^{-11}
hydrogen peroxide	$H_2O_2 \rightarrow H^+ + HO_2^-$	2.4×10^{-12}
monohydrogen phosphate ion	$HPO_4^{-2} \rightarrow H^+ + PO_4^{-3}$	4.4×10^{-13}
hydrogen sulfide ion	$HS^- \rightarrow H^+ + S^{-2}$	1.3×10^{-13}
water	$H_2O \rightarrow H^+ + OH^- \qquad [H^+][OH^-] =$	1.0×10^{-14}
hydroxide ion	$OH^- \rightarrow H^+ + O^{-2}$	$< 10^{-36}$
ammonia	$NH_3 \rightarrow H^+ + NH_2^-$	very small

From Chemistry: An Experimental Science W.H. Freeman & Co. 1963. Used with permission of Chemical Education Material Study.

Appendix 4

TABLE OF STANDARD REDUCTION POTENTIALS FOR HALF-REACTIONS

Half-reaction	$E°$ (volts)
$F_2(g) + 2 e^- \rightarrow 2 F^-$	2.87
$H_2O_2 + 2 H^+ + 2 e^- \rightarrow 2 H_2O$	1.776
$MnO_4^- + 4 H^+ + 3 e^- \rightarrow MnO_2 + 2 H_2O$	1.679
$MnO_4^- + 8 H^+ + 5 e^- \rightarrow Mn^{2+} + 4 H_2O$	1.491
$Au^{3+} + 3 e^- \rightarrow Au$	1.42
$Cl_2(g) + 2 e^- \rightarrow 2 Cl^-$	1.358
$Cr_2O_7^{2-} + 14 H^+ + 6 e^- \rightarrow 2 Cr^{3+} + 7 H_2O$	1.33
$\frac{1}{2} O_2(g) + 2 H^+ + 2 e^- \rightarrow H_2O$	1.229
$MnO_2 + 4 H^+ + 2 e^- \rightarrow Mn^{2+} + 2 H_2O$	1.208
$Br_2(l) + 2 e^- \rightarrow 2 Br^-$	1.065
$NO_3^- + 4 H^+ + 3 e^- \rightarrow NO(g) + 2 H_2O$	0.96
$Hg^{2+} + e^- \rightarrow \frac{1}{2} Hg_2^{2+}$	0.905
$Hg^{2+} + 2 e^- \rightarrow Hg(l)$	0.851
$\frac{1}{2} O_2(g) + 2H^+(10^{-7} \, kmol/m^3) + 2 e^- \rightarrow H_2O$	0.815
$2 NO_3^- + 4 H^+ + 2 e^- \rightarrow N_2O_4(g) + 2 H_2O$	0.81
$Ag^+ + e^- \rightarrow Ag$	0.800
$\frac{1}{2} Hg_2^{2+} + e^- \rightarrow Hg(l)$	0.796
$Fe^{3+} + e^- \rightarrow Fe^{2+}$	0.77
$O_2(g) + 2 H^+ + 2 e^- \rightarrow H_2O_2$	0.682
$I_2 + 2 e^- \rightarrow 2 I^-$	0.535
$Cu^+ + e^- \rightarrow Cu$	0.522
$\frac{1}{2} O_2(g) + H_2O + 2 e^- \rightarrow 2 OH^-$	0.401
$Cu^{2+} + 2 e^- \rightarrow Cu$	0.340
$SO_4^{2-} + 4 H^+ + 2 e^- \rightarrow SO_2(g) + 2 H_2O$	0.20
$Cu^{2+} + e^- \rightarrow Cu^+$	0.158
$Sn^{4+} + 2 e^- \rightarrow Sn^{2+}$	0.15
$2 H^+ + 2 e^- \rightarrow H_2(g)$	0.000
$Fe^{3+} + 3 e^- \rightarrow Fe$	−0.036
$Pb^{2+} + 2 e^- \rightarrow Pb$	−0.126
$Sn^{2+} + 2 e^- \rightarrow Sn$	−0.136
$Ni^{2+} + 2 e^- \rightarrow Ni$	−0.23
$Co^{2+} + 2 e^- \rightarrow Co$	−0.28
$Cr^{3+} + e^- \rightarrow Cr^{2+}$	−0.41
$2 H^+(10^{-7} kmol/m^3) + 2 e^- \rightarrow H_2(g)$	−0.414
$Fe^{2+} + 2 e^- \rightarrow Fe$	−0.439
$Cr^{2+} + 2 e^- \rightarrow Cr$	−0.557
$Cr^{3+} + 3 e^- \rightarrow Cr$	−0.74
$Zn^{2+} + 2 e^- \rightarrow Zn$	−0.763
$2 H_2O + 2 e^- \rightarrow H_2(g) + 2 OH^-$	−0.828
$Mn^{2+} + 2 e^- \rightarrow Mn$	−1.029
$Al^{3+} + 3 e^- \rightarrow Al$	−1.66
$Mg^{2+} + 2 e^- \rightarrow Mg$	−2.375
$Na^+ + e^- \rightarrow Na$	−2.711
$Ca^{2+} + 2 e^- \rightarrow Ca$	−2.76
$Sr^{2+} + 2 e^- \rightarrow Sr$	−2.89
$Ba^{2+} + 2 e^- \rightarrow Ba$	−2.90
$Cs^+ + e^- \rightarrow Cs$	−2.923
$K^+ + e^- \rightarrow K$	−2.924
$Rb^+ + e^- \rightarrow Rb$	−2.925
$Li^+ + e^- \rightarrow Li$	−3.045

Appendix 5

LOGARITHMS

	0	1	2	3	4	5	6	7	8	9	Differences 1 2 3	4 5 6	7 8 9
1.0	0.0000	0.0043	0.0086	0.0128	0.0170	0.0212	0.0253	0.0294	0.0334	0.0374	4 8 12	17 21 25	29 33 37
1.1	0.0414	0.0453	0.0492	0.0531	0.0569	0.0607	0.0645	0.0682	0.0719	0.0755	4 8 11	15 19 23	26 30 34
1.2	0.0792	0.0828	0.0864	0.0899	0.0934	0.0969	0.1004	0.1038	0.1072	0.1106	3 7 10	14 17 21	24 28 31
1.3	0.1139	0.1173	0.1206	0.1239	0.1271	0.1303	0.1335	0.1367	0.1399	0.1430	3 6 10	13 16 19	23 26 29
1.4	0.1461	0.1492	0.1523	0.1553	0.1584	0.1614	0.1644	0.1673	0.1703	0.1732	3 6 9	12 15 18	21 24 27
1.5	0.1761	0.1790	0.1818	0.1847	0.1875	0.1903	0.1931	0.1959	0.1987	0.2014	3 6 8	11 14 17	20 22 25
1.6	0.2041	0.2068	0.2095	0.2122	0.2148	0.2175	0.2201	0.2227	0.2253	0.2279	3 5 8	11 13 16	18 21 24
1.7	0.2304	0.2330	0.2355	0.2380	0.2405	0.2430	0.2455	0.2480	0.2504	0.2529	2 5 7	10 12 15	17 20 22
1.8	0.2553	0.2577	0.2601	0.2625	0.2648	0.2672	0.2695	0.2718	0.2742	0.2765	2 5 7	9 12 14	16 19 21
1.9	0.2788	0.2810	0.2833	0.2856	0.2878	0.2900	0.2923	0.2945	0.2967	0.2989	2 4 7	9 11 13	16 18 20
2.0	0.3010	0.3032	0.3054	0.3075	0.3096	0.3118	0.3139	0.3160	0.3181	0.3201	2 4 6	8 11 13	15 17 19
2.1	0.3222	0.3243	0.3263	0.3284	0.3304	0.3324	0.3345	0.3365	0.3385	0.3404	2 4 6	8 10 12	14 16 18
2.2	0.3424	0.3444	0.3464	0.3483	0.3502	0.3522	0.3541	0.3560	0.3579	0.3598	2 4 6	8 10 12	14 15 17
2.3	0.3617	0.3636	0.3655	0.3674	0.3692	0.3711	0.3729	0.3747	0.3766	0.3784	2 4 6	7 9 11	13 15 17
2.4	0.3802	0.3820	0.3838	0.3856	0.3874	0.3892	0.3909	0.3927	0.3945	0.3962	2 4 5	7 9 11	12 14 16
2.5	0.3979	0.3997	0.4014	0.4031	0.4048	0.4065	0.4082	0.4099	0.4116	0.4133	2 3 5	7 9 10	12 14 15
2.6	0.4150	0.4166	0.4183	0.4200	0.4216	0.4232	0.4249	0.4265	0.4281	0.4298	2 3 5	7 8 10	11 13 15
2.7	0.4314	0.4330	0.4346	0.4362	0.4378	0.4393	0.4409	0.4425	0.4440	0.4456	2 3 5	6 8 9	11 13 14
2.8	0.4472	0.4487	0.4502	0.4518	0.4533	0.4548	0.4564	0.4579	0.4594	0.4609	2 3 5	6 8 9	11 12 14
2.9	0.4624	0.4639	0.4654	0.4669	0.4683	0.4698	0.4713	0.4728	0.4742	0.4757	1 3 4	6 7 9	10 12 13
3.0	0.4771	0.4786	0.4800	0.4814	0.4829	0.4843	0.4857	0.4871	0.4886	0.4900	1 3 4	6 7 9	10 11 13
3.1	0.4914	0.4928	0.4942	0.4955	0.4969	0.4983	0.4997	0.5011	0.5024	0.5038	1 3 4	6 7 8	10 11 12
3.2	0.5051	0.5065	0.5079	0.5092	0.5105	0.5119	0.5132	0.5145	0.5159	0.5172	1 3 4	5 7 8	9 11 12
3.3	0.5185	0.5198	0.5211	0.5224	0.5237	0.5250	0.5263	0.5276	0.5289	0.5302	1 3 4	5 6 8	9 10 12
3.4	0.5315	0.5328	0.5340	0.5353	0.5366	0.5378	0.5391	0.5403	0.5416	0.5428	1 3 4	5 6 8	9 10 11
3.5	0.5441	0.5453	0.5465	0.5478	0.5490	0.5502	0.5514	0.5527	0.5539	0.5551	1 2 4	5 6 7	9 10 11
3.6	0.5563	0.5575	0.5587	0.5599	0.5611	0.5623	0.5635	0.5647	0.5658	0.5670	1 2 4	5 6 7	8 10 11
3.7	0.5682	0.5694	0.5705	0.5717	0.5729	0.5740	0.5752	0.5763	0.5775	0.5786	1 2 3	5 6 7	8 9 10
3.8	0.5798	0.5809	0.5821	0.5832	0.5843	0.5855	0.5866	0.5877	0.5888	0.5899	1 2 3	5 6 7	8 9 10
3.9	0.5911	0.5922	0.5933	0.5944	0.5955	0.5966	0.5977	0.5988	0.5999	0.6010	1 2 3	4 5 7	8 9 10
4.0	0.6021	0.6031	0.6042	0.6053	0.6064	0.6075	0.6085	0.6096	0.6107	0.6117	1 2 3	4 5 6	8 9 10
4.1	0.6128	0.6138	0.6149	0.6160	0.6170	0.6180	0.6191	0.6201	0.6212	0.6222	1 2 3	4 5 6	7 8 9
4.2	0.6232	0.6243	0.6253	0.6263	0.6274	0.6284	0.6294	0.6304	0.6314	0.6325	1 2 3	4 5 6	7 8 9
4.3	0.6335	0.6345	0.6355	0.6365	0.6375	0.6385	0.6395	0.6405	0.6415	0.6425	1 2 3	4 5 6	7 8 9
4.4	0.6435	0.6444	0.6454	0.6464	0.6474	0.6484	0.6493	0.6503	0.6513	0.6522	1 2 3	4 5 6	7 8 9
4.5	0.6532	0.6542	0.6551	0.6561	0.6571	0.6580	0.6590	0.6599	0.6609	0.6618	1 2 3	4 5 6	7 8 9
4.6	0.6628	0.6637	0.6646	0.6656	0.6665	0.6675	0.6684	0.6693	0.6702	0.6712	1 2 3	4 5 6	7 7 8
4.7	0.6721	0.6730	0.6739	0.6749	0.6758	0.6767	0.6776	0.6785	0.6794	0.6803	1 2 3	4 5 5	6 7 8
4.8	0.6812	0.6821	0.6830	0.6839	0.6848	0.6857	0.6866	0.6875	0.6884	0.6893	1 2 3	4 4 5	6 7 8
4.9	0.6902	0.6911	0.6920	0.6928	0.6937	0.6946	0.6955	0.6964	0.6972	0.6981	1 2 3	4 4 5	6 7 8
5.0	0.6990	0.6998	0.7007	0.7016	0.7024	0.7033	0.7042	0.7050	0.7059	0.7067	1 2 3	3 4 5	6 7 8
5.1	0.7076	0.7084	0.7093	0.7101	0.7110	0.7118	0.7126	0.7135	0.7143	0.7152	1 2 3	3 4 5	6 7 8
5.2	0.7160	0.7168	0.7177	0.7185	0.7193	0.7202	0.7210	0.7218	0.7226	0.7235	1 2 2	3 4 5	6 7 7
5.3	0.7243	0.7251	0.7259	0.7267	0.7275	0.7284	0.7292	0.7300	0.7308	0.7316	1 2 2	3 4 5	6 6 7
5.4	0.7324	0.7332	0.7340	0.7348	0.7356	0.7364	0.7372	0.7380	0.7388	0.7396	1 2 2	3 4 5	6 6 7
	0	1	2	3	4	5	6	7	8	9	1 2 3	4 5 6	7 8 9

	0	1	2	3	4	5	6	7	8	9	Differences								
											1	2	3	4	5	6	7	8	9
5.5	0.7404	0.7412	0.7419	0.7427	0.7435	0.7443	0.7451	0.7459	0.7466	0.7474	1	2	2	3	4	5	5	6	7
5.6	0.7482	0.7490	0.7497	0.7505	0.7513	0.7520	0.7528	0.7536	0.7543	0.7551	1	2	2	3	4	5	5	6	7
5.7	0.7559	0.7566	0.7574	0.7582	0.7589	0.7597	0.7604	0.7612	0.7619	0.7627	1	2	2	3	4	5	5	6	7
5.8	0.7634	0.7642	0.7649	0.7657	0.7664	0.7672	0.7679	0.7686	0.7694	0.7701	1	1	2	3	4	4	5	6	7
5.9	0.7709	0.7716	0.7723	0.7731	0.7738	0.7745	0.7752	0.7760	0.7767	0.7774	1	1	2	3	4	4	5	6	7
6.0	0.7782	0.7789	0.7796	0.7803	0.7810	0.7818	0.7825	0.7832	0.7839	0.7846	1	1	2	3	4	4	5	6	6
6.1	0.7853	0.7860	0.7868	0.7875	0.7882	0.7889	0.7896	0.7903	0.7910	0.7917	1	1	2	3	4	4	5	6	6
6.2	0.7924	0.7931	0.7938	0.7945	0.7952	0.7959	0.7966	0.7973	0.7980	0.7987	1	1	2	3	3	4	5	6	6
6.3	0.7993	0.8000	0.8007	0.8014	0.8021	0.8028	0.8035	0.8041	0.8048	0.8055	1	1	2	3	3	4	5	5	6
6.4	0.8062	0.8069	0.8075	0.8082	0.8089	0.8096	0.8102	0.8109	0.8116	0.8122	1	1	2	3	3	4	5	5	6
6.5	0.8129	0.8135	0.8142	0.8149	0.8156	0.8162	0.8169	0.8176	0.8182	0.8189	1	1	2	3	3	4	5	5	6
6.6	0.8195	0.8202	0.8209	0.8215	0.8222	0.8228	0.8235	0.8241	0.8248	0.8254	1	1	2	3	3	4	5	5	6
6.7	0.8261	0.8267	0.8274	0.8280	0.8287	0.8293	0.8299	0.8306	0.8312	0.8319	1	1	2	3	3	4	5	5	6
6.8	0.8325	0.8331	0.8338	0.8344	0.8351	0.8357	0.8363	0.8370	0.8376	0.8382	1	1	2	3	3	4	4	5	6
6.9	0.8388	0.8395	0.8401	0.8407	0.8414	0.8420	0.8426	0.8432	0.8439	0.8445	1	1	2	2	3	4	4	5	6
7.0	0.8451	0.8457	0.8463	0.8470	0.8476	0.8482	0.8488	0.8494	0.8500	0.8506	1	1	2	2	3	4	4	5	6
7.1	0.8513	0.8519	0.8525	0.8531	0.8537	0.8543	0.8549	0.8555	0.8561	0.8567	1	1	2	2	3	4	4	5	5
7.2	0.8573	0.8579	0.8585	0.8591	0.8597	0.8603	0.8609	0.8615	0.8621	0.8627	1	1	2	2	3	4	4	5	5
7.3	0.8633	0.8639	0.8645	0.8651	0.8657	0.8663	0.8669	0.8675	0.8681	0.8686	1	1	2	2	3	4	4	5	5
7.4	0.8692	0.8698	0.8704	0.8710	0.8716	0.8722	0.8727	0.8733	0.8739	0.8745	1	1	2	2	3	4	4	5	5
7.5	0.8751	0.8756	0.8762	0.8768	0.8774	0.8779	0.8785	0.8791	0.8797	0.8802	1	1	2	2	3	3	4	5	5
7.6	0.8808	0.8814	0.8820	0.8825	0.8831	0.8837	0.8842	0.8848	0.8854	0.8859	1	1	2	2	3	3	4	5	5
7.7	0.8865	0.8871	0.8876	0.8882	0.8887	0.8893	0.8899	0.8904	0.8910	0.8915	1	1	2	2	3	3	4	4	5
7.8	0.8921	0.8927	0.8932	0.8938	0.8943	0.8949	0.8954	0.8960	0.8965	0.8971	1	1	2	2	3	3	4	4	5
7.9	0.8976	0.8982	0.8987	0.8993	0.8998	0.9004	0.9009	0.9015	0.9020	0.9025	1	1	2	2	3	3	4	4	5
8.0	0.9031	0.9036	0.9042	0.9047	0.9053	0.9058	0.9063	0.9069	0.9074	0.9079	1	1	2	2	3	3	4	4	5
8.1	0.9085	0.9090	0.9096	0.9101	0.9106	0.9112	0.9117	0.9122	0.9128	0.9133	1	1	2	2	3	3	4	4	5
8.2	0.9138	0.9143	0.9149	0.9154	0.9159	0.9165	0.9170	0.9175	0.9180	0.9186	1	1	2	2	3	3	4	4	5
8.3	0.9191	0.9196	0.9201	0.9206	0.9212	0.9217	0.9222	0.9227	0.9232	0.9238	1	1	2	2	3	3	4	4	5
8.4	0.9243	0.9248	0.9253	0.9258	0.9263	0.9269	0.9274	0.9279	0.9284	0.9289	1	1	2	2	3	3	4	4	5
8.5	0.9294	0.9299	0.9304	0.9309	0.9315	0.9320	0.9325	0.9330	0.9335	0.9340	1	1	2	2	3	3	4	4	5
8.6	0.9345	0.9350	0.9355	0.9360	0.9365	0.9370	0.9375	0.9380	0.9385	0.9390	1	1	2	2	3	3	4	4	5
8.7	0.9395	0.9400	0.9405	0.9410	0.9415	0.9420	0.9425	0.9430	0.9435	0.9440	0	1	1	2	2	3	3	4	4
8.8	0.9445	0.9450	0.9455	0.9460	0.9465	0.9469	0.9474	0.9479	0.9484	0.9489	0	1	1	2	2	3	3	4	4
8.9	0.9494	0.9499	0.9504	0.9509	0.9513	0.9518	0.9523	0.9528	0.9533	0.9538	0	1	1	2	2	3	3	4	4
9.0	0.9542	0.9547	0.9552	0.9557	0.9562	0.9566	0.9571	0.9576	0.9581	0.9586	0	1	1	2	2	3	3	4	4
9.1	0.9590	0.9595	0.9600	0.9605	0.9609	0.9614	0.9619	0.9624	0.9628	0.9633	0	1	1	2	2	3	3	4	4
9.2	0.9638	0.9643	0.9647	0.9652	0.9657	0.9661	0.9666	0.9671	0.9675	0.9680	0	1	1	2	2	3	3	4	4
9.3	0.9685	0.9689	0.9694	0.9699	0.9703	0.9708	0.9713	0.9717	0.9722	0.9727	0	1	1	2	2	3	3	3	4
9.4	0.9731	0.9736	0.9741	0.9745	0.9750	0.9754	0.9759	0.9763	0.9768	0.9773	0	1	1	2	2	3	3	4	4
9.5	0.9777	0.9782	0.9786	0.9791	0.9795	0.9800	0.9805	0.9809	0.9814	0.9818	0	1	1	2	2	3	3	4	4
9.6	0.9823	0.9827	0.9832	0.9836	0.9841	0.9845	0.9850	0.9854	0.9859	0.9863	0	1	1	2	2	3	3	4	4
9.7	0.9868	0.9872	0.9877	0.9881	0.9886	0.9890	0.9894	0.9899	0.9903	0.9908	0	1	1	2	2	3	3	4	4
9.8	0.9912	0.9917	0.9921	0.9926	0.9930	0.9934	0.9939	0.9943	0.9948	0.9952	0	1	1	2	2	3	3	4	4
9.9	0.9956	0.9961	0.9965	0.9969	0.9974	0.9978	0.9983	0.9987	0.9991	0.9996	0	1	1	2	2	3	3	3	4
	0	1	2	3	4	5	6	7	8	9	1	2	3	4	5	6	7	8	9

Answers to Exercises

A SIMPLE WAY OF USING LOGARITHMS

1. a) $10^{0.6990}$
   b) $10^{0.7853}$
   c) $10^{0.8633}$
   d) $10^{0.6821} \times 10^1$
   e) $10^{0.6794} \times 10^2$
   f) $10^{0.6721} \times 10^{-3}$
   g) $10^{0.8096} \times 10^3$
   h) $10^{0.6637} \times 10^{-6}$
   i) $10^{0.7135} \times 10^4$
   j) $10^{0.0128} \times 10^{-3}$

2. a) 8.3
   b) 2.85×10^2
   c) 7.58×10^4
   d) 7.6×10^{-5}
   e) 1.29×10^5
   f) 1.47×10^1
   g) 3.80×10^{-3}
   h) 5.72×10^{-12}
   i) 5.70×10^{-2}
   j) 9.55×10^4

3. a) 0.8451
   b) 2.7782
   c) -2.3468
   d) -1.3233
   e) 1×10^3
   f) 0.251
   g) 2.38×10^{-8}
   h) -3.1593
   i) 5.19×10^3
   j) 5.7292
   k) 8.41×10^{-5}
   l) -9.3820

4. a) 5.92
   b) 5.39×10^1
   c) 1.54×10^1
   d) 2.53×10^{-2}
   e) 3.27×10^{-2}
   f) 9.00
   g) 4.10×10^{-1}
   h) 8.27
   i) 8.94×10^{-5}

SPECIFIC HEAT, HEAT OF FUSION AND HEAT OF VAPORIZATION

1. a) 1.82 kJ
   b) 17.2°C

2. a) 6.6 kJ
   b) 0.188 kJ
   c) 0.121 kJ

3. molar heat of vaporization = 40.5 kJ/mol
   molar heat of fusion = 6.01 kJ/mol

4. a) 3.50 kJ
   b) T(final) = 48.6°C for Al; Cu gets to higher temperature.

5. 40.6 g
6. 37.0°C
7. 19.4°C
8. 61.5 kJ
9. 157 kJ
10. a) 14.0 kJ
    b) 10.8°C

11. a) 36°C   b) 6.45°C   c) 0.13 kJ/(kg·°C)
12. 52.0°C   13. 74.0°C   14. 169 g; 160 g
15. 53.2 g   16. 403 g   17. 71.4°C
18. 5.76 g

REACTION HEATS

1. -46.3 kJ/mol NH_3 2. -45 kJ   3. 810 kJ
4. -90.0 kJ   5. -1561 kJ   6. 178 kJ
7. 78 kJ   8. -812 kJ   9. 2563 kJ
10. -394 kJ
11. a) -58.2 kJ   b) 114.7 kJ   c) 51.9 kJ
    d) -72.0 kJ
12. 4.30×10^3 kJ   13. -132 kJ   14. 227 kJ
15. 7.21×10^3 kJ   16. 946 kJ
17. i) $C_8H_{18} + 25/2\ O_2 \rightarrow 8\ CO_2 + 9\ H_2O$
ii) 0 kJ   iii) -5.52×10^3 kJ   iv) 3.40×10^4 kJ
v) 0.720 kg
18. 833 kJ   19. -3.23×10^3 kJ   20. 4.9 kJ
21. 5.64×10^3 kJ   22. 24.7 kg   23. 159 kJ
24. -178 kJ

EQUILIBRIUM EXPRESSIONS AND LE CHATELIER'S PRINCIPLE

A. Equilibrium Expressions

1. $K_{eq} = \dfrac{[Cl_2][I_2]}{[ICl]^2}$

2. $K_{eq} = \dfrac{[NO]^2}{[N_2][O_2]}$

3. $K_{eq} = \dfrac{[O_3]^2}{[O_2]^3}$

4. $K_{eq} = \dfrac{[H^+]^6}{[Bi^{3+}]^2[H_2S]^3}$

5. $K_{eq} = [CO_2]$

6. $K_{eq} = [C_2H_2]$

7. $K_{eq} = \dfrac{[C_6H_5Br][HBr]}{[C_6H_6][Br_2]}$

8. $K_{eq} = \dfrac{[Cu^{2+}]}{[Ag^+]^2}$

9. $K_{eq} = \dfrac{[H_2O]^6[NO]^4}{[NH_3]^4[O_2]^5}$

10. $K_{eq} = \dfrac{1}{[H_2][O_2]^{1/2}}$

B. Le Chatelier's Principle

1. a) shift to left
   b) shift to right
   c) shift to left
   d) no effect
2. a) shift to right
   b) shift to left
   c) shift to left
3. a) shift to left; K_{eq} decreases
   b) shift to right
   c) no effect
   d) no effect
4. a) shift to left; K_{eq} decreases
   b) shift to left
   c) no effect
5. a) K_{eq} = NC; $[H_2]$ = DEC
   b) K_{eq} = DEC; $[H_2]$ = INC
   c) K_{eq} = NC; $[H_2]$ = INC
   d) K_{eq} = NC; $[H_2]$ = NC
6. a) K_{eq} = DEC; $[F_2]$ = DEC
   b) K_{eq} = NC; $[F_2]$ = INC
   c) K_{eq} = NC; $[F_2]$ = NC, after initial increase due to abrupt pressure change
7. a) K_{eq} = INC, [Sn] = NC, but more Sn produced
   b) K_{eq} = NC; [Sn] = NC
   c) K_{eq} = NC; [Sn] = NC, but some Sn used up
   d) K_{eq} = NC; [Sn] = NC
8. a)
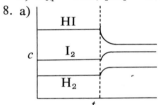
b)
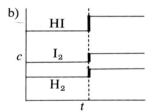
c)
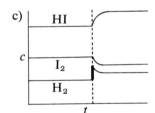
d)
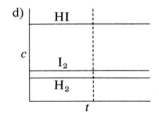
9. a)
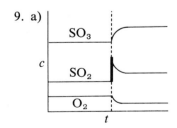
b)
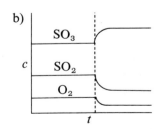

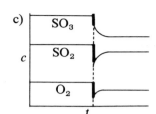

c)

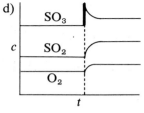

d)

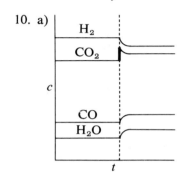

10. a)

b)

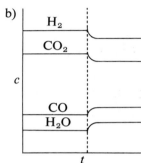

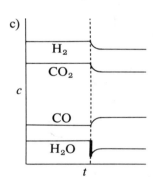

c)

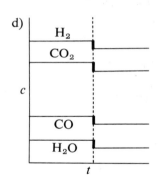

d)

EQUILIBRIUM CALCULATIONS

1. 5.0

2. 3.0

3. a) 343

b) 5.81×10^{-4}

4. 1.43×10^4

5. a) shift to right

b) shift to left

c) no shift; $K_{\text{trial}} = 4$

6. a) shift to right

b) shift to right

c) shift to right

7. 8.0×10^2 kPa

8. 0.323 kmol/m³

9. 2.2 mol

10. 0.5 mol

11. 98.7 kPa

12. $[HI] = 0.0389$ kmol/m^3, $[H_2] = [I_2] = 0.0055$ kmol/m^3

13. 0.229 kmol/m^3

14. $[H_2] = [I_2] = 0.0201$ kmol/m^3, $[HI] = 0.117$ kmol/m^3

15. product side

16. 0.044

17. 0.0492 kmol/m^3

18. 0.174 mol

19. 0.331 mol

20. 93.8 kPa

21. 61 mol

22. 6.7 g

23. $\dfrac{(3 + 0.8\ s)^2}{(2 + 0.6\ s)\ (4 - 0.4\ s)} = 1.13$

24. 4

SOLUBILITY PRODUCT

1. 1.7×10^{-10}

2. 7.75×10^{-14} kmol/m^3

3. 0.173 g

4. 4.58×10^{-4} kmol/m^3

5. 3.2×10^{-2} g

6. 3.99×10^{-5}

7. 1.36×10^{-4} kmol/m^3

8. 8.44×10^{-5} g/L

9. 4.9×10^{-3} kmol/m^3

10. 3.17×10^{-4} g/L

11. 1.0×10^{-51}

12. 1.5×10^{-32}

13. 6.1×10^{-12}

14. 1.0×10^{-8}

15. 1.0×10^{-2} kmol/m^3

16. 1.7×10^{-5} kmol/m^3

17. 3.2×10^{-4} g

18. 3.0×10^{-13} kmol/m^3

19. 5.8×10^{-5} kmol/m^3

20. 3.39×10^{-2} g/L

PRECIPITATION

1. Yes; $K_{trial} = 1.5 \times 10^{-21}$

2. No; $K_{trial} = 5 \times 10^{-18}$

3. 2×10^{-35} kmol/m^3

4. 1.06×10^{-4} kmol/m^3

5. Yes; $K_{trial} = 2.4 \times 10^{-8}$

6. 3.75×10^{-5}

7. 8.8×10^{-17}

8. Yes; $K_{trial} = 3.24 \times 10^{-14}$

9. 3.42×10^{-27}

10. 1.12×10^{-36}

11. a) 3.5×10^{-4} kmol/m^3

   b) 83.7%

12. a) 3.16×10^{-6} kmol/m^3

   b) 0.1%

13. No; $K_{trial} = 2.25 \times 10^{-12}$

14. No; $K_{trial} = 1.4 \times 10^{-8}$

15. 1.49×10^{-7} g/L

16. 3.6×10^{-4} kmol/m^3

17. a) AgBr ppts first (when $[Ag^+] = 10^{-12}$ kmol/m^3)

   b) $[Br^-] = 10^{-8}$ kmol/m^3 when Ag_2CrO_4 starts to ppt

18. a) AgCl ppts first (when $[Ag^+] = 1.6 \times 10^{-9}$ kmol/m^3)

   b) $[Cl^-] = 1.6 \times 10^{-5}$ kmol/m^3 when Ag_2CrO_4 starts to ppt

19. 2.7×10^{-8} mol
21. 1.7×10^{-6}
23. 7.74×10^{-3} g

20. 0.201 g
22. 2.4×10^{-5}

COMMON ION EFFECT

1. 5.0×10^{-12} mol
3. 2.2×10^{-3} kmol/m^3
5. a) 7.0×10^{-7} kmol/m^3
6. 2.5×10^{-11}
8. 6.1×10^{-12} g
10. 3.1×10^{-3} kmol/m^3
12. 1.56×10^{-9} kmol/m^3

2. 8.0×10^{-9} mol
4. 0.12 kmol/m^3
b) 1.7×10^{-4} g
7. 7.5×10^{-3} kmol/m^3
9. 2.0×10^{-5} mol
11. 1.4×10^{-4} g/L
13. 3.12×10^{-7} kmol/m^3

ACID-BASE REACTIONS

1. a) $[H^+] = 1.0 \times 10^{-3}$ kmol/m^3; $[OH^-] = 1.0 \times 10^{-11}$ kmol/m^3
   b) $[H^+] = 2.5 \times 10^{-15}$ kmol/m^3; $[OH^-] = 4.0$ kmol/m^3
   c) $[H^+] = 8.3 \times 10^{-13}$ kmol/m^3; $[OH^-] = 1.2 \times 10^{-2}$ kmol/m^3
   d) $[H^+] = 2.5 \times 10^{-4}$ kmol/m^3; $[OH^-] = 4.0 \times 10^{-11}$ kmol/m^3
2. $[H^+] = 2.5 \times 10^{-2}$ kmol/m^3; $[OH^-] = 4.0 \times 10^{-13}$ kmol/m^3
3. $[H^+] = 1.60 \times 10^{-13}$ kmol/m^3; $[OH^-] = 6.25 \times 10^{-2}$ kmol/m^3
4. $[H^+] = 9 \times 10^{-3}$ kmol/m^3; $[OH^-] = 1 \times 10^{-12}$ kmol/m^3
5. $[H^+] = 2.5 \times 10^{-12}$ kmol/m^3; $[OH^-] = 4.0 \times 10^{-3}$ kmol/m^3
6. $[H^+] = 3.76$ kmol/m^3; $[OH^-] = 2.66 \times 10^{-15}$ kmol/m^3
7. $[H^+] = 4.0 \times 10^{-14}$ kmol/m^3; $[OH^-] = 2.5 \times 10^{-1}$ kmol/m^3
8. 0.060 mol
9. 0.132 mol
10. 2.19 g
11. 91 g
12. 0.41 g
13. 46 mL
14. 225 mL
15. 1.24 L
16. 4.5 mL

pH AND pOH

1. a) pH = 5.00, pOH = 9.00
   c) pH = 1.60, pOH = 12.40
   e) pH = 13.903, pOH = 0.097
   g) pH = 15.097, pOH = -1.097
   i) pH = 5.307, pOH = 8.693
   k) pH = 10.810, pOH = 3.190
   m) pH = 13.497, pOH = 0.503

   b) pH = 6.48, pOH = 7.52
   d) pH = 11.877, pOH = 2.123
   f) pH = -1.000, pOH = 15.000
   h) pH = 0.000, pOH = 14.000
   j) pH = 3.498, pOH = 10.502
   l) pH = 5.152, pOH = 8.848
   n) pH = -0.021, pOH = 14.021

o) pH = 1.910, pOH = 12.090   p) pH = 5.989, pOH = 8.011
q) pH = 2.282, pOH = 11.718   r) pH = 8.678, pOH = 5.322
s) pH = 10.978, pOH = 3.022   t) pH = 9.070, pOH = 4.930

2. a) $[H^+] = 1.0 \times 10^{-3}$ kmol/m³, $[OH^-] = 1.0 \times 10^{-11}$ kmol/m³
   b) $[H^+] = 4.0 \times 10^{-12}$ kmol/m³, $[OH^-] = 2.5 \times 10^{-3}$ kmol/m³
   c) $[H^+] = 4.30 \times 10^{-9}$ kmol/m³, $[OH^-] = 2.33 \times 10^{-6}$ kmol/m³
   d) $[H^+] = 3.03 \times 10^{-8}$ kmol/m³, $[OH^-] = 3.30 \times 10^{-7}$ kmol/m³
   e) $[H^+] = 7.38 \times 10^{-16}$ kmol/m³, $[OH^-] = 13.6$ kmol/m³
   f) $[H^+] = 0.931$ kmol/m³, $[OH^-] = 1.07 \times 10^{-14}$ kmol/m³
   g) $[H^+] = 3.86 \times 10^{-7}$ kmol/m³, $[OH^-] = 2.59 \times 10^{-8}$ kmol/m³
   h) $[H^+] = 8.85 \times 10^{-10}$ kmol/m³, $[OH^-] = 1.13 \times 10^{-5}$ kmol/m³
   i) $[H^+] = 2.27$ kmol/m³, $[OH^-] = 4.41 \times 10^{-15}$ kmol/m³
   j) $[H^+] = 3.48 \times 10^{-3}$ kmol/m³, $[OH^-] = 2.87 \times 10^{-12}$ kmol/m³
   k) $[H^+] = 9.55 \times 10^{-15}$ kmol/m³, $[OH^-] = 1.05$ kmol/m³
   l) $[H^+] = 1.76 \times 10^{-6}$ kmol/m³, $[OH^-] = 5.69 \times 10^{-9}$ kmol/m³
   m) $[H^+] = 2.44 \times 10^{-13}$ kmol/m³, $[OH^-] = 4.09 \times 10^{-2}$ kmol/m³
   n) $[H^+] = 2.74 \times 10^{-5}$ kmol/m³, $[OH^-] = 3.66 \times 10^{-10}$ kmol/m³
   o) $[H^+] = 1.53 \times 10^{-8}$ kmol/m³, $[OH^-] = 6.52 \times 10^{-7}$ kmol/m³
   p) $[H^+] = 1.12 \times 10^{-4}$ kmol/m³, $[OH^-] = 8.91 \times 10^{-11}$ kmol/m³
   q) $[H^+] = 9.79 \times 10^{-16}$ kmol/m³, $[OH^-] = 10.2$ kmol/m³
   r) $[H^+] = 5.86 \times 10^{-8}$ kmol/m³, $[OH^-] = 1.71 \times 10^{-7}$ kmol/m³
   s) $[H^+] = 6.67 \times 10^{-4}$ kmol/m³, $[OH^-] = 1.50 \times 10^{-11}$ kmol/m³
   t) $[H^+] = 3.64 \times 10^{-5}$ kmol/m³, $[OH^-] = 2.75 \times 10^{-10}$ kmol/m³

3. 10.874   4. 6.500   5. 8.774
6. 5.891   7. 2.462   8. 8.851
9. 4.542   10. 8.576   11. 8.738
12. 4.923   13. 89 L   14. 133 mL
15. 155 mL

CALCULATIONS BASED ON BRÖNSTED-LOWRY THEORY

1. a) HNO_2 b) H_2CO_3
   c) $H_2PO_4^-$ d) H_2O
   e) $H_3SO_4^+$ f) $CH_3NH_3^+$
2. a) F^- b) CO_3^{2-}
   c) NH_2^- d) N_2H_4
   e) PO_4^{3-} f) $(CH_3)_2NH$
3. a) $HNO_2 + NH_3 \rightleftharpoons NO_2^- + NH_4^+$; (HNO_2, NO_2^-), (NH_3, NH_4^+)
   b) $CO_3^{2-} + HF \rightleftharpoons HCO_3^- + F^-$; (CO_3^{2-}, HCO_3^-), (HF, F^-)
   c) $HTe^- + H_3PO_4 \rightleftharpoons H_2Te + H_2PO_4^-$; (HTe^-, H_2Te), $(H_3PO_4, H_2PO_4^-)$
   d) $HCO_3^- + S^{2-} \rightleftharpoons CO_3^{2-} + HS^-$; (HCO_3^-, CO_3^{2-}), (S^{2-}, HS^-)

e) $H^- + H_2O \rightleftharpoons H_2 + OH^-$; (H^-, H_2), (H_2O, OH^-)
f) $H_2Se + HO_2^- \rightleftharpoons HSe^- + H_2O_2$; (H_2Se, HSe^-), (HO_2^-, H_2O_2)
g) $O^{2-} + H_2O \rightleftharpoons OH^- + OH^-$; (O^{2-}, OH^-), (H_2O, OH^-)
h) $H_2O + H_2SO_3 \rightleftharpoons H_3O^+ + HSO_3^-$; (H_2O, H_3O^+), (H_2SO_3, HSO_3^-)

4. a) $K_B = 1.0 \times 10^{-3}$ b) $K_A = 5.9 \times 10^{-9}$
   c) $K_B = 1.0 \times 10^{-7}$ d) $K_B = 7.7 \times 10^{-13}$
   e) $K_A = 2 \times 10^{-4}$

5. a) H_2Te b) HSO_3^-
   c) $H_2PO_4^-$

6. a) Te^{2-} b) HPO_4^{2-}
   c) OH^- d) HSe^-

7. a) $SO_3^{2-} + H_2O \rightleftharpoons HSO_3^- + OH^-$
   b) $Te^{2-} + H_2O \rightleftharpoons HTe^- + OH^-$
   c) $Al(H_2O)_5(OH)^{2+} + H_2O \rightleftharpoons Al(H_2O)_6^{3+} + OH^-$
   d) $HPO_4^{2-} + H_2O \rightleftharpoons H_2PO_4^- + OH^-$
   e) $HCO_3^- + H_2O \rightleftharpoons H_2CO_3 + OH^-$
   f) $O^{2-} + H_2O \rightleftharpoons OH^- + OH^-$
   g) no hydrolysis occurs
   h) $C_2O_4^{2-} + H_2O \rightleftharpoons HC_2O_4^- + OH^-$

8. a) basic   b) acidic
   c) acidic   d) neutral
   e) basic   f) basic

9. 1.3×10^{-20} b) 2.1×10^{-36}
   c) 1.8×10^{-10}

10. a) 1.8×10^2 b) 6.3×10^{-1}
    c) 5.7×10^4 d) 3.9×10^{-5}
    e) 4.1×10^7 f) 4.8×10^{-12}

11. a) products; $K_{eq} = 25$
    b) reactants; $K_{eq} = 8.5 \times 10^{-7}$
    c) products; $K_{eq} = 1.1 \times 10^5$
    d) reactants; $K_{eq} = 2.4 \times 10^{-5}$
    e) products; $K_{eq} = 4.4 \times 10^3$
    f) products; $K_{eq} > 10^{22}$ (acid $= H_2O$)
    g) reactants; $K_{eq} = 2.0 \times 10^{-4}$
    h) reactants; $K_{eq} = 0.14$ (HCO_3^- = base)

12. 7.1×10^{-5} kmol/m³   13. 0.14%
14. 6.16   15. 3.5×10^{-4}%
16. 0.81 kmol/m³   17. 0.010 kmol/m³
18. a) 4.88   b) 8.33
    c) 9.11   d) 13.18
    e) 11.90   f) 1.37
19. very large; HBr is 100% dissociated

20. a) 4.0×10^{-10} b) 2.9×10^{-8}
21. $0.0150 \ kmol/m^3$ 22. 2.06×10^{-9}
23. $[H^+] = 1.67 \times 10^{-11} \ kmol/m^3$, $[OH^-] = 6.00 \times 10^{-4} \ kmol/m^3$, pH $= 10.778$, pOH $= 3.222$, % hydrolysis $= 3.00\%$
24. 1.845 25. $5.88 \times 10^{-2} \ kmol/m^3$
26. 3.16×10^{-11} 27. $0.33 \ g$
28. $3.6 \times 10^{-4} \ kmol/m^3$
29. pH $= 0.956$; 10.5% of HSO_4^- dissociates
30. pH $= 2.642$; % dissociation $= 22.8\%$
31. $[NH_3] = 0.105 \ kmol/m^3$; $[OH^-] = 1.37 \times 10^{-3} \ kmol/m^3$
32. 4.745
33. a) 4.780 b) 4.710
    c) 0.284 for part a, 0.319 for part b

BUFFERS

1. a) 4.301   b) 4.301   c) 4.602
   d) 4.000   e) 5.204   f) 3.778
   g) 4.699   h) 5.255
2. 7.50   3. 0.361
4. a) 4.879   b) 9.173   c) 5.64
   d) 3.597
5. 50.8 g
6. a) 4.754   b) 4.667   c) 4.842
7. a) 7.126   b) 7.285   c) 7.062
8. $0.350 \ kmol/m^3$ 9. $0.0900 \ kmol/m^3$ 10. 0.300 mol
11. 0.0160 mol   12. 0.512   13. 2.118
14. 0.389   15. 4.751
16. a) 0.050 mol   b) 0.094 mol   c) 0.14 mol
    d) 0.350 mol
17. a) 0.025 mol   b) 0.062 mol   c) 0.085 mol
    d) 0.145 mol

TITRATION AND INDICATORS

1. blue   2. yellow   3. 2×10^{-13}
4. 4×10^{-4} 5. $0.0765 \ kmol/m^3$
6. No difference because even a small addition of HCl would change pH by several units near the end point (*e.g.*, in problem 5, going from 15.2 mL to 15.3 mL of HCl changes pH from 10.493 to 7.00)

7. $0.0358 \ kmol/m^3$ 8. $39.3 \ mL$

9. a) 4.8 b) methyl red or methyl orange

10. $pH = 8.6$; cresol red or thymolphthalein

11. Two acidic groups, one of which dissociates to a small extent ($K_A(1) = 4 \times 10^{-7}$), *i.e.*, fairly easily, and the other dissociates with great difficulty ($K_A(2) = 2 \times 10^{-12}$), and only in very basic conditions ($pH = 11.7$).

12. red   13. $38.0 \ mL$ 14. $0.0469 \ kmol/m^3$

15. 2   16. 4

17. a) When light goes out, conductance is a minimum since effectively all Cl^- ions have been precipitated out in form of $AgCl$ (which has negligible solubility). Hence $[Ag^+] = [Cl^-]$ since no excess of either ion (minimum conductance), which is the required "end point".

   b) $0.219 \ kmol/m^3$

18. $0.210 \ kmol/m^3$ 19. $0.537 \ kmol/m^3$ 20. 95.4%

ELECTROCHEMICAL CELLS AND HALF-CELL POTENTIALS

1. a) Mn is oxidized; Hg^{2+} is reduced; Hg^{2+} is oxidizing agent; Mn is reducing agent.

   b) H_2 is oxidized; Sn^{4+} is reduced; Sn^{4+} is oxidizing agent; H_2 is reducing agent.

   c) Li is oxidized; F_2 is reduced; F_2 is oxidizing agent; Li is reducing agent.

   d) Cr^{2+} is oxidized; Br_2 is reduced; Br_2 is oxidizing agent; Cr^{2+} is reducing agent.

   e) Fe^{2+} is oxidized; Sn^{4+} is reduced; Sn^{4+} is oxidizing agent; Fe^{2+} is reducing agent.

2. a) $2 I^- \rightleftharpoons I_2 + 2 e^-$; $MnO_2 + 4 H^+ + 2 e^- \rightleftharpoons Mn^{2+} + 2 H_2O$

   b) $2 I^- + MnO_2 + 4 H^+ \rightleftharpoons I_2 + Mn^{2+} + 2 H_2O$

   c) I^- is reducing agent

3. a) $Cs \rightleftharpoons Cs^+ + e^-$; $Cl_2 + 2 e^- \rightleftharpoons 2 Cl^-$

   b) $2 Cs + Cl_2 \rightleftharpoons 2 Cs^+ + 2 Cl^-$

   c) Cl_2 is oxidizing agent, Cs is reducing agent

4. a) Ni   b) Ni

   c) from Ni to Cu   d) $0.050 \ mol \ e^-$

   e) Cu

5. a) $Sn + 2 Ag^+ \rightleftharpoons Sn^{2+} + 2 Ag$ b) Ag

   c) Ag   d) from Sn to Ag

   e) gain   f) $0.020 \ mol \ e^-$

   g) $0.040 \ mol \ Ag$ h) none

6. a) $1.54 \ V$, spontaneous   b) $0.61 \ V$, spontaneous

   c) $-0.673 \ V$, not spontaneous   d) $0.62 \ V$, spontaneous

   e) $-1.46 \ V$, not spontaneous

7. a) Mg and Ag   b) Cr and Zn
8. a) no reaction
    b) reaction occurs; Sn^{2+} is formed
    c) reaction occurs; M^+ and H_2 are formed
    d) no reaction
    e) no reaction
    f) reaction occurs; I_2, Mn^{2+} and H_2O are formed
9. a) Zn^{2+} b) Cu^{2+}
    c) Br_2
10. a) Mn   b) SO_2
    c) $Hg(l)$ in $Hg_2{}^{2+}(aq)$
11. a) no dissolving   b) A dissolves to form A^+
12. a) no dissolving, $E^{\circ}_{cell} = -0.80$ V   b) Ag dissolves, $E^{\circ}_{cell} = 0.15$ V
13. a) I_2 and Fe^{3+} b) H_2 and H_2O_2
    c) Pb   d) Cu^{2+}, acidic $NO_3{}^-$
    e) Cu, OH^-
    f) I_2, O_2 in 1 $kmol/m^3$ H^+, O_2 in 1 $kmol/m^3$ OH^-
    g) 1 $kmol/m^3$ H^+, 1 $kmol/m^3$ Fe^{3+} h) none
14. a) $Cu + Cl_2 \rightarrow Cu^{2+} + 2\,Cl^-$
    b) $Al + 3\,Cr^{3+} \rightarrow Al^{3+} + 3\,Cr^{2+}$
    c) $3\,Sn + 2\,NO_3{}^- + 8\,H^+ \rightarrow 3\,Sn^{2+} + 2\,NO + 4\,H_2O$
    d) $3\,Cu + 8\,H^+ + 2\,NO_3{}^- \rightarrow 3\,Cu^{2+} + 2\,NO + 4\,H_2O$
    e) $Cu + \frac{1}{2}\,O_2 + 2\,H^+ \rightarrow Cu^{2+} + H_2O$
    f) $3\,Hg + MnO_4{}^- + 4\,H^+ \rightarrow \frac{3}{2}\,Hg_2{}^{2+} + MnO_2 + 2\,H_2O$
    g) $2\,H_2O_2 \rightarrow 2\,H_2O + O_2$
15. Cathodic protection occurs; the Mg is oxidized (*i.e.*, corroded) instead of the aluminum casing.
16. a) $2\,In^{2+} \rightarrow In^{3+} + In^+$; $E^{\circ}_{cell} = 0.09$ V
    b) $3\,H_2SO_3 \rightarrow S + 2\,SO_4{}^{2-} + 4\,H^+ + H_2O$; $E^{\circ}_{cell} = 0.25$ V
    c) $4\,HNO_2 \rightarrow N_2O + 2\,NO_3{}^- + H_2O + 2\,H^+$; $E^{\circ}_{cell} = 0.33$ V
17. a) decrease   b) increase
    c) decrease   d) decrease
    e) E°_{red} decreases, but E°_{oxid} increases for the reaction given
    f) E°_{red} decreases, but E°_{oxid} increases for the reaction given
18. a) O_2 bubbled through 1 $kmol/m^3$ H_2SO_4
    b) $KMnO_4$ in 2 $kmol/m^3$ HCl   c) 2 $kmol/m^3$ Pb^{2+}
    d) $Cr_2O_7{}^{2-}$ in 0.2 $kmol/m^3$ H^+
19. a) H_2 in 1 $kmol/m^3$ NaCl
    b) SO_2 bubbled through 1 $kmol/m^3$ NaOH
    c) N_2O_4 bubbled through 1 $kmol/m^3$ $NaNO_3$
    d) 0.5 $kmol/m^3$ Sn^{2+}
20. greater than 1.10 V

21. a) 1.23 V   b) -0.69 V
    c) 1.26 V   d) 1.47 V
    e) -1.66 V

ELECTROLYSIS

1. $Cu(s)$ at cathode, $Cl_2(g)$ at anode
2. $Ni(s)$ at cathode, $O_2(g)$ at anode; 1.05 V
3. a) $2 H^+(10^{-7} \text{ kmol/m}^3) + 2 I^- \rightarrow H_2(g) + I_2$
   b) $2 H^+(10^{-7} \text{ kmol/m}^3) + 2 Cl^- \rightarrow H_2(g) + Cl_2(g)$
   c) $Cu^{2+} + H_2O \rightarrow Cu(s) + \frac{1}{2} O_2(g) + 2 H^+(10^{-7} \text{ kmol/m}^3)$
   d) $Ni^{2+} + 2 OH^- \rightarrow Ni(s) + \frac{1}{2} O_2(g) + H_2O$; basic
   e) $H_2O \rightarrow H_2(g) + \frac{1}{2} O_2(g)$; neutral
   f) $2 H^+ + 2 I^- \rightarrow H_2(g) + I_2$
   g) $Cu^{2+} + H_2O \rightarrow Cu + \frac{1}{2} O_2(g) + 2 H^+(10^{-7} \text{ kmol/m}^3)$
   h) $2 H_2O + Fe \rightarrow H_2(g) + Fe^{2+} + 2 OH^-$; $Fe^{2+} + 2 OH^- \rightleftharpoons Fe(OH)_2(s)$
   i) $2 H^+ + Cu \rightarrow H_2(g) + Cu^{2+}$
   j) $Ni^{2+} + 2 e^- \rightarrow Ni$ (cathode); $Ni \rightarrow Ni^{2+} + 2 e^-$ (anode)
      $\therefore$ Ni dissolves at anode and is redeposited at cathode.
4. $Cu(s)$ will oxidize to Cu^{2+}, $Ag(s)$ will not oxidize, $Pb(s)$ will oxidize to Pb^{2+}; Cu^{2+} will be reduced to $Cu(s)$, Pb^{2+} will not be reduced. Note that Cu is purified since some impurities will not oxidize and the impurities which do oxidize cannot be reduced.
5. 1.36 V; $Cl_2(g)$ at anode, $H_2(g)$ at cathode
6. red around anode, blue around cathode; pH = 7.0
7. water will be reduced instead of Al^{3+}
8. 0.0518 mol   9. 247 C
10. 48.3 g of Pb at cathode, 3.73 g of $O_2(g)$ at anode
11. 1.21×10^6 C   12. 39.9 g   13. 13.2 g
14. 133 u ($=$ Cs); produced at cathode
15. $+4$ 16. 1.16×10^4 s   17. 1.60×10^{-19} C/e$^-$
18. a) 0.533 g Cu   b) 648 s   19. $+3$
20. 1.55×10^3 A   21. 305 g   22. 1.59×10^4 s
23. 128 u, cathode   24. Sb_2O_5 25. U^{4+}
26. 80.0 g/mol   27. 50.9 g/mol   28. ZCl_4
29. 665 s

BALANCING HALF-CELLS

1. $Ce^{4+} + 2 e^- \rightleftharpoons Ce^{2+}$
2. $I_2 + 2 e^- \rightleftharpoons 2 I^-$

3. $Mn^{2+} + 2 H_2O \rightleftharpoons MnO_2 + 4 H^+ + 2 e^-$

4. $O_2 + 2 H^+ + 2 e^- \rightleftharpoons H_2O_2$

5. $S_2O_8{}^{2-} + 2 H^+ + 2 e^- \rightleftharpoons 2 HSO_4{}^-$

6. $H_3AsO_4 + 2 H^+ + 2 e^- \rightleftharpoons HAsO_2 + 2 H_2O$

7. $H_2SeO_3 + 4 H^+ + 4 e^- \rightleftharpoons Se + 3 H_2O$

8. $N_2H_4 + 4 OH^- \rightleftharpoons N_2 + 4 H_2O + 4 e^-$

9. $HO_2{}^- + OH^- \rightleftharpoons O_2 + H_2O + 2 e^-$

10. $Cr_2O_7{}^{2-} + 14 H^+ + 6 e^- \rightleftharpoons 2 Cr^{3+} + 7 H_2O$

11. $HXeO_4{}^- + 4 OH^- \rightleftharpoons HXeO_6{}^{3-} + 2 H_2O + 2 e^-$

12. $HC_2H_3O_2 + 4 H^+ + 4 e^- \rightleftharpoons C_2H_5OH + H_2O$

13. $Cr(OH)_3 + 5 OH^- \rightleftharpoons CrO_4{}^{2-} + 4 H_2O + 3 e^-$

14. $CH_3CHO + 2 H^+ + 2 e^- \rightleftharpoons CH_2CH_2 + H_2O$

15. $2 KNO_3 + H_2SO_4 + 2 H^+ + 2 e^- \rightleftharpoons 2 NO_2 + 2 H_2O + K_2SO_4$

16. $KClO_3 + NH_4HSO_4 + 6 H^+ + 6 e^- \rightleftharpoons NH_4Cl + 3 H_2O + KHSO_4$

17. $FeHPO_3 + 6 OH^- \rightleftharpoons PO_4{}^{3-} + Fe(OH)_3 + 2 H_2O + 3 e^-$

18. $Cu_2S + 3 H_2O \rightleftharpoons 2 Cu^{2+} + H_2SO_3 + 4 H^+ + 8 e^-$

19. $FeS + 4 H_2O \rightleftharpoons Fe^{3+} + SO_4{}^{2-} + 8 H^+ + 9 e^-$

20. $Hg_2PbS_2 + 26 OH^- \rightleftharpoons 2 SO_4{}^{2-} + Pb(OH)_6{}^{2-} + 2 Hg(OH)_2 + 8 H_2O + 20 e^-$

21. $(NH_4)_2S + 2 OH^- \rightleftharpoons S + 2 H_2O + 2 NH_3 + 2 e^-$

BALANCING REDOX EQUATIONS USING HALF-CELLS

1. $2 H_2O + 5 U^{4+} + 2 MnO_4{}^- \rightarrow 2 Mn^{2+} + 5 UO_2{}^{2+} + 4 H^+$

2. $6 Zn + As_2O_3 + 12 H^+ \rightarrow 2 AsH_3 + 6 Zn^{2+} + 3 H_2O$

3. $6 Fe^{2+} + Cr_2O_7{}^{2-} + 14 H^+ \rightarrow 2 Cr^{3+} + 6 Fe^{3+} + 7 H_2O$

4. $Cl_2 + SO_2 + 2 H_2O \rightarrow 2 Cl^- + SO_4{}^{2-} + 4 H^+$

5. $3 Cu + 2 NO_3{}^- + 8 H^+ \rightarrow 3 Cu^{2+} + 2 NO + 4 H_2O$

6. $3 S^{2-} + ClO_3{}^- + 3 H_2O \rightarrow 3 S + Cl^- + 6 OH^-$

7. $3 OCl^- \rightarrow 2 Cl^- + ClO_3{}^-$

8. $3 CN^- + IO_3{}^- \rightarrow I^- + 3 CNO^-$

9. $Sn^{2+} + H_2O_2 \rightarrow Sn^{4+} + 2 OH^-$

10. $2 Mn^{2+} + 5 HBiO_3 + 9 H^+ \rightarrow 5 Bi^{3+} + 2 MnO_4{}^- + 7 H_2O$

11. $5 HSO_3{}^- + 2 IO_3{}^- \rightarrow I_2 + 5 SO_4{}^{2-} + 3 H^+ + H_2O$

12. $3 HNO_2 \rightarrow HNO_3 + 2 NO + H_2O$

13. $3 Br_2 + 6 OH^- \rightarrow 5 Br^- + BrO_3{}^- + 3 H_2O$

14. $Sb_2S_3 + 22 H^+ + 28 NO_3{}^- \rightarrow 3 SO_4{}^{2-} + Sb_2O_5 + 28 NO_2 + 11 H_2O$

15. $3 As_2S_3 + 4 H_2O + 10 H^+ + 28 NO_3{}^- \rightarrow 9 SO_4{}^{2-} + 6 H_3AsO_4 + 28 NO$

16. $3 H_2O_2 + 2 Cr(OH)_4{}^- + 2 OH^- \rightarrow 2 CrO_4{}^{2-} + 8 H_2O$

17. $FeS + 3 NO_3{}^- + 4 H^+ \rightarrow SO_4{}^{2-} + Fe^{3+} + 3 NO + 2 H_2O$

18. $2 FeHPO_3 + Cr_2O_7{}^{2-} + 14 H^+ \rightarrow 2 H_3PO_4 + 2 Fe^{3+} + 2 Cr^{3+} + 5 H_2O$

19. $SnS_2O_3 + 2\,MnO_4^- + 6\,H^+ \rightarrow 2\,SO_4^{2-} + Sn^{4+} + 2\,Mn^{2+} + 3\,H_2O$

20. $6\,Hg_4Fe(CN)_6 + 66\,H^+ + 47\,ClO_3^- \rightarrow$
$36\,NO + 36\,CO_2 + 6\,Fe^{3+} + 24\,Hg^{2+} + 47\,Cl^- + 33\,H_2O$

21. $Fe_2Fe(CN)_6 + 24\,H^+ + 15\,NO_3^- \rightarrow 21\,NO + 6\,CO_2 + 3\,Fe^{3+} + 12\,H_2O$

22. $2\,FeHPO_3 + 5\,H_2O + 3\,OCl^- \rightarrow 2\,PO_4^{3-} + 2\,Fe(OH)_3 + 6\,H^+ + 3\,Cl^-$

23. $Cu_2SnS_2 + 26\,OH^- + 10\,S_2O_8^{2-} \rightarrow$
$22\,SO_4^{2-} + Sn(OH)_6^{2-} + 2\,Cu(OH)_2 + 8\,H_2O$

24. $CuS + 8\,HNO_3 \rightarrow Cu(NO_3)_2 + 4\,H_2O + 6\,NO_2 + SO_2$

25. $3\,FeAsS + 17\,H^+ + 14\,NO_3^- \rightarrow$
$3\,SO_4^{2-} + 3\,H_3AsO_4 + 3\,Fe^{3+} + 14\,NO + 4\,H_2O$

26. $Sn(S_2O_3)_2^{2-} + 10\,H_2O + 6\,FeS_2O_8^+ \rightarrow Sn^{4+} + 16\,SO_4^{2-} + 20\,H^+ + 6\,Fe^{2+}$

27. $2\,Ca_3(PO_4)_2 + 6\,SiO_2 + 10\,C \rightarrow P_4 + 6\,CaSiO_3 + 10\,CO$

28. $2\,KMnO_4 + 5\,H_2S + 3\,H_2SO_4 \rightarrow K_2SO_4 + 2\,MnSO_4 + 8\,H_2O + 5\,S$

29. $3\,C_2H_5OH + 2\,K_2Cr_2O_7 + 8\,H_2SO_4 \rightarrow$
$3\,CH_3COOH + 2\,Cr_2(SO_4)_3 + 2\,K_2SO_4 + 11\,H_2O$

30. $10\,K_4Fe(CN)_6 + 122\,KMnO_4 + 299\,H_2SO_4 \rightarrow$
$162\,KHSO_4 + 5\,Fe_2(SO_4)_3 + 122\,MnSO_4 + 60\,HNO_3 + 60\,CO_2 + 188\,H_2O$

31. $5\,NH_4SCN + 14\,MnO_4^- + 32\,H^+ \rightarrow$
$5\,N_2 + 5\,CO_2 + 5\,SO_4^{2-} + 14\,Mn^{2+} + 26\,H_2O$

32. $2\,CrSCN^{2+} + 9\,H_2O + 19\,BrO^- \rightarrow$
$2\,NO_3^- + 2\,CO_3^{2-} + 2\,SO_4^{2-} + 2\,CrO_4^{2-} + 18\,H^+ + 19\,Br^-$

33. $2\,Fe(CrO_2)_2 + 7\,Na_2O_2 \rightarrow Fe_2O_3 + 4\,Na_2CrO_4 + 3\,Na_2O$

34. $16\,NH_3 + 6\,CuF_2 \rightarrow 2\,Cu_3N + 12\,NH_4F + N_2$

OXIDATION NUMBERS

(*Note:* a "*" denotes a problem in which we have assumed at least one oxidation number. The assumed numbers are underlined.)

1. a) $S = +6$, $O = -2$ b) $P = +3$, $F = -1$
   c) $P = +5$, $Cl = -1$ d) $Na = +1$, $P = -3$
   e) $S = +5$, $F = -1$ f) $S = +7$, $O = -2$
2. a) $N = +5$, $O = -2$ b) $N = +4$, $O = -2$
   c) $N = +3$, $O = -2$ d) $N = +2$, $O = -2$
   e) $N = +1$, $O = -2$ f) $N = 0$
   g) $N = -\frac{1}{3}$ h) $N = -2$, $H = +1$
   i) $N = -3$, $H = +1$
   [note possible numbers for N in this question]
3. a) $U = +3$, $O = -2$ b) $U = +16/3$, $O = -2$

196

c) $U = +5, O = -2$ d) $K = +1, U = +6, O = -2$
e) $Mg = +2, U = +6, O = -2$

4. a) $Mn = +2, S = +6, O = -2$ b) $Mn = +4, O = -2$
c) $K = +1, Mn = +7, O = -2$ d) $Mn = +7, O = -2$
e) $Mn = +3, Cl = -1$

5. a) $H = +1, S = +5, O = -2$ b) $H = +1, S = +2, O = -2$
c) $H = +1, S = +6, O = -2$ d) $K = +1, H = +1, S = +6, O = -2$
e) $S = 0$ f) $S = +2, O = -2$

6. a) $Sr = +2, Si = +4, O = -2$ b) $S = +3, O = -2, Cl = -1$
c) $S = +5, O = -2, Cl = -1$ d) $H = +1, S = +8, O = -2$
e) $S = +6, O = -2, Cl = -1, F = -1$
f) $N = -1, H = +1, O = -2$

7. a) $C = +3, O = -2$ b) $W = +6, O = -2$
c) $N = +3, O = -2$ d) $Cl = +7, O = -2$
e) $H = +1, I = +7, O = -2$ f) $P = +5, O = -2$
g) $Cl = +7, F = -1$

8. a) $Y = +3, O = -2, H = +1$ b) $N = -3, H = +1, S = +4, O = -2$
c) $Pb = +4, C = +4, O = -2$ d) $Cd = +2, N = +5, O = -2$
e) $Hg = +2, I = +5, O = -2$

9. a) $C = -4, H = +1$ b) $C = -2, H = +1, Cl = -1$
c) $C = 0, H = +1, Cl = -1$ d) $C = -2, H = +1, O = -2$
e) $C = -4/3, H = +1, O = -2$

10. a) $C = -3/2, H = +1$ b) $C = -2, H = +1, O = -2$
c*) $C = -2, H = +1, \underline{S} = -2$ d*) $C = -2, H = +1, \underline{N} = +3, O = -2$
e*) $C = -2, H = +1, \underline{S} = +4, O = -2$

11. a) $C = +1/2, H = +1, O = -2$ b) $C = -8/5, H = +1, O = -2$
c) $C = 0, H = +1, O = -2$ d) $C = -2/3, H = +1, Cl = -1$
e) $C = -2/7, H = +1, O = -2$

12. a*) $C = -3/2, H = +1, \underline{N} = +3, O = -2$
b*) $C = -2/3, H = +1, \underline{S} = +4, O = -2$
c*) $C = 0, H = +1, \underline{N} = +3, O = -2$

13. a *) $\underline{Ge} = +4, C = -8/3, H = +1$
b*) $\underline{B} = +3, C = -2, H = +1, O = -2$
c*) $\underline{Sn} = +4, S = -2, C = -2, H = +1$
d*) $\underline{C} = -4/5, H = +1, \underline{Hg} = +2, Cl = -1$
e*) $C = +4, H = +1, \underline{Sn} = +4, O = -2$

Note: In C-13 we assume the following groups are present: $C_3H_7^-$, $C_2H_5O^-$, CH_3S^-, CH_3^-. Similarly, in B-10 we assume the presence of OH^-, SH^-, NO_2^-, SO_3^{2-}.

BALANCING REDOX EQUATIONS USING OXIDATION NUMBERS

1. $SeO_3{}^{2-} + 4\,I^- + 6\,H^+ \rightarrow Se + 2\,I_2 + 3\,H_2O$
2. $I_2 + 5\,HOCl + H_2O \rightarrow 2\,IO_3{}^- + 5\,Cl^- + 7\,H^+$
3. $4\,Zn + NO_3{}^- + 7\,OH^- \rightarrow 4\,ZnO_2{}^{2-} + NH_3 + 2\,H_2O$
4. $3\,SO_3{}^{2-} + Cr_2O_7{}^{2-} + 8\,H^+ \rightarrow 3\,SO_4{}^{2-} + 2\,Cr^{3+} + 4\,H_2O$
5. $2\,AuCl_4{}^- + 3\,C_2O_4{}^{2-} \rightarrow 2\,Au + 8\,Cl^- + 6\,CO_2$
6. $3\,H_2PO_2{}^- + 2\,TeO_4{}^{2-} \rightarrow 3\,PO_4{}^{3-} + 2\,Te + 2\,H_2O + 2\,H^+$
7. $3\,CdS + 2\,NO_3{}^- + 8\,H^+ \rightarrow 3\,Cd^{2+} + 3\,S + 2\,NO + 4\,H_2O$
8. $As_4 + 10\,NaOCl + 6\,H_2O \rightarrow 4\,H_3AsO_4 + 10\,NaCl$
9. $3\,PbS + 8\,NO_3{}^- + 8\,H^+ \rightarrow 3\,Pb(NO_3)_2 + 2\,NO + 3\,S + 4\,H_2O$
10. $CH_3NO_2 + 6\,Ti^{3+} + 6\,H^+ \rightarrow CH_3NH_2 + 6\,Ti^{4+} + 2\,H_2O$
11. $Cr_2O_7{}^{2-} + 3\,HCHO + 8\,H^+ \rightarrow 2\,Cr^{3+} + 3\,HCOOH + 4\,H_2O$
12. $Pt + 2\,NO_3{}^- + 6\,Cl^- + 8\,H^+ \rightarrow PtCl_6 + 2\,NO + 4\,H_2O$
13. $Tl_2SO_4 + 4\,K_3Fe(CN)_6 + 6\,KOH \rightarrow Tl_2O_3 + 4\,K_4Fe(CN)_6 + K_2SO_4 + 3\,H_2O$
14. $4\,MnO_4{}^- + 5\,Sb_2O_3 + 12\,H^+ \rightarrow 4\,Mn^{2+} + 5\,Sb_2O_5 + 6\,H_2O$
15. $2\,Al_2O_3 + 2\,Co(NO_3)_2 \rightarrow 2\,CoAl_2O_4 + 4\,NO_2 + O_2$
16. $2\,MnO_4{}^- + 10\,HN_3 + 2\,SO_4{}^{2-} + 6\,H^+ \rightarrow 2\,MnSO_4 + 15\,N_2 + 8\,H_2O$
17. $2\,H_2SeO_3 + SCN^- + H^+ \rightarrow 2\,Se + CO_2 + NH_4{}^+ + HSO_4{}^-$
18. $2\,VO_4{}^{3-} + 3\,I^- + IO_3{}^- + 4\,Cl^- + 9\,H_2O \rightarrow 2\,VO^{2+} + 4\,ICl + 18\,OH^-$
19. $2\,Sb_2O_4 + 6\,Na_2CO_3 + 23\,S \rightarrow 4\,Na_3SbS_4 + 7\,SO_2 + 6\,CO_2$
20. $Co(NO_3)_2 + 7\,KNO_2 + 2\,HC_2H_3O_2 \rightarrow$
$$K_3Co(NO_2)_6 + KNO_3 + 2\,KC_2H_3O_2 + NO + H_2O$$
21. $Cr_2(SO_4)_3 + 5\,Na_2CO_3 + 3\,KNO_3 \rightarrow$
$$2\,Na_2CrO_4 + 3\,KNO_2 + 3\,Na_2SO_4 + 5\,CO_2$$
22. $(NH_4)_2PtCl_6 + N_2H_4\cdot 2\,HCl + 6\,NH_3 \rightarrow 8\,NH_4Cl + N_2 + Pt$
23. $2\,MnSO_4 + 5\,Ag_2O_2 + 10\,NO_3{}^- + 4\,H^+ \rightarrow$
$$2\,MnO_4{}^- + 10\,AgNO_3 + 2\,SO_4{}^{2-} + 2\,H_2O$$
24. $7\,IO_3{}^- + 4\,CuSCN + 7\,Cl^- + 18\,H^+ \rightarrow$
$$7\,ICl + 4\,Cu^{2+} + 4\,HSO_4{}^- + 4\,HCN + 5\,H_2O$$
25. $2\,FeS_2 + 15\,Na_2O_2 \rightarrow Fe_2O_3 + 4\,Na_2SO_4 + 11\,Na_2O$

ELECTRON CONFIGURATIONS

1. a) $P(1s^2 2s^2 2p^6 3s^2 3p^3)$
   b) $Ti(1s^2 2s^2 2p^6 3s^2 3p^6 4s^2 3d^2)$
   c) $Co(1s^2 2s^2 2p^6 3s^2 3p^6 4s^2 3d^7)$
   d) $Br(1s^2 2s^2 2p^6 3s^2 3p^6 4s^2 3d^{10} 4p^5)$
   e) $Sr(1s^2 2s^2 2p^6 3s^2 3p^6 4s^2 3d^{10} 4p^6 5s^2)$
   f) $Tc(1s^2 2s^2 2p^6 3s^2 3p^6 4s^2 3d^{10} 4p^6 5s^2 4d^5)$
   g) $As(1s^2 2s^2 2p^6 3s^2 3p^6 4s^2 3d^{10} 4p^3)$
   h) $Cd(1s^2 2s^2 2p^6 3s^2 3p^6 4s^2 3d^{10} 4p^6 5s^2 4d^{10})$

i) $Ca(1s^22s^22p^63s^23p^64s^2)$

j) $Kr(1s^22s^22p^63s^23p^64s^23d^{10}4p^6)$

k) $Cs(1s^22s^22p^63s^23p^64s^23d^{10}4p^65s^24d^{10}5p^66s^1)$

l) $Ar(1s^22s^22p^63s^23p^6)$

m) $Ga(1s^22s^22p^63s^23p^64s^23d^{10}4p^1)$

n) $Y(1s^22s^22p^63s^23p^64s^23d^{10}4p^65s^24d^1)$

o) $Mo(1s^22s^22p^63s^23p^64s^23d^{10}4p^65s^14d^5)$

p) $Au(1s^22s^22p^63s^23p^64s^23d^{10}4p^65s^24d^{10}5p^66s^14f^{14}5d^{10})$

2. a) $P([Ne]\ 3s^23p^3)$ b) $Ti([Ar]\ 4s^23d^2)$

c) $Co([Ar]\ 4s^23d^7)$ d) $Br([Ar]\ 4s^23d^{10}4p^5)$

e) $Sr([Kr]\ 5s^2)$ f) $Tc([Kr]\ 5s^24d^5)$

g) $As([Ar]\ 4s^23d^{10}4p^3)$ h) $Cd([Kr]\ 5s^24d^{10})$

i) $Ca([Ar]\ 4s^2)$ j) $Kr([Ar]\ 4s^23d^{10}4p^6)$

k) $Cs([Xe]\ 6s^1)$ l) $Ar([Ne]\ 3s^23p^6)$

m) $Ga([Ar]\ 4s^23d^{10}4p^1)$ n) $Y([Kr]\ 5s^24d^1)$

o) $Mo([Kr]\ 5s^14d^5)$ p) $Au([Xe]\ 6s^14f^{14}5d^{10})$

3. a) $H^-(1s^2)$ b) $Sr^{2+}([Ar]\ 4s^23d^{10}4p^6)$

c) $Br^-([Ar]\ 4s^23d^{10}4p^6)$ d) $N^{3+}([He]\ 2s^2)$

e) $Ti^{2+}([Ar]\ 3d^2)$ f) $N^{2-}([He]\ 2s^22p^5)$

g) $Mn^{2+}([Ar]\ 3d^5)$ h) $Cu^+([Ar]\ 3d^{10})$

i) $Au^{3+}([Xe]\ 4f^{14}5d^8)$ j) $Ge^{2+}([Ar]\ 4s^23d^{10})$

k) $Ru^{3+}([Kr]\ 4d^5)$ l) $Sb^{3+}([Kr]\ 5s^24d^{10})$

4. a) $P([Ne]\ 3s^13p^4)$ b) $Ti([Ar]\ 4s^13d^3)$

c) $Co([Ar]\ 4s^13d^8)$ d) $Br([Ar]\ 4s^13d^{10}4p^6)$

e) $Sr([Kr]\ 5s^14d^1)$ f) $Tc([Kr]\ 5s^14d^6)$

g) $As([Ar]\ 4s^13d^{10}4p^4)$ h) $Cd([Kr]\ 5s^14d^{10}5p^1)$

i) $Ca([Ar]\ 4s^13d^1)$ j) $Kr([Ar]\ 4s^23d^{10}4p^55s^1)$

k) $Cs([Xe]\ 4f^1)$ l) $Ar([Ne]\ 3s^23p^54s^1)$

m) $Ga([Ar]\ 4s^13d^{10}4p^2)$ n) $Y([Kr]\ 5s^14d^2)$

o) $Mo([Kr]\ 4d^6)$ p) $Au([Xe]\ 4f^{14}5d^{10}6p^1)$

5. a) 6 b) 0

c) 0 d) 2

e) 0 f) 0

g) 2 h) 6

i) 3 j) 2

6. a) 3, element = B b) 5, element = P

c) 1, element = Li d) 2, element = Mg

e) 7, element = F

7. a) +1, element = Na b) +3, element = Co

c) +4, element = Pb d) +5, element = Nb

e) +5, element = V f) +3, element = Al

g) +3, element = Tl

LEWIS STRUCTURES AND SHAPES OF MOLECULES

1. a)   H:S̈:H

       b)   :C̈l:P:C̈l:
                  :C̈l:

c) $\left[:\ddot{S}:\ddot{S}: \right]^{2-}$

     d) $\left[:\ddot{O}:H \right]^{-}$

e)   :Ï:Be:Ï:

     f)   :Ö:C̈l:

g) $\left[H:\ddot{N}:H \right]^{-}$

     h) $\left[H:\ddot{O}:H \right]^{+}$
             H

i)   H:C::N:

     j)   H
         H:C:Ö:H
           H

k) $\left[\begin{array}{cc} .\ddot{O}. & .\ddot{O}. \\ C:C & \\ :\ddot{O}. & .\ddot{O}: \end{array} \right]^{2-}$

     l)   :C̈l:Ge:C̈l:
              :C̈l:

m)   H :Ö:
     H:C : C:H
        H

     n)   H:Ö:C̈l:

o)   H:C::C:B̈r:

     p)   :O:
         H:C:Ö:H

q)   :F̈:B:F̈:
       :F̈:

     r)   H:C::C:C::C:H

s)   :C̈l::C̈l:
    :C̈l:N : B:C̈l:
      :C̈l::C̈l:

     t)   :C̈l:Al:C̈l:
            :C̈l:

u) $\left[\begin{array}{cc} :\ddot{O}: \\ Si \\ :\ddot{O}. & .\ddot{O}: \end{array} \right]^{2-}$

     v) $\left[:\dot{N}:N::N: \right]^{-}$ or $\left[\dot{N}::N::\dot{N} \right]^{-}$

w) $\left[\begin{array}{cc} .\ddot{O}. & .\ddot{O}. \\ S & \\ :\ddot{O}. & .\ddot{O}. \end{array} \right]^{2-}$

     x)   :F̈:N::N:F̈:

y) $\ddot{\text{O}}::\text{N}:\ddot{\text{O}}:$

z)
```
      :O:
       ⋮
       S
   .Ö.  .Ö.
```

aa)
```
  :O:        :Ö:
     .  N:N  .
  :Ö.        :Ö.
```

bb)
```
 ⌈   :O:    ⌉ 2-
 |    ⋮⋮    |
 |     C    |
 ⌊ :Ö.  .Ö: ⌋
```

cc)
```
 ⌈ :Ö.  .Ö: ⌉ 3-
 |     P    |
 ⌊ :Ö.  .Ö: ⌋
```

dd)
```
              .Ö.
   .Ö.  N:N
   :Ö.        :Ö.
```

2. f, l, y

3. a)
```
      :Ḟ:
       |    .Ḟ.
   :—Se
       |    .F.
      :Ḟ:
```
irregular
tetrahedron

b)
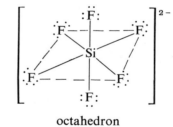
octahedron

c)
```
 ⌈    :Ḟ:    ⌉ -
 |     |     |
 |     B     |
 | .F.   .F. |
 ⌊    .F.    ⌋
```
tetrahedron

d)
```
        :Cl:
              .Cl.
   :Cl—Sb
              .Cl.
        :Cl:
```
trigonal bipyramid

e)
```
   :Cl:
    S—:
      .Cl.
```
V-shape

f)
```
          |
          N
     .Cl.    .Cl.
        :Cl:
```
trigonal pyramid

201

g) $\left[\,:\!\ddot{B}r\!-\!Ag\!-\!\ddot{B}r\!:\,\right]^{-}$

linear

h)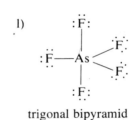

square plane

i) $\left[\begin{array}{c}:\!\ddot{O}\!:\\ |\\ I\\ / \ \ \backslash\\ :\!\ddot{O}\quad\quad\ddot{O}\!:\\ \ddot{O}\!:\end{array}\right]^{-}$

tetrahedron

j)

V-shape

k)

square pyramid

l)

trigonal bipyramid

m) $\left[\begin{array}{c}:\!\ddot{I}\!:\\ |\\ :\!-\!I\\ \backslash\\ :\!\ddot{I}\!:\end{array}\right]$

linear

n)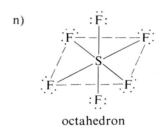

octahedron

o)

T-shape

p)

trigonal pyramid

202

q)

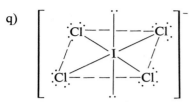

square plane

r)

tetrahedron

s)

square pyramid

t)

V-shape

u)

trigonal pyramid

v)

octahedron

w)

V-shape

x)

trigonal pyramid

y)

trigonal pyramid

z)

tetrahedron

aa)

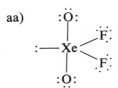

irregular tetrahedron
(other isomers possible)

bb)

$$\left[\begin{array}{c} \ddot{O} \\ Cr \\ O \quad O \end{array} \right]^{2-}$$

tetrahedron

cc)

:F: :F:
 | |
 O   or   O
 :O: :O:

V-shape

dd)

:O:
 ‖
 Zr
F   F

triangular plane

ee)

$$\left[\begin{array}{c} \ddot{O} \\ Ti \\ O \quad O \end{array} \right]$$

triangular plane

ff)

Sn
Br   Br

V-shape

4. w, cc

5. a, e, f, j, k, o, p, s, t, u, w, x, y, z, aa, cc, dd, ff

6. a) $BiCl_3$ b) AlF_3 c) BaO d) SrO e) FrF

7. a)

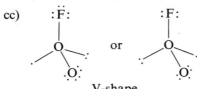

linear
triangular planar

b)

C—N
V-shaped
triangular planar

c)

$^{-}\overset{+}{O}$ H
   C—N—H
 O   H
 tetrahedral
 triangular planar

d)

S—C≡N:
Cl
linear
V-shaped

e)

H
   H
 C   H
C   C
H   C
H   H
H
tetrahedral

f)

H—C≡C—N   H
              N—C—H
linear   H
V-shaped
V-shaped

204